Table of Contents

Geographical Features and Places of Interest

Across The State

Regional

Inns And Restaurants

Educational Institutions

History

North Carolina People

Natural History And Phenomenon

Flora And Fauna

Rocks And Minerals

Weather

Arts And Leisure

Sports

Parks And Campgrounds

Agriculture, Business And Industry

Transportation

North Carolina Potpourri

Geographical Features
and
Places of Interest

Crabtree Falls, off Blue Ridge Parkway

Our Four Fine National Forests

Having four national forests within its borders allows North Carolina to not only showcase its natural beauty, but also provide many forms of outdoor recreation for both native Tar Heels and tourists alike. See if you can figure out the facts about these forests in this quiz.

1. Through the efforts of a wide range of citizens going back to the turn of the century, North Carolina is blessed with four national forests. What branch of the US Department of Agriculture administers the nation's 156 national forests?
    (a) US Woodlands Service   (b) US Forest Service   (c) Federal Forest Commission

2. Counting both government and privately owned land within the boundaries of North Carolina's four national forests, how many total acres are contained within the tracts?
    (a) approximately 3,000,000 acres   (b) approximately 5,000,000 acres   (b) exactly 5,658,000 acres

3. Covering more than one million acres, half of which is federally owned, Nantahala National Forest was established in 1911. Nantahala takes its name from the Indian word for "land of the noon day sun." What North Carolina mountain tribe gave Nantahala its name?
    (a) Meherrin Indians   (b) Cherokee Indians   (c) Osawa Indians

4. Covering parts of 12 North Carolina counties, Pisgah National Forest includes such attractions as Lake Tahoma and Hawksbill Mountain. Pisgah takes its name from the mountain where what Biblical figure was said to have viewed the Promised Land?   (a) Saul   (b) Abraham   (c) Moses

5. Located on the North Carolina coast just south of New Bern, Croatan National Forest holds approximately 300,000 acres within its borders. In what "depressing" year was Croatan National Forest established?
    (a) 1915   (b) 1933   (c) 1959

6. The "baby" of North Carolina's national forests, little Uwharrie National Forest, was established by order of President John F. Kennedy in 1961. What lake on the Yadkin River forms part of the western boundary of Uwharrie?   (a) Badin Lake   (b) Blewett Falls Lake   (c) High Rock Lake

7. The majority of acreage in Uwharrie National Forest lies within Montgomery County. What highway cuts across Montgomery from Albemarle to Troy where Uwharrie's ranger headquarters is located?
    (a) NC 24/27   (b) US 29   (c) NC 134

8. Joyce Kilmer Memorial Forest is a 3,800-acre stand of virgin timber within Nantahala National Forest. Kilmer, a poet famous for his work "Trees," lost his life in World War I in what European nation?
    (a) Bosnia   (b) England   (c) France

9. One of Pisgah National Forest's most popular sites, 6,2300-foot Roan Mountain, straddles the Tennessee-North Carolina border in Mitchell County. What type of foliage brings thousands of visitors to Roan Mountain each June?   (a) Azalea   (b) Multiflora Rose   (c) Rhododendron

10. With 11 species represented, Croatan National Forest can boast of having more carnivorous plants than any national forest in the nation. Which one of the following insect eating plants would *not* be found in Croatan?   (a) Venus Flytrap   (b) Waterwheel plant   (c) Pitcher plant

11. In addition to its unusual plant life, Croatan National Forest also boasts many unique raised swampy areas where, among other things, blueberries thrive. What are these elevated bogs called?
    (a) Pocosins   (b) Monadnocks   (c) Escarpments

12. Good fishing for walleye and bass can be found on Hiwassee Lake in the Nantahala National Forest. Formed in 1940 by a Tennessee Valley Authority dam, Hiwassee Lake is located in what North Carolina county?   (a) Clay County   (b) Macon County   (c) Cherokee County

A Cascade Of Waterfall Trivia

No matter if one visits North Carolina's scores of waterfalls by vehicle or well-worn hiking boot, the cascades inspire awe and tranquility in the spirits of all who see them. Check your maps and memories for the places and particulars of this quiz.

1. What North Carolina county, with more than 200 waterfalls of various sizes within its boundaries, lays claim to the title "Land of Waterfalls?" (a) Swain County (b) Transylvania County (c) Clay County

2. The majority of waterfalls in our state are located along a unique geological feature of the southern Appalachians. What is this sharp change in terrain responsible for all those waterfalls called?
    (a) Blue Ridge Escarpment (b) Smoky Mountains Watershed (c) The Great Divide

3. A North Carolina superlative, Whitewater Falls near Cashiers is the highest waterfall in the eastern United States. How far do the upper falls of this spectacular cascade tumble?
    (a) 200 feet (b) 325 feet (c) 411 feet

4. Visitors to Dry Falls near Highlands can experience an exhilarating treat by walking behind the falls which plunge 75 feet into a deep ravine carved by what river?
    (a) Catawba River (b) Cullasaja River (c) French Broad River

5. Located on NC 276, a little over nine miles north of Brevard, Looking Glass Falls roars down a 60-foot cliff that, when wet and frozen, is mirrorlike. What National Forest is Looking Glass Falls located in?
    (a) Pisgah National Forest (b) Uwharrie National Forest (c) Nantahala National Forest

6. Crabtree Falls, just off the Blue Ridge Parkway at milepost 340, is a popular sight for travelers. What tiny village of distinctly European air is about six miles down the road from the falls?
    (a) Bavarianton (b) Little Switzerland (c) Valle Crucis

7. Glen Burnie Falls near Blowing Rock has since 1906 been part of the Blowing Rock Recreation Area. What creek named after a holiday does Glen Burnie's 75-foot drop happen on?
    (a) Thanksgiving Creek (b) Christmas Creek (c) New Year's Creek

8. Stone Mountain Falls, on Big Sandy Creek near Roaring Gap, is a 200-foot slope of rushing whitewater. Which one of the following states also has a Stone Mountain? (a) Wyoming (b) Georgia (c) Texas

9. With a 150-foot drop, Cullasaja Falls near Franklin is the premier falls on the Cullasaja River. What Spanish explorer, in search of gold, was the first non-Native American to see Cullasaja Falls and its gorge? (a) Hernando de Soto (b) Lazaro Torres (c) Juan DeCordoba

10. Between Shelby and Morganton lies a range of mountains that contain Jacob Fork River, its lovely 80-foot High Shoals Falls, and a 7,000-acre state park. What are these low, yet rugged, mountains called?
    (a) South Mountains (b) Craggy Mountains (c) Brushy Mountains

11. Moravian Falls is located just off NC 16, not too many miles from where it intersects with US 421. The falls, the creek they are on and a nearby village all took their name from the German Moravians who settled the area as early as 1752. What county is Moravian Falls located in?
    (a) Forsyth County (b) Alexander County (c) Wilkes County

12. Not all waterfalls in NC are located in the western part of our state. North of Winston-Salem in the Sauratown Mountains, Lower Cascades Falls tumbles through a series of 30-foot steps for 120 feet. In what 6,000-acre park near the town of Danbury is Lower Cascades Falls found?
    (a) Hanging Rock State Park (b) Sliding Rock State Park (c) Chimney Rock Park

13. Soco Falls, located just off NC 19 in the Great Smoky Mountains, is said to have been the spot where some angry Native Americans threw an early Spanish explorer to his demise. Soco Falls is located within the boundaries of what Indian reservation?
    (a) Catawba Reservation (b) Tuscarora Reservation (c) Qualla Reservation

Follow A North Carolina River

Whether flowing lazily through the coastal plain, or tumbling down a Great Smoky Mountains stream, North Carolina's rivers add to the beauty of our state. Follow the course of these waterways as you answer the questions to this quiz.

1. Rising in southwest Henderson County, the Green River flows through Lake Summitt and Lake Adger on its way to the Broad River at the Rutherford County line. On this journey the Green River is spanned by the tallest bridge in North Carolina on what highway near Saluda?
   (a) US 64   (b) Interstate 26   (c) NC 107

2. A favorite of canoeists, the New River passes through scenic Ashe County as its heads toward Virginia and West Virginia. The New River is said to be the only large river in the nation to flow northward in imitation of what famous African waterway?   (a) Congo River   (b) Zambezi River   (c) Nile River

3. With its headwaters in Onslow County, the White Oak River drifts southeastward along the Jones-Onslow and Carteret-Onslow county lines to its final destination of Bogue Inlet. On its journey, the White Oak River passes by what Onslow town whose name is similar to that of former Yugoslavia's capital city?   (a) Budapest   (b) Ploesti   (c) Belgrade

4. Once called Gow-ta-no or "pine in water" by the Tuscarora Indians, the Neuse River begins its path to Pamlico Sound in Durham County. At its coastal junction with the Trent River in Craven County, the Neuse flows by what town that was once our state's capital city?
   (a) Bath   (b) Washington   (c) New Bern

5. From headwaters in Burke County, the Jacob Fork River winds its way through Catawba County where it joins the Henry Fork. A favorite of folks fishing for trout, Jacob Fork River tumbles over what spectacular 80-foot waterfall in South Mountains State Park?
   (a) High Shoals Falls   (b) Catawba Falls   (c) Lauren's Falls

6. The Tuckasegee River has its origins at the junction of Panthertown and Greenland creeks in Jackson County. Before it enters the Little Tennessee River in Swain County, the Tuckasegee passes through what popular Swain tourist town that was once known as Charleston?
   (a) Cherokee   (b) Birdtown   (c) Bryson City

7. Popular vacation and day trip destinations, Chimney Rock and Lake Lure in Rutherford County are part of spectacular Hickory Nut Gorge. What river, flowing from its head in Buncombe County to a junction with the Green River, was dammed in 1928 to form Lake Lure's 1,500 acres?
   (a) Hickory River   (b) Linville River   (c) Broad River

8. Cascading a total of 800 feet in several cataracts, one of which is more than 400 feet, Whitewater Falls on the Whitewater River is among the highest in eastern America. For part of its run to the Toxaway River, the Whitewater forms the boundary between Jackson and what other county that takes its name from the Latin "across woods"?   (a) Swain County   (b) Transylvania County   (c) Yancey County

9. Beginning in Person County, the Tar River runs all the way to Beaufort County where it forms the Pamlico River. Once known as the Pampticough River, the Tar's name has several explanations—an Indian word, "tau," meaning river of health; "tar" for the region's naval stores; and "Taw" for a river in Devonshire in what country?   (a) Ireland   (b) Scotland   (c) England

10. At least nine North Carolina waterways go by the name "Little River." Originally known as the Yeopim River, the Little River that rises in eastern Perquimans County and forms the border between that and Pasquotank County passes a community that goes by what name reminiscent of our nation's 37th president?   (a) Johnsonville   (b) Nixonton   (c) Kennedy Creek

Creeks And Streams

Bubbling from countless springs, North Carolina's lacework of waterways is the lifeblood of our state. Remember the good ol' days by a swimming hole with the answers to this quiz.

1. Bryson Creek originates in eastern Transylvania County and flows southeast into Henderson County where it converges with the French Broad River. This mountain stream shares its name with Bryson City, which is located on the Tuckasegee River and is the seat of what Tar Heel mountain county?
    (a) Cherokee County   (b) Buncombe County   (c) Swain County

2. Named for a type of tree, this creek flows from Northampton County northeast into Virginia where it enters the Meherrin River. No less than 10 Tar Heel waterways share the name of what evergreen species that thrives where the water is brackish?   (a) Cypress   (b) Laurel   (c) Balsam

3. From its origin in eastern Madison County, this stream cascades south to its rendezvous with a branch known as Paint Fork. This North Carolina stream goes by what name, which is also the capital of California?   (a) Los Angeles Creek   (b) San Francisco Creek   (c) Sacramento Creek

4. Waxhaw Creek rises in western Union County then flows southwest until it joins the Catawba River near the South Carolina state line. The area through which Waxhaw Creek flows was once known as "a rich oasis in the pine barrens" and was the home of what US president?
    (a) Andrew Jackson   (b) Andrew Johnson   (c) James K. Polk

5. Western Warren County is home to a creek and plantation house that was the birthplace of two Confederate generals of the same surname. This creek and former home of Robert and Matthew Ransom go by what title, reminiscent of a piece of horse tack?
    (a) Shoe Creek   (b) Bridle Creek   (c) Saddleback Creek

6. A coastal tributary, Taylor Creek separates Carrot Island from the mainland as it flows from Lenox Point to the mouth of the Newport River. Name the county—with communities such as Bertie, Stacy, and Davis—where Taylor Creek is located.   (a) Dare County   (b) Carteret County   (c) Pender County

7. Flowing from eastern Brunswick County, this creek makes its way from McKenzie Pond to the Cape Fear River. The plantation house of former North Carolina official Eleazer Allen (1692-1750) is named for and located on this creek that takes its moniker from what imaginary country in the book *Gulliver's Travels?*   (a) Oz   (b) Shangri-La   (c) Lilliput

8. Beginning in Clay County near Julie Ridge, this creek flows past Deadline Ridge before joining Tusquitee Creek. It takes its name from what directional instrument that was dropped into its waters by Revolutionary War veteran Robert Henry?
    (a) Transponder Creek   (b) Compass Creek   (c) Transit Creek

9. Pearson's Falls in Polk County tumbles over a 75-foot drop. Surrounded by a 300-acre wildflower and herbarium maintained by the Tryon Garden Club, the land around Pearson's Falls is watered by what creek, whose name has an equestrian ring to it?   (a) Horse Path Creek   (b) Mare Branch   (c) Colt Creek

10. Named for a type of small chestnut, this creek rises in Yadkin County before flowing into Davie County where it eventually joins Dutchmans Creek. What stream bears a name similar to a famous Reidsville mansion?   (a) Chinquapin   (b) Japanese Chestnut   (c) Chiskapen

11. At least four North Carolina waterways go by the name of Alligator Creek. One of these creeks begins as a tidal stream on Eagles Island in Brunswick County. Flowing southward, Alligator Creek eventually joins what river that empties into the Atlantic Ocean at Corncake Inlet?
    (a) New River   (b) Cape Fear River   (c) Pee Dee River

Playing The Name Game
With Tar Heel Towns

With the passage of time and taste, many North Carolina locales have seen their names change. Grab a gazetteer or talk to an old-timer for the answers to this quiz.

1. Prior to taking its present moniker in 1712, Craven County was named for a Quaker politician who was the governor of Carolina from 1694-96. Keeping his surname in mind, what was Craven County once known as? (a) Archdale County (c) Tryon County (c) White County

2. The seat of Carteret County, Beaufort, was incorporated in 1723. Prior to that time it went by a name that reflected what is still an important commodity in the town's economy. What was Beaufort's original name? (a) Lumberton (b) Tarboro (c) Fishtown

3. The home of Western Carolina University, Cullowhee in Jackson County, lies close to the Tuckasegee River. Cullowhee was first known by an Indian word meaning "place of the lilies." What was Cullowhee originally called? (a) Sagaway (b) Kullaughee (c) Ka-nu-ga

4. Delco is a small community on US Highway 74 in Columbus County. For about six months in 1918 residents of the region saw fit to honor the general known as "Black Jack" who was leading American troops in World War I. What general lent his name to the area that would one day be Delco? (a) Pershing (b) McArthur (c) Stillwell

5. Situated on the Tar River, Greenville took its present name in 1786. For seven years prior to that time Greenville had based its name on the last royal governor of North Carolina. What was it called? (a) Johannesburg (b) Martinsville (c) Martinsborough

6. Located in Sampson County, the town of Ivanhoe takes its present name for Sir Walter Scott's novel. Prior to the 1880s Ivanhoe was a community that was named after what river that flows from Sampson County to the Cape Fear River? (a) Tar River (b) Black River (c) Catawba River

7. A major furniture center, Hickory, dates back to the 1850s when the "town" consisted of a rustic way station. In 1863 Hickory was incorporated with what name that reflected its origin? (a) Hickory Tavern (b) Hickory Alehouse (c) Pub in the Hickories

8. One of the largest lakes in North Carolina, Lake Phelps in Washington and Tyrrell Counties, is part of Pettigrew State Park. Early maps give Lake Phelps a name after what type of native grape? (a) Lake Tokay (b) Lake Chablis (c) Scuppernong Lake

9. Site of a state port facility, Morehead City is on Bogue Sound and the Newport River. Before selecting its present name in 1861, the spit of land Morehead City is situated on was once known by what pastoral-sounding title? (a) Shepherd's Point (b) Lamb Acres (c) Sheep Run

10. The last major town on US Highway 64 in western North Carolina, Murphy sits where the Hiwassee and Valley rivers meet. An earlier name for Murphy has a different origin but similar spelling to what north Mecklenburg County town on NC Highway 115 just south of Davidson? (a) Pineville (b) Huntersville (c) Long Creek

11. Rising 1,500 feet about ground level, Pilot Mountain sits serenely surveying the Surry County landscape. On early maps, Pilot Mountain was referred to by a name similar to the peak that Moses' ark landed on. What mount was this? (a) Mt. Carmel (b) Mt. Everest (c) Mt. Ararat

12. Our North Carolina state capital of Raleigh was founded in 1792. Prior to that time the area was a center for Wake County politics and business. In 1771 through 1792, the land that would be Raleigh went by what name? (a) Wake Court House (b) Sir Walterville (c) Wakesboro

13. Famous now for golf resorts, the piney woods region of our state between the Pee Dee and Cape Fear rivers is called the Sandhills. In past years this rolling terrain was known as "Deserta Arenosa" and what other name reflective of a famous desert? (a) Tar Heel Gobi (b) Carolina Kalahari (c) Sahara of North Carolina

How They Were Named

When it comes to naming communities, Tar Heels are anything but unoriginal. Our towns are named for everything from famous novels to Latin phrases, from vice presidents to flowers. See how well you know the origins of our town names by answering the questions below. We provide the word origins; you provide the towns.

1. This town on the Black River was named in the 1880s for the hero in a novel by Sir Walter Scott.
   (a) Lancelot (b) Merlin (c) Ivanhoe

2. Inundated by Fontana Lake, this community had been named for a type of clover that grew in the area. After Pearl Harbor, locals started calling the town MacArthur because its original name had become quite unpopular. What was this name? (a) Tojo (b) Japan (c) Nakajima

3. This Eno River town was named in 1766 after Wills Hill, President of the Board of Trade and Plantations and secretary of state for the Colonies. (a) Hillsborough (b) Willisville (c)Hillton

4. An 18th century New York mineralogist and a gem found only in North Carolina gave this town its name. (a) Micaville (b) Johnstone (c) Hiddenite

5. The Ohio city that provided steel for a bridge being built over the nearby Pigeon River gave this mountain town its name. (a) Canton (b) Cleveland (c) Dayton

6. This Gaston County town was named for the 11th vice president of the United States.
   (a) Dallas (b) Belmont (c) Lowell

7. This furniture-producing town was named after the unique position it occupied on the old North Carolina Railroad. (a) Lowesville (b) High Point (c) Midland

8. Originally named for the Japanese city Togo, this town was renamed for a Confederate leader after December 7, 1941. (a) Genlee (b) Davisboro (c) Jacksonville

9. The Confederate ironclad *Neuse* was built near this town, named for the number of mineral springs around which a local resort once operated. (a) Five Springs (b) Six Springs (c) Seven Springs

10. This town shares its name with an adjacent peak, the site of the old WBTV transmitting tower.
    (a) Spencer Mountain (b) Pilot Mountain (c) Mount Gilead

11. In Watauga County, this community takes its name from the Latin phrase for "Valley of the Cross."
    (a) Crucis Vale (b) Valcrosse (c) Valle Crucis

12. On Roanoke Island, this village was named after one of two Indians taken to England by explorers in 1584. (a) Ocracoke (b) Wanchese (c) Hatteras

13. This community takes its name from a mineral discovered nearby. The mineral is the birthstone for December. (a) Garnet (b) Corundum (c) Zirconia

14. Benjamin Franklin was an envoy to the court of the French monarch for whom this town was named in 1779. (a) Charlestown (b) Richardsville (c) Louisburg

15. William Byrd's estate lent its name to this town on the Dan and Smith rivers.
    (a) Eden (b) Valhalla (c) Magnolia

16. A local resident named this Catawba County town after an Italian who sculpted a statue of George Washington that once stood in Raleigh. (a) Garibaldi (b) Antonio (c) Conover

17. Incorporated in 1869, this town took the name of Lafayette's estate near Paris.
    (a) Sans Souci (b) LaGrange (c) Fountain bleau

18. Birthplace of Governor Charles Aycock, this town was named after the chief engineer of the Wilmington and Weldon Railroad. (a) Edwards (b) Smithfield (c) Fremont

19. Frequent floods in the valley below this community gave it the look of a famous Italian bay...hence its name. (a) Venice (b) Naples (c) Biscayne

20. This college town, a center of Lumbee Indian affairs, was named for a railroad official.
    (a) Pembroke (b) Carnegie (c) Pullman

7

Tar Heel Crossroads

Crossroads in North Carolina can range from the intersection of teeming interstate highways to sleepy little spots where country roads meet one another near field and forest. Don't lose your way as you search for the Carolina crossroads in this quiz.

1. Once home to its own little Grand Ole Opry, but more recently known for apple orchards and a feline moniker, the intersection of state roads 1002 and 1113 in northwest Lincoln County goes by what name? (a) Tiger Crossing (b) Cat Square (c) Tomcat Crossroads

2. The little Surry County community of Ararat is located near the junction of State Road 2019 and State Road 2017 along the banks of the Ararat River. Ararat took its name from the Biblical spot where what famous ship came to rest? (a) Noah's Ark (b) King David's fleet (c) John's fishing boat

3. It's a place at crossroads of a different type that makes the Montgomery County town of Star unique. Sometimes called Twinkletown, Star is the geographical center of North Carolina where what type of lines intersect? (a) longitude and altitude (b) latitude and magnitude (c) longitude and latitude

4. Said to have once been the largest strawberry market in the country, Tin City in Duplin County is one mile east of Wallace at the junction of NC 11 and NC 41. Things are quiet in Tin City, but just to the east thousands of cars roar down what major highway? (a) I-95 (b) I-85 (c) I-40

5. Dating back to before the Civil War, Silk Hope in Chatham County fills the junction of State Road 1003 and State Road 1346. Silk Hope takes its name from the story that in the 1800s a resident tried to raise silkworms there on what type of trees? (a) Longleaf Pine (b) Mulberry (c) Cypress

6. Snow Camp at the intersection of State Road 1005 and State Road 1004 was given its name by British soldiers who camped there during a snow storm in March 1781. Snow Camp is located in what county seated by Graham? (a) Alamance County (b) Madison County (c) Camden County

7. Just east of Whiteville in Columbus County, the little crossroads of Red Bug is at the junction of State Road 1904 and State Road 1907. Red Bug got its name after area loggers suffered countless bites from what insects known as "red bugs"? (a) mosquitoes (b) flies (c) chiggers

8. Residents of the little Bladen County community at the juncture of NC 87 and NC 131 have the unique distinction of living where our state's nickname is home. Name this hamlet, once famous for its naval stores. (a) Turpentine (b) Tar Heel (c) Tarboro

9. Three miles west of Bonlee at the merging of State Road 1005 and State Road 1006, the community of Rabbits Crossroads was once the center of a lively bunny trapping trade. What county, seated by Pittsboro, is the site of Rabbits Crossroads? (a) Orange County (b) Chatham County (c) Wake County

10. Calico is a small community in southern Pitt County whose name comes from a type of cloth that sold well at a local store. What two highways running from Greenville and Ayden intersect and form the Calico crossroads? (a) NC 43 and 102 (b) US 74 and 421 (c) NC 306 and 101

11. The Granville County community of Tally Ho was a popular hunting spot and stagecoach stop in the early 1800s. Located at the juncture of Tally Ho Road and State Road 1136, this hamlet takes its name from the cry hunters give as they chase what animal? (a) deer (b) possums (c) foxes

12. The town of Turkey in Sampson County has had everything from a thriving pepper trade to a school known as Turkey Male Academy. Located at the crossing of NC 24 and State Road 1909, Turkey is about a 10-mile strut east of what community that is Sampson's seat?
(a) Roseboro (b) Piney Green (c) Clinton

13. The cool little Surry County community of Zephyr sits at the juncture of State Road 1001 and State Road 1315. Zephyr is located just east of what river that flows into the Yadkin?
(a) Mitchell River (b) Pisgah River (c) Clingman's River

Name That Town

Many North Carolina towns take their names from folks who have made a significant contribution to either our state or nation. With this quiz, measure your memory of Tar Heel municipalities named for people.

1. A college town, Transylvania County's seat also is the home of a popular summer music festival and the Cradle of Forestry in America historic site. Name this community, incorporated in 1889 and titled for a Revolutionary War surgeon. (a) Brendletown (b) Brevard (c) Boone

2. The little community of Jackson Hill in Davidson County dates back to 1828. Located on NC Highway 8 just a few miles from the Yadkin River, Jackson Hill was named for what Southern military man? (a) Andrew Jackson (b) Stonewall Jackson (c) Jackson Browne

3. Perched in Perquimans County between the Little and Perquimans rivers, Durants Neck takes its name from George Durant who settled nearby during the mid-1600s. Name the large body of fresh water near Durants Neck that was originally known as the Sea of Rawnocke. (a) Lake Norman (b) Rattan Bay (c) Albemarle Sound

4. A textile town in Gaston County, Bessemer City dates back to the Victorian era. Locally known for its "Jiggers" 1950s-style drive-in restaurant, Bessemer City was named after Sir Henry Bessemer (1813-1898), who discovered the process of making what important modern metal? (a) steel (b) aluminum (c) titanium

5. Located on a site that was originally a militia muster grounds before campaigns against the Indians and the Battle of Kings Mountain, Newland was incorporated in 1913. Flanked by the Linville and Toe rivers, Newland is in what county? (a) McDowell County (b) Avery County (c) Ashe County

6. Once called Lonesome Valley by an early settler homesick for his native Virginia, Henderson in Vance County takes its name from 19th-century jurist Leonard Henderson. That Virginian would probably be surprised to see what teeming highway skimming the outskirts of Henderson these days? (a) I-26 (b) I-95 (c) I-85

7. Incorporated in 1852, the seat of Montgomery County was laid out as early as 1843. Bisected by NC Highways 24/27, this Tar Heel town's name is said to have come from either a 19th-century UNC trustee, a former member of the General Assembly, or what ancient Mediterranean city? (a) Athens (b) Troy (c) Memphis

8. Formed at the junction of NC 16 and the Alexander Railroad, this Tar Heel town dates back to 1847 and takes its name from the 12th President of the United States. Name this town called after the man known as "Old Rough and Ready." (a) Taylorsville (b) Jacksonville (c) Lincolnton

9. Not as populous as the city of the same name in Ohio, North Carolina's town of Cleveland is located about 10 or so miles northwest of Salisbury in Rowan County. Originally known as Third Creek, Cleveland takes its name after what former US Commander-in-Chief? (a) Theodore Cleveland (b) Benjamin Cleveland (c) Grover Cleveland

10. Our state's only deepwater port north of Wilmington, Morehead City takes its name from former governor John Motley Morehead (1796-1866). Situated on Bogue Sound and the Newport River, Morehead City is in what county? (a) New Hanover County (b) Onslow County (c) Carteret County

11. The seat of Stanly County, Albemarle is a thriving North Carolina city that also offers wilderness recreation in nearby Uwharrie National Forest. Albemarle takes its name from George Monck (1608-1679), who also went by what title? (a) Lord Proprietor of Carolina (b) Carolina's Royal Gubernator (c) Royal Carolina Highness

Street Wise

A love of whimsy coupled with active imaginations has given North Carolina towns a wealth of unique street names. Take a walk on the sunny side as you guess these Tar Heel streets.

1. Perhaps more than any other state, North Carolina has a special relationship with its stock-car driving heroes. What 1998 Daytona 500 winner calls our state home and has both a modern four-lane highway in Cabarrus County and a sandy little lane in Robeson County near Maxton named for him?
   (a) Dale Jarrett   (b) Dale Earnhardt   (c) Rusty Wallace

2. The little community of Killians Crossroads must have felt an uncontrollable itch to chuckle when it named a street Fuzzy Road. Killians residents and the rest of what Piedmont county seated by Newton can claim Fuzzy Road as their own?   (a) Catawba County   (b) Iredell County   (c) Robeson County

3. Kinston in Lenoir County is known for the CSS Neuse State Historic Site and the Richard Caswell Memorial. What street in Kinston takes its name from the organization whose motto is "Always be Prepared"?   (a) Boy Scout Lane   (b) 4-H Highway   (c) Girl Scout Road

4. Not to be confused with its same name city in South Carolina, Greenville in Pitt County is the home of East Carolina University. No doubt having brought on many a chuckle, one thoroughfare in Greenville goes by what rather provincial name?
   (a) Bubba Boulevard   (b) Redneck Road   (c) White Lightning' Lane

5. Residents and visitors to the historic coastal town of New Bern have much to feast their eyes on, including magnificent Tryon Palace and its gardens. Considering the fact that New Bern has been a sailor's town for 300 years, in earlier days what street name might have meant "a short stroll"?
   (a) Wharf Way   (b) Gangplank Road   (c) Blackbeard Boulevard

6. Located in a rich agricultural region of our state, Wilson in Wilson County also is the home of Barton formerly Atlantic Christian College. The farm crop that put Wilson on the map lends its name to what street that shares its name with a novel by Erskine Caldwell?
   (a) Tobacco Road   (b) Watermelon Way   (c) Poke Sallet Annie Street

7. The seat of Swain County, Bryson City, was once known as Charleston. It is a popular tourist destination and station for the Great Smoky Mountains Railway. What road named here heads north out of town, passes through an eerie tunnel, then comes to a dead end in the forest?
   (a) Last Stop Lane   (b) End of the Line Road   (c) The Road to Nowhere

8. Well known for its furniture industry, the city of Hickory also is the home of the Waldensian Winery. An excellent place to call home, Hickory has one street whose name is like what destination most everyone would like to arrive at?   (a) Easy Street   (b) Millionaire Way   (c) Rich Avenue

9. In addition to its nickname as barbecue capital of North Carolina, Lexington is the seat of Davidson County. Hopefully not the true state of any resident's financial condition, what street in Lexington nonetheless conjures up thoughts of hard times?
   (a) Bankruptcy Boulevard   (b) Penniless Place   (c) Poverty Lane

10. Monroe in Union County is in the heart of North Carolina's poultry-farming district. Named for President James Monroe, the town also pays tribute to one of its own politicians by having at least five streets bear the last name of what famous US senator from North Carolina?
    (a) Jesse Helms   (b) Harvey Gantt   (c) Lauch Faircloth

11. Home of many mountain attractions including "Ghost Town In the Sky," Maggie Valley in Haywood County was named in 1909 for the postmaster's daughter, Maggie Mae Setzer. Echoing an old nursery rhyme, what Maggie Valley road is named after the item "daddy had gone a-hunting to wrap his baby bunting in"?   (a) Silk Street   (b) Rabbit Skin Road   (c) Lace Lane

County Courthouses Past And Present

Like each of the 100 counties they serve, North Carolina's courthouses have their own unique style. Cast your verdict for the correct answers to this quiz on our state's magnificent "temples of justice."

1. Completed in 1927 at a cost of $256,000, the present Cherokee County Courthouse in Murphy is a two-story example of Neo-Classical Revival architecture. What material mined just a few miles from Murphy is the building constructed of? (a) slate (b) limestone (c) marble

2. Built in 1881, the Chatham County Courthouse sits smack in the middle of an English-style traffic roundabout formed by US Highway 64 and US Highway 15-501. What town is both the location of the courthouse and the seat of Chatham? (a) Pittsboro (b) Silk Hope (c) Matthews

3. A national historic landmark, the 1767 Chowan County Courthouse has been called the finest example of Georgian public architecture in our state. Though a more modern structure now handles most of Chowan's legal business, the old courthouse still sits proudly overlooking what bay?
    (a) Carolina Bay (b) Edenton Bay (c) Pamlico Bay

4. Perched high on a hill in beautiful downtown Sylva, the Jackson County Courthouse was built in 1914 for $30,000. Almost a tune-up for hiking in the mountains that surround its clock-faced cupola, visitors to this courthouse can opt to climb how many steps to the front door? (a) 107 (b) 60 (c) 45

5. The Victorian-style courthouse in Transylvania County is located at Brevard. During our nation's bicentennial, citizens in Transylvania buried a time capsule in the courthouse yard to be dug up in another 100 years. Name the year that event will occur. (a) 2081 (b) 2076 (c) 2077

6. Built in the Beaux Arts Neo-Classical style, the Wilkes County Courthouse dates back to 1903. Located on ground that has seen Tories hung and Tom Dula jailed, this courthouse is in what town?
    (a) Fairplains (b) Boomer (c) Wilkesboro

7. The present Brunswick County Courthouse was built in 1979 and is a sleek one-story structure surrounded by earthen berms. What central Brunswick County town, whose name has a South American ring to it, is this court's site? (a) Bolivia (b) Columbia (c) Chile

8. The old Burke County Courthouse in Morganton is on the National Register of Historic Places and dates back to 1833. Though a courthouse built in 1976 serves Burke today, the old building witnessed much history, including what first for a Tar Heel woman?
    (a) first woman lawyer (b) first woman hanged in North Carolina (c) first woman judge

9. Costing $28,000 to construct, the 1861 Caswell County Courthouse at Yanceyville was designed by one of the most influential architects of pre-Civil War North Carolina. Name this builder, who also counted among his works the 1858 New East and New West buildings at the University of North Carolina at Chapel Hill. (a) Christopher Wrenn (b) Frank Wright (c) William Percival

10. A state highway historical marker telling the tale of Cherokee Indian Tsali's bravery graces the front lawn of the Swain County Courthouse. Built on the banks of the Tuckasegee River in 1908, this hall of justice is in what Swain town? (a) Bryson City (b) Birdtown (c) Stecoah

11. Hertford County's fourth courthouse was built in 1956. During what war was one of Hertford's previous courthouses, at the county seat of Winton, burned with the rest of the town?
    (a) War of 1812 (b) Civil War (c) Revolutionary War

12. The Craven County Courthouse combines both French and Roman architecture into its imposing 1883 structure. What town, our state capital from 1746 until 1792, is the location of this brick bastion?
    (a) New Bern (b) Bath (c) Morehead City

13. Replaced by a granite, brick and marble structure built in 1959, the older Davidson County Courthouse at Lexington had served its citizens since its completion in 1858. With its majestic columns, this courthouse took its style from Virginia's capitol in what city?
    (a) Appomattox (b) Alexandria (c) Richmond

North Carolina Military Camps

Thanks to its mild climate and strategic location, North Carolina has long been a place where soldiers, sailors and airmen have earned their stripes and wings. Salute our state's military camps past and present with the correct answers to this quiz.

1. During World War I many US Army soldiers learned to operate tanks at a huge training facility located in Raleigh. Situated just off Hillsborough Road, the camp took its name from a Revolutionary War colonel and was called what? (a) Camp Lee (b) Camp Jackson (c) Camp Polk

2. Located about two miles north of Fort Fisher in New Hanover County, Camp Wyatt was a Civil War training facility. This camp was named for a rebel soldier, Henry Wyatt, who had what distinction? (a) first Confederate killed in Civil War (b) oldest soldier in Confederate army (c) youngest soldier in Confederate army

3. With 110,000 acres of land and nearly 60,000 personnel, the US Marine complex in Onslow County bills itself "the world's most complete amphibious training base." Name this famous post which was started in 1942. (a) Camp Pendelton (b) Camp Lejeune (c) Camp Pyle

4. Camp Greene was a World War I training camp that occupied 6,000 acres in Mecklenburg County just west of Charlotte. Able to house up to 60,000 troops, this camp was named for Nathanael Greene, a general in what war? (a) Revolutionary War (b) Spanish-American War (c) Boer War

5. The second-largest paratrooper training base in the US during World War II, Camp Mackall saw Airborne soldiers from the 82nd and 101st divisions by the thousands learn their trade. Located in east Richmond and northwest Scotland counties, Camp Mackall was closest to which of the following towns? (a) Elmer (b) Marston (c) Hasty

6. Used to train Confederate conscripts, Camp Vance in Burke County operated from 1861 until its capture in 1864 by Union Colonel George Kirk. Camp Vance was named for what famous Tar Heel, our Civil War governor and a brave soldier in his own right? (a) General A.D. Vance (b) Colonel Vance Burke (c) Colonel Zebulon B. Vance

7. Names for Tar Heel native Major General Richmond Davis (1866-1937), Camp Davis was a World War II anti-aircraft training base that at times held as many as 60,000 soldiers. Camp Davis operated from 1941-45 near Holly Ridge in what county? (a) Onslow (b) Pender (c) Nash

8. Camp Chronicle was a World War I training facility that was located near present-day S. Linwood Street in Gastonia. Camp Chronicle operated in conjunction with a nearby artillery range situated at the base of what Gaston County mountain? (a) Little Mountain (b) Pilot Mountain (c) Crowders Mountain

9. Another Civil War training camp once located in our state was Camp Alamance. This camp was situated in Alamance County near the North Carolina Railroad repair depot named Company Shops. What modern city now occupies the site? (a) Snow Camp (b) Burlington (c) Union Ridge

10. Camp Clingman operated in Asheville during the Civil War on French Broad Avenue. This camp was named for Confederate Brigadier General and statesman Thomas L. Clingman. What mountain in Swain County also carries on the Clingman name? (a) Clingmans Dome (b) Mount Clingman (c) Clingmans Peak

11. During the Revolutionary War, Tar Heel patriot and military leader William Davidson was with his men at Camp Rocky River on October 10, 1780, when he received news of a great American victory to the west. What triumph over the British led by Colonel Patrick Ferguson had just taken place? (a) Battle of Guilford Courthouse (b) Battle of Kings Mountain (c) Battle of Catawba Heights

12. One of the 14 military bases and camps located in our state during World War II, Camp Butner was established in 1942. Serving as an infantry training post, hospital and relocation center, Butner straddled the lines of what counties? (a) Stanly/Cabarrus (b) Martin/Pitt (c) Durham/Granville/Person

All You Wanted To Know About Tar Heel Mansions

Built by skilled craftsmen of fine native stone, bricks or timber, the mansions of North Carolina offer plenty to brag about. Put your architectural knowledge to the test with the answers to this quiz on our state's many stately homes.

1. The largest private residence in the United States, Asheville's Biltmore House was built for George Washington Vanderbilt by Richard Morris Hunt. In what year was this 255-room edifice completed? (a) 1895 (b) 1880 (c) 1910

2. Built in the shape of a cross by the Hairston family in 1854, Cooleemee Plantation house sits overlooking the Yadkin River. What county, whose seat is Mocksville, is the home of this fine "Anglo-Grecian villa?" (a) Henderson County (b) Iredell County (c) Davie County

3. Now part of an historical museum complex, the 1774 Hezekiah Alexander House was once the home of a successful Scotch-Irish planter. Constructed of native stone, this two-story structure is located in what North Carolina county, the first to declare independence from Great Britain?
    (a) Wake County (b) Mecklenburg County (c) Rowan County

4. Located at 100 Hermitage Road in Charlotte, the historic mansion "White Oaks" has been owned over the years by men like James Cannon of Cannon Mills and textile magnate Henry Lineberger. During the 1920s the home achieved its full glory under the ownership of what tobacco and electricity tycoon?
    (a) James B. Duke (b) Phillip Morris (c) Joe "Bull" Durham

5. Constructed in 1825 and located just off NC Highway 133 near Winnabow, one of our state's most popular tourist attractions centers around the plantation house of rice planter "King" Roger Moore. Name this mansion, famous for its azalea gardens.
    (a) Evergreen Gardens (b) Moore Manor (c) Orton Plantation

6. The home of our state's chief executive, Raleigh's Governor's Mansion, was built on Burke Square in 1891. When money to complete the project ran short, the man in charge of construction, W.J. Hicks, employed men from what nearby institution as laborers and brickmakers?
    (a) State Prison (b) UNC-Chapel Hill (c) NC State University

7. An 1850 Greek Revival mansion, Poplar Grove Plantation was once a thriving 600-acre estate worked by more that 60 slaves. Now on the National Record of Historic Places, Poplar Grove is located in what community on US Highway 17 just north of Wilmington? (a) Oleander (b) Greenfield (c) Scotts Hill

8. A coastal landmark, Cupola House is a unique two-story frame structure that dates to the early 18th century. Fine woodworking and, of course, the cupola on top are features of this home in what Chowan County town, once our colony's capital from 1722 to 1743? (a) New Bern (b) Edenton (c) Yeopim

9. Completed in 1770, New Bern's Tryon Palace and its gardens are both an architectural and botanical treasure. A top tourist destination, Tryon Palace was known as "the most beautiful building in the colonial Americas." What royal governor had this stately brick home constructed?
    (a) William Tryon (b) Thomas Tryon (c) Sir Tryon Featherstone

10. A 27-room mansion full of fabulous art treasures and antiques, Chinqua-Penn Plantation's stone construction features a large clock tower and 20 acres of gardens. Originally owned by Mr. and Mrs. Thomas Jefferson Penn, the estate is now open to the public near what town north of Greensboro? (a) Thomasville (b) Reidsville (c) Marston

11. An antebellum estate dating back to 1820, the Dr. Josephus Hall House is a fine Tar Heel home that still contains many pieces of Federal and Victorian furniture. After the Civil War, Hall House was used as Union headquarters in what town, the seat of Rowan County?
    (a) China Grove (b) Mount Ulla (c) Salisbury

12. The former home of Governor David Stone (1808-1810), Hope Plantation house is a stately, two-story Federal structure of Georgian design. Still containing Stone's 1,400-volume library, the home is open to the public near the town of Windsor in what county? (a) Chowan (b) Bertie (c) Halifax

13. The former residence of railroad and lumber tycoon John Wilkinson, River Forest Manor in Belhaven is an opulent reminder of turn-of-the-century Tar Heel wealth. Modern visitors to River Forest Manor enter the home through huge Ionic columns after they dock their boats at what nearby river?
    (a) Pungo River (b) Rocky River (c) Black River

Historic North Carolina Churches

With literally thousands of churches scattered across our state, North Carolina could be called the "buckle of the Bible Belt." Be one of those who faithfully answer the questions to this quiz on Tar Heel church lore and locations.

1. Dating back to 1734, Saint Thomas Episcopal Church is said to be the oldest house of worship in North Carolina. Saint Thomas' two-foot-thick walls have stood the test of time in what Beaufort County location, the oldest in our state? (a) Pinetown (b) Bath (c) Leechville

2. The burial site of three North Carolina colonial governors, Saint Paul's Episcopal Church was started in 1736 but not completed until 30 years later. Described as a "large, handsome brick church, with a steeple," Saint Pauls is located in what county seat on the Albemarle Sound?
    (a) Valhalla (b) Durants Neck (c) Edenton

3. Christ Church in Raleigh was under construction from 1848 to 1861. Designed by English-born architect Richard Upjohn, the church is built of stone in the Gothic Revival style. What shape does the ground plan of this National Historic Landmark assume? (a) cruciform (b) rectangle (c) pentagon

4. Situated at the corner of Trade and Church streets in Charlotte, First Presbyterian Church dates all the way back to 1832. For many years the widow of Stonewall Jackson lived next door to First Presbyterian. Known as the "First Lady of the South," what was her name?
    (a) Varina Jackson (b) Mary Anna Morrison Jackson (c) Brenda Kay Jackson

5. Painted by internationally known artist Ben Long, the magnificent fresco of the Last Supper in Holy Trinity Church at Glendale Springs fills visitors with reverent awe. Located on NC Highway 16, Holy Trinity and Glendale Springs are in what county? (a) Catawba Co. (b) Wilkes Co. (c) Ashe Co.

6. Saint James Episcopal, the oldest church in Wilmington still in use, has an original structure that dates back to 1770. Much history surrounds Saint James, including the fact that its graveyard is the burial place of what patriot whose last name is given to the county that is seated by Lillington?
    (a) Cornelius Harnett (b) Joseph Johnston (c) John Stokes

7. Another notable Wilmington house of worship is Saint Therese Catholic Church. Located on Market Street, this church was first known as St. Mary by the Sea. Rebuilt in 1955, Saint Therese was nearly destroyed by what famous October 1954 hurricane?
    (a) Hurricane Hugo (b) Hurricane Hazel (c) Hurricane Dorothy Jean

8. Designed in 1852 by prominent Charleston, South Carolina, architect E.C. Jones, Saint John in the Wilderness is located in Henderson County, not far from poet Carl Sandburg's Connemara estate. What town is home for this quaint mountain church? (a) Saluda (b) Bat Cave (c) East Flat Rock

9. In 1819 Presbyterian citizens of Craven County's seat began construction of a 70-by-50-foot church that is still touted as the finest example of a Federal-style house of worship in our state. Designed by Uriah Sandy, First Presbyterian is located in what town? (a) New Bern (b) Bath (c) Havelock

10. Designed in 1895 by Richard Morris Hunt, All Souls Episcopal Church is a small-but-powerful example of the Byzantine style. In addition to All Souls, Hunt also designed what nearby Buncombe County mansion for the same patron? (a) Bryn Avon (b) Cooleemee (c) Biltmore House

11. A splendid brick structure topped by a baroque Germanic steeple, Home Church in Winston-Salem was completed in 1800. What religious group, the people who founded Salem, were the driving force behind the construction of Home Church? (a) Catholics (b) Moravians (c) Jesuits

12. Belmont Abbey, the name of a monastery and college in Gaston County, was founded by Benedictine monks in 1876. Dominating the Abbey campus is a Gothic Revival church whose stained-glass windows won the 1893 prize at the Columbian Exhibition in Chicago. What denomination is Belmont Abbey aligned with? (a) Catholic (b) Lutheran (c) Episcopalian

13. Situated at the corner of Seventh and North Tryon streets in uptown Charlotte, Saint Peter's Protestant Episcopal Church hosted worshippers on its present site as early as 1858. In April 1865, Saint Peter's received guests in the form of what fleeing Confederate president and his cabinet?
    (a) Jubal Early (b) Jefferson Davis (c) Joseph E. Johnston

Graves And Graveyards Of The Tar Heel State

Though most rest in peace, there are always a few spirits up and about. Don't get spooked as you answer the questions in this quiz about some of our state's most interesting graves and graveyards.

1. Raleigh's old City Cemetery dates back to around 1792 when its first five acres were laid out. By 1810 the town had hired a "Pastor to the City" at a salary of $500 annually to perform burial ceremonies there. What street just east of town was this graveyard originally located on?
   (a) Blount Street   (b) East Street   (c) Fayetteville Street

2. Peter Ney died in 1846 in Rowan County. Buried at Third Creek Presbyterian Church, Ney was said by some to really be marshal Michel Ney, a hero of the French Revolution who escaped to this country in 1816 following the downfall of what French leader?
   (a) Napoleon Bonaparte   (b) Maurice Chevalier   (c) Paul Bruchon

3. On Ocracoke Island the British Sailors' Cemetery contains the graves of four Royal Navy sailors who lost their lives off our North Carolina shores. Victims of a German submarine, these men and their ship, the *Bedfordshire,* went down in what year?   (a) 1918   (b) 1940   (c) 1942

4. Buried at Pleasant Grove Baptist Cemetery just north of Fuquay-Varina in 1890, Rebecca Alford's tombstone recounts the time during the Civil War when she threw scalding water on Yankee scalawags. Name the county where Rebecca's grave is located.   (a) Orange Co.   (b) Wake Co.   (c) Hoke Co.

5. As his tombstone attests, Alton Stewart was in 1926 the first person in North Carolina to earn an airplane pilot's license. Sadly, Stewart's flying career came to a sudden end with his fatal crash in 1929 near the town of Coats in what eastern Tar Heel county?   (a) Harnett   (b) Rutherford   (c) Hoke

6. An oddity to some and an inspiration to many, George Harrill of Shelby moved at the age of 63 to an abandoned bomb shelter south of Kure Beach. Dispensing a special brand of philosophy until his death in 1972, Harrill took what nickname from the Civil War fort he's buried near?
   (a) "Fort Shaw Socrates"   (b) "Fort Fisher Hermit"   (c) "Bard of Fort Barnwell"

7. Dating back to the early 1700s, the historic graveyard in Carteret County's seat includes among others the tombstone of an 18th-century naval officer who was buried standing upright. What is the name given to Beaufort's cemetery?   (a) Hallowed Hill   (b) Centennial Cemetery   (c) Old Burying Ground

8. Though he lived on until 1969, Jesse Maness of Montgomery County lost in a 1913 accident a part of himself that was buried with its own separate tombstone. Sharing this distinction with Stonewall Jackson, Maness was buried separately from which one of his bodily parts?   (a) his arm   (b) his leg   (c) his ear

9. Dating back to the 1850s, Charlotte's Elmwood Cemetery holds many unique tombs and tombstones. One of the most famous graves belongs to a Hollywood actor who starred in films such as "Virginia City," "Colt 45," and "Ride The High Country." Name this star who died in 1987.
   (a) Rudolph Valentino   (b) Tom Mix   (c) Randolph Scott

10. A bit of debate still swirls around whether the stone angel in Hendersonville's Oakdale Cemetery or another in a graveyard near Bryson City is the figure Thomas Wolfe made famous in one of his novels. Name the title to Wolfe's book that made use of one of these heavenly creatures.
    (a) *Angel On My Shoulder*   (b) *Look Homeward, Angel*   (c) *Angel in the Outfield*

11. Goshen Cemetery in the Gaston County community of North Belmont is the burial place for at least a dozen Revolutionary War patriots, some of whom fought at the Battle of Kings Mountain. Goshen was the first graveyard in our state west of what nearby river?   (a) Yadkin   (b) Uwharrie   (c) Catawba

12. Near Godwin in Cumberland County lies the grave of David Williams, who died in 1975. A gunsmith and inventor, Williams perfected the design for a new type of rifle while serving a prison sentence. What type of light, rapid-fire weapon did Williams invent that World War II soldiers liked so well?
    (a) Carbine   (b) Bofors gun   (c) Flak gun

13. Wilmington's first municipal burial ground, Oakdale Cemetery, opened for business in 1855. Among its many unusual and historical monuments is the one to Nance Martin, who died at sea in 1857. Martin had the distinction of being pickled, then buried at Oakdale in a large casket of what grog?
    (a) rum   (b) root beer   (c) sarsaparilla

Much Ado About Museums

Whether you're interested in Native American history or traditional wooden boats, North Carolina has a museum for you. How well do you know your options?

1. Housed in a restored 19th century doctor's office, the Country Doctor Museum has instruments, supplies and furnishings from that era. What Nash County town is its home?
   (a) Stanhope   (b) Bailey   (c) Red Oak

2. What town on US 74, just west of Lumberton, is home to the Indian Museum of the Carolinas, with Native American artifacts and exhibits?   (a) Laurinburg   (b) Hamlet   (c) Pembroke

3. Rock hounds delight in the specimens on display at the Museum of North Carolina Minerals. Just off the Blue Ridge Parkway at milepost 331, what town, named for a type of tree, is nearby?
   (a) Juniper   (b) Cypress   (c) Spruce Pine

4. A carriage collection and information on textile history are just a few of the exhibits at the Gaston County Museum of Art and History. Name the town, once the county seat, where the museum is housed in an 1852 hotel.   (a) Abilene   (b) Dallas   (c) Waco

5. Lovers of small, traditional wooden boats and their lore enjoy the North Carolina Maritime Museum. Name the town, seat of Carteret County, where the museum is located.
   (a) Smyrna   (b) Sealevel   (c) Beaufort

6. Don't expect to find Rambo's headband at the JFK Special Warfare Museum, but you will find lots of other artifacts from unconventional and psychological warfare. What famous North Carolina paratrooper base hosts the museum?   (a) Fort Bragg   (b) Fort Benning   (c) Fort Jackson

7. Puffers, chewers, dippers and others curious about the history and production of tobacco can have their cravings satisfied at the Tobacco Museum of North Carolina. What Johnston County town, along US 301, houses this museum?   (a) Four Oaks   (b) Bagley   (c) Kenly

8. Interested in pre-1820s home furnishings and decorating? Then it would behoove you to visit the Museum of Early Southern Decorative Arts. Name the city, Forsyth County's most populous, where the museum has been since 1965.   (a) Winston-Salem   (b) Clemmons   (c) Kernersville

9. The oldest house (circa 1872) in this Lee County town holds not only a collection of rail memorabilia, but also pottery and local history documents. Where is the Railroad House Museum located?
   (a) Tramway   (b) Sanford   (c) Lemon Springs

10. Owned by the Eastern Band of Cherokee Indians and containing artifacts from their rich heritage, the Museum of the Cherokee Indian is located on US 441. Pinpoint the popular mountain town where the museum is located.   (a) Smokemont   (b) Maggie Valley   (c) Cherokee

11. One need not be a Methodist to find the World Methodist Museum interesting. What mountain lake, named for a Cherokee chief, is nearby?   (a) Lake Junaluska   (b) Lake Sequoyah   (c) Lake Hiawatha

12. A former Civil War blockade runner port is the present-day home of the Cape Fear Museum. What waterfront city houses this broad collection of lowland lore?
    (a) Sea Breeze   (b) Wilmington   (c) Wrightsville Beach

13. Moon rock, dinosaur replicas and a petting zoo are just a few of the attractions at the North Carolina Museum of Life and Science. What town claims this museum?
    (a) Durham   (b) Wake Forest   (c) Raleigh

14. Housed in a former branch of the US Mint, the Mint Museum of Art has hosted everything from the casket of an Egyptian pharaoh to the treasures of Russian royalty. What Piedmont city is home to the mint?   (a) Raleigh   (b) Statesville   (c) Charlotte

15. The Waldensians are a religious group that traces its roots back to 12th century Italy. In 1893, 29 members came to Burke County, where the Waldensian Museum chronicles their way of life. What town, whose name is Italian for "Valley of Our Lord," is home to this unique showplace?
    (a) Val Dor   (b) Valdese   (c) Valle Crucis

Public Gardens In North Carolina

Showcasing an incredible variety of indoor and outdoor plant life, North Carolina offers nearly 40 public gardens and arboretums for visitors' viewing pleasure. See if you can pinpoint each Tar Heel plant paradise with this quiz.

1. Located on US 421, all but 20 of Greenfield Gardens' 200 acres consist of a lovely cypress- and azalea-lined lake. Its Old South ambience is situated just two miles from the downtown area of what coastal North Carolina city? (a) Surf City (b) Morehead City (c) Wilmington

2. The Elizabethan Gardens have brought an elegant bit of the 16th century to Manteo since 1951. Overlooking Roanoke Sound, the gardens are located near what fort?
(a) Fort Caswell (b) Fort Raleigh (c) Fort Fisher

3. Once the domain of "King" Roger Moore, Orton Plantation began life as a rice plantation in 1725. Featuring camellias, azaleas and a host of other flowering shrubs, the gardens at Orton were started 100 years ago. Name the river that Orton Plantation Gardens overlooks.
(a) Catawba River (b) Cape Fear River (c) Tar River

4. With nine gardens scattered over 25 acres, Sandhills Community College Gardens have plantings in everything from roses to vegetables. In what Moore County recreation mecca are these gardens located?
(a) Pinehurst (b) Eagle Springs (c) Glendon

5. Blooming from late spring until October, more than 1,000 roses fill the grounds of Raleigh's Municipal Rose Garden with incredible fragrance and beauty. Behind what Raleigh cultural landmark are all those roses situated?
(a) Raleigh Symphony Hall (b) Raleigh Little Theatre (c) Raleigh Museum of Art

6. Laid out in 1916 on the grounds of R.J. Reynolds' estate, the 130-acre Reynolda Gardens spotlight Japanese cherry trees, magnolias and an All-America rose collection. What Forsyth County town is home to Reynolda Gardens? (a) Winston-Salem (b) Clemmons (c) Vienna

7. Under the care of the North Carolina Botanical Garden, Penny's Bend Nature Preserve near Durham is actually the property of the US Army Corps of Engineers. Rare plants and hiking trails are features of this 84-acre natural garden located on what river? (a) French Broad (b) Rocky (c) Eno

8. Part of the Duke University campus, the 55-acre Sarah P. Duke Gardens are an eclectic botanical collection that includes iris, native plants and an Asian arboretum. Which campus of Duke University is home to these gardens? (a) South Campus (b) West Campus (c) North Campus

9. Located at Red Springs, Flora Macdonald Gardens were created over a 40-year span by Charles Vardell, the first president of Flora Macdonald Academy. Name the county where Red Springs and Flora Macdonald Academy are located. (a) Chatham County (b) Randolph County (c) Robeson County

10. Since its founding in 1869, Davidson College in Mecklenburg County has considered its entire 85-acre campus to be an arboretum. Over 1,600 labeled varieties of plant life occupy Davidson's grounds located on what highway? (a) NC 115 (b) US 64 (c) NC 49

11. The Botanical Gardens of Asheville offer visitors 800 types of plants, a half-mile trail and a special garden for the blind. At 151 Weaver Boulevard, these gardens are near what Asheville institution of higher learning? (a) Asheville Academy (b) Buncombe County College (c) UNC at Asheville

12. Open daily from May to September, Daniel Boone Native Garden in Boone displays indigenous plants and a log cabin. What famous outdoor drama theater is located near these gardens?
(a) Lost Colony Theater (b) Horn in the West Theater (c) Unto These Hills Theater

13. Comprising 155 acres near Wilmington, Airlie Gardens are on the former estate of rice magnate Pembroke Jones. Famous for its water oaks, tranquil ponds with swans and masses of azaleas, Airlie Gardens overlook what coastal sound? (a) Pamlico Sound (b) Wrightsville Sound (c) Albemarle Sound

14. Featuring a nature trail that skirts the base of Mount Noble, Cherokee Botanical Garden displays 150 species of plants. Located on US 441, this mountain garden is situated beside what Cherokee Indian settlement? (a) Qualla Village (b) Sequoyah Village (c) Oconaluftee Village

Inlets And Islands

A sandy band of filigree, our state's coastline is in constant motion. Travel down east with this quiz on North Carolina's wind- and waveswept inlets and islands.

1. The notorious chap Edward Teach (Blackbeard) once called this Hyde County hideout home. Now the site of a US Coast Guard station and a favorite stop for tourists, what coastal Carolina island has previously been known as Wococon and Okok?
   (a) Ocracoke Island   (b) Okisko Island   (c) Wohanoke Island

2. Brown's Inlet in Onslow County has appeared on maps as early as 1733. Just a few miles north of the New River's mouth, Brown's Inlet is part of what US military post in our state?
   (a) Fort Bragg   (b) Cherry Point Marine Air Station   (c) Camp Lejeune Marine Base

3. Cutting its watery way to the Cape Fear River at the south end of Federal Point, Corncake Inlet is a prime surf fishing spot. What island's northern end forms Corncake's shore?
   (a) Harkers Island   (b) Smith Island   (c) Durant Island

4. Folks traveling to the Outer Banks via Morehead City can catch a ferry-boat from an island north of town then enjoy the hour-long ride to Ocracoke. What Carteret County island is this ferry's base?
   (a) Pine Island   (b) Cedar Island   (c) Great Island

5. Flowing between Portsmouth Island and Core Banks, Drum Inlet has also been called Whalebone Inlet. Appearing on maps as early as 1711, Drum Inlet takes its name from what type of animal?
   (a) fish   (b) turtle   (c) shorebird

6. Located at the extreme northeastern corner of our state, Knotts Island is the site of a National Wildlife Refuge. An excellent place to observe waterfowl, Knotts Island sits where Virginia's Back Bay flows into what North Carolina sound?   (a) Albemarle Sound   (b) Currituck Sound   (c) Pamlico Sound

7. The world famous Cape Hatteras Lighthouse has been an Outer Banks landmark since 1870. Other Hatteras Island attractions include Pea Island National Wildlife Refuge and Chicamacomico Life Saving Station. What thin ribbon of asphalt connects Hatteras Island with the outside world?
   (a) NC 49   (b) NC 94   (c) NC 12

8. Once known as Topsail Inlet, Beaufort Inlet is just east of Atlantic Beach and slightly south of the town of Beaufort. Beaufort Inlet forms the passageway between the Atlantic Ocean and what sound?
   (a) Bogue Sound   (b) Croatan Sound   (c) Albemarle Sound

9. Roanoke Island in Dare County was the site where 16th-century English colonists first attempted settlement in our country. What famous play seen each summer on Roanoke tells the tale of these intrepid pioneers who disappeared with scarcely a trace?
   (a) "Unto These Hills"   (b) "The Lost Colony"   (c) "Hail and Farewell"

10. Lockwoods Folly Inlet slips between Holden Beach and Long Beach where Lockwoods Folly River flows into Long Bay. Also near Sunset Harbor, this inlet is in what county?
    (a) Pender County   (b) Columbus County   (c) Brunswick County

11. Tubbs Inlet in Brunswick County is the southernmost inlet on our Tar Heel coast. To the north of Tubbs Inlet is Ocean Isle Beach. What beach, only accessible by drawbridge, is just to the south?
    (a) Sunset Beach   (b) Long Beach   (c) Topsail Beach

12. A treacherous barrier between the Outer Banks' Bodie Island and Pea Island, Oregon Inlet was formed by a hurricane in 1846. What bridge, completed in 1964 and nearly wrecked in 1990, spans Oregon Inlet?   (a) Elwood P. Suggins Bridge   (b) Herbert C. Bonner Bridge   (c) Zebulon Vance Bridge

13. Shallotte Inlet in Brunswick County cuts between Big Beach and Hales Beach. What important transportation artery does this inlet connect with the Atlantic Ocean?
    (a) Intracoastal Waterway   (b) Intercoastal Waterway   (c) Dismal Canal

14. An outer barrier island stretching from Cape Lookout to Swash Inlet, Core Banks has also been known as Endesoakes and Salvage Island. What type of people is Core Banks named after?
    (a) Spaniards   (b) Germans   (c) Native Americans

15. Bogue Inlet in Onslow County is located just northeast of Hammocks Beach State Park. Before it flows into the Atlantic Ocean, what 20-mile long river passes through Bogue Sound and Inlet?
    (a) Little River   (b) White Oak River   (c) New River

Curiosities Of Our Colonial Capital

Few towns in America can match New Bern's historical significance or well-preserved charm. Uncover some interesting facts about New Bern's past and present with this quiz.

1. First settled in 1710, New Bern took its name from the capital of the home of its founder, Christoph de Graffenreid. What European country's capital was this?
    (a) Bavaria (b) Austria (c) Switzerland
2. Incorporated in 1723, New Bern quickly rose to prominence and became North Carolina's capital. During what years did New Bern serve as our colonial and state center of government?
    (a) 1746-1792 (b) 1715-1799 (c) 1727-1800
3. Long before the white man came to the Craven County-New Bern area, Native Americans lived there. What tribe frequented those pre-New Bern environs?
    (a) Pocosins (b) Chippewas (c) Tuscaroras
4. Because of its historical, cultural and educational contributions to our state's society, New Bern has for many years had a nickname that tied it to an ancient city of prominence. What is that nickname?
    (a) The Rome of Carolina (b) The Athens of NC (c) The Cairo of Carolina
5. Being a waterfront town, New Bern's elevation above sea level is only 12 feet. At the junction of what two rivers is New Bern located?
    (a) Trent and Neuse (b) Tar and Pamlico (c) Chowan and Pungo
6. Many visitors to New Bern choose the watery route and tie their boats up at the town docks. Most folks coming to town, however, make it by land down what major highway from Kinston?
    (a) US 74 (b) US 70 (c) I-95
7. One of the finest buildings in colonial America, and still a magnificent New Bern attraction, Tryon Palace was named for Royal Governor William Tryon, who was its first resident. In what year was this imposing structure completed? (a) 1750 (b) 1760 (c) 1770
8. Several New Bern citizens have had the honor and privilege of being the governor of our state. Which governor below was not from New Bern?
    (a) Terry Sanford (b) Abner Nash (c) Richard Dobbs Spaight Sr.
9. Innovative and progressive in many fields, New Bernians scored a coup when they became the first city in America to celebrate the birthday of what US President?
    (a) James Madison (b) George Washington (c) Rutherford B. Hayes
10. The Civil War saw New Bern become a battlefield during March 1862. What Union general commanded the assault against New Bern during those turbulent days?
    (a) Ambrose Burnside (b) Joshua Chamberlain (c) Pinklon Thomas
11. A labor of love for Carteret County native Will Gorges, his New Bern Civil War Museum displays among other things more than 700 weapons from that conflict. Located at the corner of Pollock and Metcalf streets, what year did the museum open? (a) 1975 (b) 1980 (c) 1989
12. New Bern's many churches have seen much history. Built in 1822 by Uriah Sandy, the First Presbyterian Church on New Street served in what capacity during the Civil War?
    (a) ammo dump (b) hospital (c) horse stable
13. Christ Episcopal Church on Pollock Street in New Bern owns a bit of history as well in the form of a silver communion service that's more than 200 years old. The service has survived both fire and theft. Name the English monarch who presented this silver treasure to Christ Episcopal in 1752.
    (a) King George II (b) King James (c) King Edward VII
14. New Bern takes great pride in its many gardens, flower beds and ornamental trees. With more than 2,000 of its species growing in town, what flowering tree do New Bernians rank as their favorite?
    (a) dogwood (b) cottonwood (c) crape myrtle
15. As enduring and timeless as New Bern itself, the Hall of Fame cypress tree on East Front Street is said to be one of the oldest trees in North Carolina. About how old is this towering landmark?
    (a) 300 years old (b) 600 years old (c) 1,000 years old

Wandering Through Wilmington

Steeped in history, Wilmington is a place full of fascination from the past and present. Have no fear as you travel up the Cape Fear River toward the answers to this quiz.

1. Wilmington was known by several names before its incorporation in 1739-1740. One of these monikers reflected an English seaport that in the 1960s would launch the Beatles unto our shores. What was Wilmington once known as? (a) New London (b) Old Blimey (c) New Liverpool

2. In addition to its role as a major port, Wilmington has since 1729 been the seat of New Hanover County. Covering 225 square miles, New Hanover is bound by the Cape Fear River, the Atlantic Ocean, Brunswick County and what other county to the north?
(a) Pender County (b) Onslow County (c) Duplin County

3. Now home to a museum of history and design arts, the four-story, 22-room mansion at 503 Market Street is considered by many to be Wilmington's premiere example of pre-Civil War architecture. Completed in 1861, this Greek Revival and Italianate edifice is known by what name?
(a) Boscoe House (b) Bellamy Mansion (c) Orton Acres

4. Once a spot where the crop known as "king" of Southern commodities was traded, the center with more than 30 stores and several acclaimed restaurants on North Front Street in downtown Wilmington was one of the city's first revitalization efforts during the 1970s. Name this popular tourist stop.
(a) The Cotton Exchange (b) Indigo Lane (c) Rice Row

5. Having a World War II battleship parked in its back yard definitely sets Wilmington apart from most coastal cities. Reminding thousands of visitors who step on board each year of the price of freedom, the *USS North Carolina* came home in October of what year? (a) 1970 (b) 1960 (c) 1952

6. Once a route where slaves were transported out of Wilmington, the present-day highway that runs north-south through town has been called "Negro Head Road." Name this thoroughfare that has been the subject of ghost stories and legends. (a) NC 211 (b) US 74 (c) US 421

7. Sponsored by the Colored Industrial Exposition Association, the first fair for blacks in North Carolina was held in 19th-century Wilmington. What year did this premiere event take place at the city fairgrounds?
(a) 1855 (b) 1875 (c) 1895

8. Since 1858, thespians and theater-lovers have enjoyed fabulous shows in the Wilmington landmark located at Third and Chestnut streets. Name this building, which also shares its space with City Hall.
(a) Thalian Hall (b) The Palace (c) Beauregard's Theatre

9. With names like the *Cape Fear Mercury* (1769-1775), *Wilmington Daily Herald* (1854-1863) and the *True Republican* (1809-1810), many newspapers have come and gone in Wilmington. What newspaper, founded in 1867 and with a current circulation of 60,000, still serves the town?
(a) *New Hanover Herald* (b) *Wilmington Observer* (c) *Wilmington Morning Star*

10. On February 22, 1865, the city of Wilmington was officially surrendered by Mayor John Dawson to Union forces during the Civil War. This same date in February 1732 was also the birthday of what United States president? (a) John Adams (b) George Washington (c) Thomas Jefferson

11. The 28th president of the United States lived as a young man with his parents in Wilmington during the 1870s. His stay was commemorated with a historical marker at Third and Orange streets. Name this chief executive who saw our nation through World War I.
(a) Woodrow Wilson (b) Theodore Roosevelt (c) Calvin Coolidge

12. Another famous person who once called Wilmington home is basketball superstar Michael Jordan. As a lad during the late 1970s, Jordan honed his hoop skills as a student and player at what Wilmington high school? (a) Cape Fear High School (b) Laney High School (c) Hanover High School

13. In 1905 corporate investors constructed a huge music and dancing pavilion at Wrightsville Beach just a few miles east of Wilmington. Name this entertainment mecca, whose thousands of lights brightened the coastal sky for nearly 70 years and where folks shagged until dawn.
(a) The Palm Room (b) The Crow's Nest (c) Lumina

Go East, Young Man

Although the state's agriculture heartland, North Carolina's coastal plain is more than fields and farms. Test your knowledge of the lands east of Raleigh and west of Greenville in this quiz.

1. In 1961, a B-52 bomber carrying two nuclear bombs crashed in eastern North Carolina. Although the US Department of Defense at the time said the bombs could not have gone off, later evidence indicated that one was a safety catch away from exploding. What Goldsboro air base had the plane come from? (a) Shaw Air Force Base   (b) Seymour Johnson Air Force Base   (b) Pope Air Force Base

2. In addition to boasting North Carolina's largest dollar value in farm receipts, Johnston County is also the birthplace of movie legend Ava Gardner. Married three times, Gardner was first married to what actor who starred with Elizabeth Taylor in *National Velvet?* (a) Cary Grant   (b) Frank Sinatra   (c) Mickey Rooney

3. The seat of Lenoir County, Kinston is also the home of the CSS *Neuse* State Historic Site. Another Kinston highlight is the city's self-guided museum depicting the life of what man who was North Carolina's first elected governor?   (a) Richard Caswell   (b) John White   (c) James Eaker

4. The town of Wilson was founded in 1849 from Tosnot Depot and Hickory Grove on the present CSX rail line. Located in the heart of North Carolina tobacco country, and the site of the largest tobacco market in the nation, Wilson is also home to what popular science museum? (a) Discovery Place   (b) Imagination Station   (c) Natural Science Center

5. Home to one of North Carolina's finest historic districts, Tarboro showcases everything from the plantation of General Thomas Blount (1759-1812) to a walking tour of the entire 45-block district. Finding your way to Tarboro is easy because it sits next to the intersection of NC Highway 33, US Highway 258, and what other highway that crosses the length of our state? (a) US Highway 74   (b) US Highway 64   (c) US Highway 158

6. Located in Sampson County at the junction of US Highway 421 and US 13, Spivey's Corner was once known as West Crossroads. Since 1969, Spivey's Corner has made a worldwide reputation for itself by holding what type of contest each year? (a) National Hollerin' Contest   (b) National Watermelon Eatin' Contest   (c) National Shad Festival

7. The first patriot victory in the South during the American Revolution, the battle of Moores Creek Bridge took place in Pender County. Site of a national battlefield near Currie, the fight that saw the British skedaddle took place on February 27 in what year?   (a) 1775   (b) 1776   (c) 1777

8. A popular recreation area, Bladen Lakes Educational State Forest and its associated waters are located just northeast of Elizabethtown. Which one of the following lakes is not part of the state forest? (a) White Lake   (b) Singletary Lake   (c) Bay Tree Lake

9. Rose Hill in Duplin County is located about halfway between Magnolia and Teachey. The oldest of North Carolina's operating wineries there uses a 200-year-old recipe to produce wine from muscadine grapes. Name this winery that offers tours and tastings of its wares. (a) Muscadine Winery   (b) Duplin Winery   (c) Westbend Wines

10. Rocky Mount has a colorful history that includes being the birthplace of the Hardee's hamburger chain. Besides something for the body, Rocky Mount also offers something for the mind by being the hometown of what college? (a) Rocky Mount Union College   (b) East Carolina University   (c) North Carolina Wesleyan College

11. Site of a state park in western Halifax County, Medoc Mountain is near the town of Hollister. Medoc Mountain took its name from late-19th-century vineyards in the area that were named Medoc in honor of a famous wine region in what country?   (a) Italy   (b) France   (c) Germany

A Capital Quiz

Raleigh became the Wake County seat in 1771, the state capital in 1792 and was named for Sir Walter Raleigh of Lost Colony fame. If you need more help with this quiz on our capital, try reading the story by Betty Work on page 24 of *The State* August 1991 issue.

1. In what year was Wake County formed from parts of Orange, Johnston and Cumberland counties? (a) 1775   (b) 1769   (c) 1771

2. Wake was Governor Tryon's wife's maiden name, and the person for whom the county was named. What was her first name? (a) Mary   (b) Margaret   (c) Sarah

3. What Wake County town is home of the Southeastern Baptist Seminary?
    (a) Cary   (b) Wake Forest   (c) Fuquay-Varina

4. Completed in 1840, the state Capitol building is an example of what architectural style?
    (a) Greek Revival   (b) Gothic   (c) Baroque

5, What river flows through Wake County, providing recreational opportunities for its population?
    (a) Neuse River   (b) Haw River   (c) Tar River

6. In mid-April 1865, Raleigh was surrendered to Union Army forces. What Union general accepted the surrender? (a) U.S. Grant   (b) William Tecumseh Sherman   (c) William Rosecrans

7. What US President was born in Raleigh?
    (a) James K. Polk   (b) Andrew Jackson   (c) Andrew Johnson

8. With Dr. W.R. Valentiner as its first director, what year did the North Carolina Museum of Art in Raleigh open? (a) 1938   (b) 1956   (c) 1975

9. Christmas Day 1886 saw the beginning of streetcar operation in Raleigh. What powered those first streetcars? (a) steam   (b) mules   (c) electricity

10. Which Raleigh building, on the National Register of Historic Places, was the first reinforced concrete skyscraper to be erected in North Carolina?
    (a) Masonic Temple Building   (b) Federal Building   (c) Seaboard Cost Line Building

11. Founded by Lamar Stringfield and based in Raleigh, the North Carolina Symphony began playing in what year? (a) 1910   (b) 1932   (c) 1965

12. What was that great Wake County institution of higher learning, now known as NC State University, originally called? (a) NC Institute of Agricultural Science   (b) NC Farmer's College   (c) NC College of Agriculture and Mechanic Arts

13. William B. Umstead State Park in Wake County is one of North Carolina's most popular parks. Who was William B. Umstead? (a) a former North Carolina governor (b) a former United States ambassador to Great Britain   (c) a tobacco magnate and financier

14. Who was the first governor to occupy the Executive Mansion in Raleigh?
    (a) Thomas Holt   (b) Alfred Scales   (c) Daniel Fowle

15. The first coeducational college for blacks in the US, Shaw University in Raleigh was founded by Dr. Henry Tupper in what year? (a) 1865   (b) 1895   (c) 1932

Mountain Trivia

Going to the mountains this fall? Better brush up on your knowledge of Western North Carolina history and culture. It'll impress your traveling companions—and make you appreciate the sites even more.

1. Connemara, Carl Sandburg's home in Flat Rock, was a productive place not only for poetry but also for livestock. What type of animal did Mrs. Sandburg raise there?
   (a) chickens   (b) cows   (c) goats

2. Constructed during World War II, Fontana Dam is 480 feet tall and a popular attraction. Who built it?
   (a) Duke Power   (b) Tennessee Valley Authority   (c) Carolina Power and Light

3. Qualla Indian Reservation is home to the Eastern Band of Cherokee Indians. What does the Cherokee word "qualla" mean?   (a) Old Woman   (b) Mighty Chief   (c) Big Bear

4. Called the "clogging capital of the world," what area also boasts a "wild west"-style town?
   (a) Cove Creek   (b) Bryson City   (c) Maggie Valley

5. Sports car buffs flock to Rutherford County each spring to race to the top of a well-known monolith. What is this popular race called?
   (a) Chimney Rock Hillclimb   (b) Spindale Rally   (c) Thermal City Grand Prix

6. Lake Junaluska is a resort area named for an Indian chief credited with saving Andrew Jackson's life. What tribe did Junaluska belong to?   (a) Tuscarora   (b) Cherokee   (c) Catawba

7. Every summer the outdoor drama *Horn in the West* is performed near Appalachian State University. What mountain explorer's adventures are featured in the play?
   (a) Johnny Appleseed   (b) Davy Crockett   (c) Daniel Boone

8. What foothills resort town gained new-found fame after the 1987 movie *Dirty Dancing* was filmed there?   (a) Lakes James   (b) Lake Lure   (c) Lake Nebo

9. At 6,684 feet, Mount Mitchell is the tallest peak east of the Mississippi. What was it called in the early 1800s?   (a) Black Dome   (b) Crabtree Mountain   (c) Mount Tryon

10. The fresh mountain air has lured many famous writers to Asheville. One of them, O. Henry, is buried there. What was O. Henry's real name?
    (a) James Simpson Riley   (b) Francis Barton   (c) William Sydney Porter

11. County seat of Transylvania County, Brevard has become a popular retirement community. What is Brevard's other claim to fame?
    (a) apple orchards   (b) Brevard Music Center   (c) antique shopping

12. Bridal Veil Falls near Highlands is formed when the Cullasaja River tumbles 120 feet. What does "cullasaja" mean in Cherokee?   (a) Sugar Water   (b) Laughing Water   (c) Fire Water

13. A taste of the Alps can be found at what stop just off the Blue Ridge Parkway and Highway 226A near Crabtree Meadows Campground?
    (a) Little Bavaria   (b) Little Matterhorn   (c) Little Switzerland

14. Inspiration for the song "On Top of Old Smoky," Clingmans Dome is the highest point in the Smokies. How tall does "Old Smoky" stand?   (a) 6,500 feet   (b) 6,643 feet   (c) 6,156 feet

Highland Heritage

Heart of the "Land of the Sky," Asheville offers a cool blend of mountain and city life. Trace the past and present of this Tar Heel gateway as you answer the questions to this quiz.

1. The seat of Buncombe County, Asheville was incorporated in 1797 and is named for Samuel Ashe, governor from 1795 until 1798. Before the city took its present name, what was Asheville known as? (a) Averytown (b) Montford (c) Morristown

2. No visit to the Asheville area is complete without a tour of the Biltmore House and Estate. Built by George Vanderbilt in 1895 and the largest private residence in the world, Biltmore has how many rooms? (a) 195 (b) 250 (c) 300

3. After years of construction and dozens of lost lives, railway lines are completed to Asheville and the first train pulls into town on October 2, 1880. Name the railroad company that built the tracks that eventually would stretch from Salisbury to Asheville.
(a) Piedmont Railway (b) Western North Carolina Railroad (c) Great Smoky Mountains Railway

4. In the heart of downtown Asheville, Pack Square and Pack Place comprise a complex of art galleries, studios, and museums that include the Colburn Gem and Mineral Museum. This hub of Asheville culture is bordered by what highway that begins as Merrimon Avenue, then heads on out of town as Biltmore Avenue? (a) US 25 (b) NC 213 (c) US 12/23

5. In 1906 two important gentlemen arrived in Asheville by steam-powered car to scout Jackson County for the mineral cobalt. One of these fellows was Harvey Firestone of tire manufacturing legend. His companion was what man credited with inventing the phonograph?
(a) Victor Victrola (b) James Zenith (c) Thomas Edison

6. In 1921, Asheville native Exum Clement became the first woman to serve in the North Carolina General Assembly. Prior to her service in the legislature, Clement also had made history as the first woman to pursue what profession in Asheville? (a) attorney (b) physician (c) dentist

7. The year 1949 saw students at Lee H. Edwards High School receive the first TV broadcast in the Asheville area on a crude set they had built. What popular movie actress known as "America's Sweetheart" applied for a license to build a TV station in Asheville that same year?
(a) Shirley Temple (b) Joan Crawford (c) Mary Pickford

8. One of Asheville's most famous native sons, novelist Thomas Wolfe, used his hometown as a backdrop for many of his works. As a child, Wolfe lived with his mother at her boardinghouse on Spruce Street that went by what name in his epic autobiographical novel *Look Homeward, Angel?*
(a) Dixieland (b) Hillview (c) Biltmore

9. Weather data from around the country is gathered, analyzed, and stored in Asheville at a US government building near Battery Park. Available to the public are tours of this unique facility with what name?
(a) Weather Center USA (b) The Atmospheric Center (c) National Climatic Center

10. Built around the turn of the century, one of Asheville's most beautiful buildings is a Spanish Baroque-style house of worship that was the first Catholic church consecrated in North Carolina. Name this church whose dome rises above Haywood Street.
(a) St. Mary's Church (b) St. Paul's Cathedral (c) Basilica of St. Lawrence

11. The Asheville area has been a popular location for motion picture makers since 1921, when North Carolina's first film production, *Conquest of Canaan,* was shot there. In 1958, filmmakers came to Asheville and shot a story about mountain moonshiners that starred Robert Mitchum. What was this movie called? (a) *Thunder Road* (b) *White Lightnin'* (c) *Whisky Mountain*

High And Mighty

Rise to the challenge with this quiz on North Carolina mountains whose elevations top out at more than 5,000 feet.

1. At 6,684 feet, Mount Mitchell is not only the tallest peak in North Carolina, but also in the eastern United States. Called Attakulla by the Cherokees, Mount Mitchell had what previous name?
(a) Mount Elisha   (b) Black Dome   (c) Mount Holly

2. At 6,647 feet, Mount Craig in Yancey County ranks as the second-highest mountain in our state. Mount Craig was one of two peaks named Black Brothers until 1947 when it was renamed in honor of Locke Craig (1860-1924) who has held what political post?
(a) Governor of North Carolina   (b) Mayor of Asheville   (c) Supreme Court Justice

3. Jones' Knob rises 6,240 feet and is named after a man who falsely claimed to have scaled its slopes. Once called Jones' Folly, this mountain sits on the line between Haywood and what other county that is home to Western Carolina University?   (a) Clay County   (b) Jackson County   (c) Cherokee County

4. Cold Mountain in Haywood County is near the Little East Fork of the Pigeon River and has an altitude of 6,030 feet. In 1997, a creative work by Charles Frazier used the mountain as its title and won a national award. What genre did Frazier use to tell his tale?   (a) Poem   (b) Short story   (c) Novel

5. Located on the Swain-Haywood county line between Tricorner Knob and Luftee Knob, Mount Yonaguska rises 6,150 feet. Part of the Great Smoky Mountains National Park, Mount Yonaguska is named for the great Indian chief who lived to be approximately 100 years old as leader of what tribe?
(a) Cherokee Tribe   (b) Catawba Tribe   (c) Tuscarora Tribe

6. A popular spot for hikers, Mount Pisgah stands 5,721 feet above the Buncombe-Haywood county line and on clear days affords a view of five states. Mount Pisgah is named for the mountain from which what biblical character saw the Promised Land?   (a) Nicodemus   (b) Saul   (c) Moses

7. The highest point in the Blue Ridge Mountains stands 5,964 feet above the junction of Avery, Caldwell, and Watauga counties. A privately owned tourist attraction, what North Carolina mountain hosts the annual Gathering of the Scottish Clans and has a swinging mile-high bridge?
(a) Grandfather Mountain   (b) Black Mountain   (c) Chimney Rock

8. Potrock Bald is a 5,250-foot mountain that takes its name from a story about an Indian shaman who made his medicines in a hollowed out stone on the hilltop. Potrock Bald is near the head of Potrock Branch and Compass Creek in what county whose seat is Hayesville?
(a) Cleveland County   (b) Swain County   (c) Clay County

9. Straddling Swain County in North Carolina and Sevier County in Tennessee, Mount Sequoyah is just a hair more than 6,000 feet tall. Mount Sequoyah is named after the brilliant Cherokee who lived from 1770 to 1843 and introduced what type of system to his people?
(a) Monetary system   (b) Alphabet   (c) Numerical system

10. Plott Balsam in western Haywood County stands 6,088 feet tall and takes its name from pioneer settler Amos Plott. The Plotts also gave their name to what type of canine that is the official state dog of North Carolina?   (a) Plott hound   (b) Plott terrier   (c) Plott retriever

11. Soaring 6,224 feet above Yancey County at the head of Shuford Creek, Gibbs Mountain is named for Billy Gibbs, who was a circuit rider. What was Gibbs' job as a rider of the circuit?
(a) Rodeo star   (b) Horse jockey   (c) Minister

September 2000

Tar Heel Mountain Names And Places

Many of North Carolina's mountain peaks have a name or story attached to them as colorful as the autumn leaves that blanket their slopes. Get out your gazetteer and map for guidance to the answers in this quiz.

1. Located in central Wilkes County, Rendezvous Mountain stands 2,450 feet. This peak takes its name from the story that Revolutionary War patriots gathered there before they marched to what famous battle site just west of Gastonia? (a) Kings Mountain (b) Moores Creek Bridge (c) Bentonville

2. Soaring 5,721 feet in elevation, Mount Pisgah on the Buncombe-Haywood County line offers a five-state view. Pisgah takes its name from the mountain in the Bible that gave what person a glimpse of the promised land? (a) Lot (b) Joseph (c) Moses

3. On the Tennessee-North Carolina border, 6,400-foot Mount Kephart was named in 1928 for naturalist and author Horace Kephart. What was the title of Kephart's famous book on the people and places of our hill country?
   (a) *Mountain Folk and Facts* (b) *Our Southern Highlanders* (c) *Cover and Crags of Carolina*

4. Just east of Tryon, 1,831-foot Round Mountain was the setting for a 1776 battle between whites under Captain Thomas Howard and Cherokee warriors led by a fellow with the impressive name of Big Wayah. In what county are Round Mountain and Tryon located?
   (a) Polk County (b) Macon County (c) Rutherford County

5. Towering 6,000 feet over Swain County and Tennessee's Sevier County on the North Carolina-Tennessee line, Mount Sequoyah is named for the Cherokee Indian genius who developed what system for his people? (a) alphabet (b) numerical system (c) monetary system

6. Near Skyuka Creek in Polk County, Tryon Mountain rises 3,231 feet. Tryon Mountain takes its name from Governor William Tryon who was our state's chief executive during what years?
   (a) 1850-1854 (b) 1900-1904 (c) 1765-1771

7. Called "sokassa" by the Cherokee Indians, 3,200-foot Rumbling Bald Mountain is located in an area that was shaken by several earthquakes in 1874. What county is the locale for Rumbling Bald Mountain?
   (a) Rutherford County (b) Clay County (c) Macon County

8. Whiteside Mountain in Jackson County near Highlands is at the head of the Chattooga River. An inscription in Spanish found on Whiteside Mountain was attributed to what explorer who trekked that region circa 1540? (a) Juan Carlos (b) Hernando de Soto (c) Tio Montero

9. Covered with mysterious hummocks that are said to be the remains of trees blown down in a storm long ago, 5,516-foot Big Bald is an impressive Yancey County mountain. What town on highway US 19 near Big Bald has a decidedly alpine ring to its name? (a) Matterhorn (b) Swiss (c) Innsbruck

10. On the Swain County line in the Great Smoky Mountains National Park sits 6,150-foot Mount Yonaguska. This majestic peak takes its name from the last great chief of what North Carolina Indian tribe?
    (a) Pamlicos (b) Waxhaws (c) Cherokees

11. The second-highest mountain in North Carolina at 6,663 feet elevation, Mount Craig was named for former Tar Heel Governor Locke Craig. What North Carolina state park is the site for Mount Craig and its slightly higher neighbor? (a) Mount Mitchell State Park (b) Roan Mountain State Park
    (c) Mount Sterling State Park

12. In the 1880s a group of Mormons attempted to settle in the hills of Haywood County, but their polygamous ways meant that they had to move on. What mountain near Fulbright Cove in central Haywood County takes its name from the state that might be considered the headquarters for Mormons in the US?
    (a) Nevada Mountain (b) Arizona Mountain (c) Utah Mountain

13. Another Haywood County peak, 5,071-foot Junaluska Mountain, is named in honor of the Cherokee chief who saved the life of a future US president during battle with a hostile tribe. Who did Junaluska save that became our 7th president? (a) James Madison (b) Andrew Jackson (c) James Monroe

North Carolina Inns Abound
From Mountains To Sea

To North Carolina innkeepers, Southern hospitality is not a cliche but a way of life. Scattered across the landscape from mountains to coast like jewels, all the inns in our state offer something special to their guests in a wide variety of styles. Test your knowledge of some of these unique lodgings with this quiz.

1. Located in downtown Highlands, the Old Edwards Inn has treated guests royally for more than 100 years. What twisty highway leads guests to Old Edwards from the neighboring town of Cashiers? (a) US 64   (b) NC 281   (c) NC 107

2. Just up the road from Cashiers the Greystone Inn houses its guests in a fine example of Swiss Revival architecture. What large Transylvania County lake does the Greystone Inn grace the shores of? (a) Lake Rhodhiss   (b) Lake James   (c) Lake Toxaway

3. An Asheville landmark, the Grove Park Inn's 400 rooms have seen politicians, authors and celebrities. What year was the Grove Park Inn erected?   (a) 1887   (b) 1913   (c) 1925

4. Dating back to the turn of the century, the Claddagh Inn in Hendersonville features a library for its guests. Aptly named, as its customers discover, "Claddagh" means love and lasting friendship in what language?   (a) Swedish   (b) Hungarian   (c) Gaelic

5. Situated near Lake Lure and Bat Cave, the Esmeralda Inn has not only served as a stagecoach stop but was once lodging for a Hollywood silent film star known as "America's Sweetheart." Who was this box office favorite?   (a) Mary Pickford   (b) Lauren Bacall   (c) Dale Evans

6. Under new ownership, but sill employing its fourth generation of Wray family members, the Nu-Wray Inn dates back to an original log structure built in 1833. In what NC town, the seat of Yancey County, is the Nu-Wray Inn located?   (a) Bandana   (b) Burnsville   (c) Micaville

7. Boasting the only heated swimming pool on Ocracoke Island, the Island Inn caters to life in the slow lane. Around in various guises since 1901, the inn has also served what purpose in its past? (a) Naval officers' quarters   (b) auto garage   (c) fish house

8. Listed on the National Register of Historic Places, the Holly Inn in Pinehurst welcomes golfers with open arms. What gentleman, the original developer of Pinehurst, built the Holly Inn in 1895? (a) Benson Casey   (b) Richard Rosenthal   (c) James Tufts

9. The Tar Heel Inn, located in the Carolina coastal town of Oriental, has been praised by more than one patron for its Belgian waffle breakfasts. What sound is just a hop and a skip from this 19th century establishment?   (a) Masonboro Sound   (b) Pamlico Sound   (c) Albemarle Sound

10. The Trestle House Inn, an Edenton treat, acquired its name from redwood timbers bought at auction that went into its construction. What railroad had originally utilized the beams as part of an actual trestle?   (a) Southern Railroad   (b) Union Pacific Railroad   (c) Raleigh-Gaston Railroad

11. Dating back to 1775 Durham, the Arrowhead Inn was once part of a large estate. Outside the inn, a five-foot tall stone arrowhead marks what historic path once used by Indians and early settlers? (a) Great Westward Path   (b) Great Spirit Trail   (c) Great Trading Path

12. On the National Register, the Waverley Inn in Hendersonville also claims to be the oldest hostelry in that town. Guests will find many attractions nearby, including the home of what famous poet? (a) Wallace Stevens   (b) William Wordsworth   (c) Carl Sandburg

13. The building complex housing Winston-Salem's Brookstone Inn dates back to 1836. Moravian buns for breakfast please many guests at this inn. What 19th century purpose did Brookstone's structure originally serve?   (a) Grist mill   (b) Cotton mill   (c) Hosiery mill

March 1993

Tar Heel Eats And Eateries

Fine fare and a variety of places to enjoy it characterize the North Carolina culinary tradition. With this quiz providing food for thought, see how many correct answers you can pile on your plate.

1. In 1987 the North Carolina General Assembly passed a resolution naming our official Tar Heel state beverage. With over 140 million gallons produced here annually, what is this tasty quaff? (a) apple cider   (b) milk   (c) scuppernong wine

2. If any dish were to be voted the state food of NC, it would have to be barbecue. Down east they go for a peppery, vinegary sauce, while proponents of Lexington or "western" style barbecue favor what base for their basting?   (a) tomato base   (b) onion base   (c) molasses base

3. In the hill country of West Jefferson, the Ashe County Cheese Company operates the only cheese factory in North Carolina. What type of tangy cheese hoops roll out of this 50-year-old factory? (a) Gouda   (b) Swiss   (c) Cheddar

4. A tasty dish that contains corn, lima beans, chicken, pork and occasionally the odd squirrel, Brunswick stew is said to have been invented by what group that founded what is now Winston-Salem? (a) Moravians   (b) Adventists   (c) Huguenots

5. More than 25 million jars of tasty North Carolina pickles flow out of the works at the Mount Olive Pickle Company each year. Mount Olive calls itself the "Pickle Capital of the South." In what county are Mount Olive and all those pickles located?   (a) Bertie Co.   (b) Martin Co.   (c) Wayne Co.

6. The oldest fruit festival in the South is still held in the Columbus County town of Chadbourn. At one time entire trainloads of the fruit grown there were shipped to market. What succulent morsels is Chadbourn famous for?   (a) cherries   (b) strawberries   (c) raspberries

7. Dating back to the 1930s, the annual Waynesville Ramp Convention celebrates the eating and lore of a tangy tuber called a "ramp." Which of the following roots is most closely related to the famous rampion? (a) onion   (b) Tara root   (c) Irish potato

8. Down on the North Carolina coast, the shrimp reigns supreme with diners who crave the very freshest in shellfish. The fisherman who harvest the capricious shrimp crop have their own humorous name for their quarry. What is it?   (a) skeeters   (b) croakers   (c) bugs

9. Many a frosty Carolina morning has been given a good start with fried livermush nestled in a homemade biscuit. Besides hog livers and a whole lot of spices, what other ingredient gives livermush its unique texture?   (a) cracklins   (b) lard   (c) cornmeal

10. Located at Blowing Rock's historic Green Park Inn, Madison's Restaurant received a prestigious 4 1/2 star rating in 1992. Uniquely situated, the Inn and Madison's straddle what invisible boundary line? (a) Mason and Dixon Line   (b) Continental Divide   (c) Carolina Fault Line

11. Plenty of home-style grub characterizes Dillsboro's Jarrett House restaurant, where, in the 1800s, a meal could be had for a dime. Name the mountain river that flows through Dillsboro and close by the Jarrett House.   (a) Nantahala River   (b) Tuckasegee River   (c) New River

12. Shatley Springs Restaurant is as famous for its fried chicken as it is for the curative waters that patrons can tote home in a jug. Shatley Springs is located just off of what highway near the community of Crumpler?   (a) NC 16   (b) US 64   (c) NC 108

13. Doing wonders with seafood purchased locally, the Harvey Mansion Restaurant in New Bern is housed in a structure that dates back to the late 1700s. Located on Tryon Palace Drive, Harvey's gives diners a view of what historic river?   (a) Tar River   (b) Trent River   (c) Cape Fear River

14. The building that houses the restaurant at The Colonial Inn in Hillsborough also dates back to the 1700s. Legend says that during the Civil War the inn was spared by Yankees because the owner's wife flew what flag?   (a) Masonic flag   (b) white flag   (c) Stars and Stripes

The Inn Crowd

The Grove Park Inn Resort boasts a tradition of elegance and an eclectic roster of guests. Test your knowledge of one of North Carolina's grandest hotels in this quiz.

1. The Grove Park Inn Resort has been called "the finest resort hotel in the world." Designed by architect Fred L. Seely and originally owned by Edwin W. Grove—also known as the "Father of Modern Asheville"—the inn first opened in the summer of what year? (a) 1900 (b) 1903 (c) 1913

2. One inspiration for the design of The Grove Park Inn Resort came when a secretary handed Edwin Grove a copy of a brochure titled "The Hotels of Yellowstone Park." Looking for a spot in Asheville to build his hotel, Grove eventually decided on a slope on the side of what mountain?
    (a) Sunset Mountain (b) Grandfather Mountain (c) Beaucatcher Mountain

3. Fine food has been a part of The Grove Park Inn Resort since its first days. Early menus lauded the inn's California prunes, fresh seafood, and plenty of milk and cream from what neighboring dairy and estate? (a) Coble Dairy (b) Harvey B. Hunter Dairy (c) Biltmore Dairy

4. During the summers of 1935 and 1936, one of America's most famous novelists called The Grove Park Inn Resort home. Name this author who wrote such works as *This Side of Paradise,* and whose wife, Zelda, was a patient at nearby Highland Hospital.
    (a) Ernest Hemingway (b) William Faulkner (c) F. Scott Fitzgerald

5. The year 1936 also saw another famous visitor spend some time at The Grove Park Inn Resort. On a tour of the Great Smoky Mountains, the 32nd President of the United States called on the inn just as his wife had done in 1934. Name this New Yorker who had 50 rooms reserved for himself and his staff.
    (a) Franklin D. Roosevelt (b) Warren G. Harding (c) Calvin Coolidge

6. During World War II, The Grove Park Inn Resort offered its services as a rest and recreation facility for the armed forces. Following the war, the chief of staff of the US Army and his wife visited the Grove Park in April 1947. Name this five-star general and The Grove Park Inn Resort patron whose spouse was named Mamie. (a) George Patton (b) Dwight Eisenhower (c) Jimmy Doolittle

7. In 1955, The Grove Park Inn Resort was purchased by Charles A. Sammons. During Sammons' ownership, the inn's two-story Fairway Lodge opened with 50 rooms in 1964 and the seven-story North Wing opened in 1964. In 1973, The Grove Park Inn Resort saw its name added to what prestigious list? (a) Michelin Honor Hotel Roster (b) National Register of Historic Places
    (c) NC Architectural Awards List

8. Built shortly after the main inn, the Presidental Cottage was named in honor of Philippine President Manuel Quezon. The Presidential Cottage was originally known as the Anne Hathaway Cottage because it was constructed to the exact dimensions of the birthplace of the wife of what English bard?
    (a) William Wordsworth (b) Robert Browning (c) William Shakespeare

9. Much of The Grove Park Inn Resort's style reflects the strong influence of a particular design movement that was popular in the United States in the early 20th century. Roycroft Shops in East Aurora, New York, provided much of the inn's furnishings in what design style?
    (a) Arts and Crafts design style (b) Prairie design style (c) Art Nouveau design style

10. In 1988, The Grove Park Inn Resort completed a $65 million expansion program. Part of that work included the addition of a new 413,250-square-foot wing that brought the total number of rooms at The Grove Park Inn Resort up to 510. The addition was named the Vanderbilt Wing in honor of what owner of the Biltmore House? (a) Calvin Vanderbilt (b) William Vanderbilt (c) George Vanderbilt

Historic Restaurants

Culinary delights combine with memorable settings to create North Carolina's most charming eateries. Experience the food and history of these restaurants as you sample this quiz.

1. Known for generous portions served family style, the restaurant at historic Jarrett House dates back to 1884 when its original structure was built by William Dills. Once a stop on the Western NC Railroad, Jarrett House is part of what Jackson County town? (a) Dillsboro (b) Dilltown (c) Dillburg

2. Shatley Springs Inn and Restaurant near Crumpler was once a spa where visitors came to partake of waters said to have healing effects. Fried chicken, country ham, biscuits, and vegetables are drawing cards at this historic restaurant located in what county?
   (a) Buncombe County (b) Jefferson County (c) Ashe County

3. A tar Heel favorite, the Nu-Wray Inn in Burnsville dates back to 1833 when it was built of constructed logs. Dishes at the Nu-Wray's restaurant include cream gravy, tipsy cake, and smothered lettuce salad. Built on the town square in Burnsville, the inn is included on what prestigious list?
   (a) National Register of Historic Places (b) National Trust Registry (c) NC Historic Sites Roster

4. Opened in 1882, The Green Park Inn features a championship-quality golf course in addition to elegant accommodations and gourmet meals. The Green Park's Laurel Room Restaurant is located in Caldwell County on US Highway 321 in what town? (a) Boone (b) Blowing Rock (c) Candler

5. Listed on the National Register of Historic Places since 1995, Josephine's Restaurant at Lone Beech in Marion serves lunch and dinner in a refined atmosphere. The 7,000-square-foot house in which Josephine's is located was built in 1902 as a cottage ordered from what catalog?
   (a) Sears (b) Montgomery Ward (c) JC Penney

6. Featuring a fine restaurant, pub, and art gallery, the Harvey Mansion in New Bern is housed in a 200-year-old structure that was once a home, office, and warehouse for a planter and businessman John Harvey. Located at 221 Front Street, the Harvey Mansion sits by what river?
   (a) Tar River (b) Cape Fear River (c) Trent River

7. Located on 28 acres of rolling Henderson County landscape, the Woodfield Inn dates back to 1852 when it served as a stagecoach station. Featuring three dining rooms seating 200 guests, the Squires Restaurant at the Woodfield Inn stands near what famous author's residence?
   (a) Thomas Wolfe (b) Carl Sandburg (c) Fred Chappell

8. On the National Register of Historic Places since 1972, Mast Farm dates back to the late 1700s. Now a gracious lodging and dining establishment, the Mast Farm Inn is located in what Watauga County town whose name means "valley of the cross?" (a) Crusi Valle (b) Val Crucifix (c) Valle Crucis

9. An architectural gem of the Victorian age, Richmond Hill Inn in Asheville features elegant lodging in each of its 36 rooms as well as fine dining in the mansion's Gabrielle's restaurant, which has won what prestigious AAA award for its cuisine?
   (a) Four Diamond Award (b) Silver Spoon Award (c) Traveler's Best Award

10. Charles and Mary Clawson, immigrants to North Carolina from Sweden and Iceland, originally owned Clawson's 1905 Restaurant and Pub in Beaufort. On Front Street, Clawson's building has been used for many purposes, including a bakery and what other type of store operated by the Clawsons?
    (a) Harness shop (b) Grocery (c) Fish house

11. In the early 20th century, Captain Amos Frye built the rustic Fryemont Inn and its restaurant, which are listed on the National Register of Historic Places. Featuring native trout prepared at least four ways, the Fryemont Inn and its dining room are located in what Swain County town once known as Charleston?
    (a) Cherokee (b) Cullowhee (c) Bryson City

The Lowdown On NC College Regalia

Get out those dusty raccoon coats, megaphones, scrapbooks and pom-poms. Reviving memories of the old alma mater, see if you can come up with the correct fight song, yearbook title, school colors or mascot for the Tar Heel colleges and universities featured in this quiz.

1. Nestled in a scenic mountain valley at Cullowhee, Western Carolina University's 5,500 students stay warm in the winter with a healthy dose of school spirit. Purple and gold are the colors WCU sports on the field. What feline is their mascot? (a) jaguar (b) bobcat (c) catamount

2. Dating back to 1947, the University of North Carolina at Wilmington is located on a 650-acre campus in one of our state's most historic cities. Just minutes from fine ocean fishing and swimming, UNCW appropriately takes what symbol as its mascot? (a) seagull (b) seahawk (c) pelican

3. Originally known as Trinity College, Durham's Duke University occupies more than 8,000 acres. No matter what the sport, Duke's navy blue and white clad Blue Devils always give the opposition a real contest. In quieter moments, Duke students past and present enjoy looking at their yearbook that goes by what title? (a) *Chanticleer* (b) *Crier* (c) *Pitchfork*

4. Established in 1899, Appalachian State University helped put Boone on the map. Led by their mascot, "Yosef," and singing fight songs such as "Hail To The Brave Hearts," Appalachian students cheer on teams dressed in what colors? (a) red and white (b) orange and white (c) black and gold

5. Located in the Cleveland County town of Boiling Springs, Gardner-Webb University is a coed school of about 1,500 students. Established in 1904, Gardner-Webb's school colors are black and red. What tenacious canine is their mascot? (a) Sooner hound (b) bulldog (c) bloodhound

6. Going all the way back to 1891, North Carolina Agricultural and Technical State University began life as the "Agricultural and Mechanical College for the Colored Race." Nicknamed the "Aggies," and with a bulldog mascot, NC A&T teams sport what school colors?
(a) green and gold (b) blue and gold (c) white and green

7. Once strictly a teachers' college, East Carolina University in Greenville now offers degrees in many subjects, including medicine. Known as the "Pirates," East Carolina students carry that swashbuckling theme over to their yearbook that goes by what title?
(a) *Buccaneer* (b) *Treasure Chest* (c) *Blackbeard's Book*

8. A member of the Central Intercollegiate Athletic Association and the NCAA Division II, North Carolina Central University in Durham had its roots as the National Religious Training School and Chautauqua established by James Shepard in 1910. When the Eagles swoop onto the field, what colors do they wear? (a) brown and gold (b) black and white (c) burgundy and gray

9. The first state university to open its doors, the University of North Carolina at Chapel Hill dates back to 1795. With colors of Carolina blue and white, the Tar Heels of UNC have what hardheaded animal as their mascot? (a) mule (b) ram (c) mustang

10. Gaston County's Belmont Abbey College was founded by Benedictine monks in the 1880s. Today it is a thriving campus serving the needs of both Roman Catholic and Protestant students. Clad in their crimson and cream school colors, the Abbey's athletes take what name as they march onto their fields of play? (a) Crusaders (b) Irish Invaders (c) Mad Monks

11. Raleigh's North Carolina State University was first known as the Agriculture and Mechanical Arts. Red and white are the school colors of the Wolfpack. Name the title of State's yearbook.
(a) *Howlings* (b) *Wolf Call* (c) *Agromeck*

12. The little Harnett County community of Buies Creek (population 600) is the home of Campbell University. Founded by J.A. Campbell in 1887, it was originally known as Buies Creek Academy. Name the unique school mascot that helps get Campbell teams through the toughest dry spells.
(a) camel (b) tortoise (c) lizard

Making The Grade

Go to the head of the class with the answers to this quiz on North Carolina public schools whose names start with the letter A.

1. Located on a 22-acre campus, Atkinson Elementary School in Hendersonville has 454 students and a staff of 66. Since 1996, Atkinson has been both a School of Distinction and Exemplary Growth. What feline, also known as a mountain lion, is Atkinson's mascot? (a) Panther (b) Cheetah (c) Cougar

2. Atlantic Elementary School in the town of Atlantic features an annual Battle of the Books and a Quiz Bowl for its students. Atlantic Elementary also has at least three computers in each classroom and a computer lab with more than 25 terminals. Atlantic Elementary is located in what coastal county?
   (a) Carteret County (b) Dare County (c) Onslow County

3. Annie H. Snipes Elementary School is located in New Hanover County and named for one of that area's great teachers and principals. Providing quality education for students in grades K-5, Snipes Elementary even has its own Web site to help tutor students. Annie Snipes Elementary is located on Chestnut Street in what New Hanover County port city? (a) Delco (b) Wilmington (c) Kure Beach

4. Located in northeastern Cumberland County, Armstrong Elementary School has more than 400 students who are full of what denizens call "All-Star Pride." With a yellow jacket as its mascot, the Armstrong Elementary team can be found in what community? (a) Rockfish (b) Hope Mills (c) Eastover

5. Alexander Graham Middle School on Runnymede Lane in Charlotte educates students in grades 6-8 and includes in its curriculum leadership classes unique to the school. Alexander Graham has a rich history and is one of the oldest schools in Charlotte. How old is it?
   (a) 25 years old (b) 40 years old (c) 77 years old

6. Apple Valley Middle School on Fruitland Road in Hendersonville has won many awards, including School of Distinction and scoring exemplary on the state end-of-grade tests for the last three years. Apple Valley also serves four other nearby towns, including Edneyville, Dana, Balfour, and what other community on US Highway 25 south of Arden? (a) Enka (b) Fletcher (c) Saluda

7. One of North Carolina's smallest high schools, Andrews High School in the town of Andrews has fewer than 300 students in grades 9-12. An exemplary progress school, Andrews High has strong programs in academics, athletics, and cultural arts. What county, the westernmost in our state, is home to Andrews? (a) Cherokee County (b) Swain County (c) Madison County

8. Alexander Central High School is a grade 10-12 facility that has more than 900 students and 70 classroom teachers, and an attendance rate of nearly 95 percent. Also featuring enrichment classes with after-school tutoring and the selection of a Student of the Month, Alexander Central can be found in what town that's the seat of Alexander County? (a) Love Valley (b) Millersville (c) Taylorsville

9. Archdale-Trinity Middle School in Randolph County has a bulldog as its mascot and sports school colors of blue and gold. A North Carolina School of Distinction, Archdale-Trinity is located in the town that was the original site for what current university that moved to Durham in 1892?
   (a) Wake Forest University (b) Duke University (c) Campbell University

10. Ayden-Grifton High School in Ayden has more than 500 students who enjoy the school's newspaper, *The Charger Express*. A staff of 62 educates grades 9-12 at this Exemplary Growth school in what county? (a) Pitt County (b) Beaufort County (c) Hyde County

History

Tryon Palace

Tar Heel Patriots To Remember

When the time to fight for independence came to the American colonies in 1776, North Carolinians from all walks of life did their part. Be "revolutionary" in your thinking to this quiz on Tar Heels who gave their all for freedom.

1. A delegate from North Carolina to the Continental Congress and an officer in the militia who was active in politics until his death in 1797, Whitmel Hill was one of the leaders of our state's independence movement. What county, bordered on the east by the Chowan River and Albemarle Sound, was Hill born in? (a) Bertie County (b) Washington County (c) Tyrrell County

2. The accolades that could be heaped upon North Carolina patriot William R. Davie are many indeed. In addition to being a famous Revolutionary War colonel and having Davie County named in his honor, he also held what Tar Heel political office. (a) secretary of state (b) state treasurer (c) governor

3. North Carolinian Griffith Rutherford (1731-1800) was a member of the Provincial Congress and also a military leader in the western part of our state where it was believed the British were stirring up the Native American population. What mountain tribe did Rutherford and his men fight during the years 1776 and 1777? (a) Chowan Indians (b) Cherokee Indians (c) Choctaw Indians

4. Richard Dobbs Spaight Sr. (1758-1802) saw military action in the Revolution, including the Battle of Camden. After the war, Spaight was governor of our state from 1792 to 1795. What unusual event ended Spaight's life at the age of 44? (a) pistol duel (b) mule kick (c) carriage wreck

5. Revolutionary War General Thomas Person (1733-1800) was given the honor in 1791 of having Person County named after him. In addition to his political and military contributions during the war for independence, Person was also instrumental in the development of what Tar Heel school?
(a) Appalachian State University (b) Wake Forest University (c) UNC at Chapel Hill

6. One of the officers in charge of the "Overmountain Men" who defeated the British at Kings Mountain, Revolutionary War hero John Sevier would later be chosen as governor of what short-lived area in the western region of our state? (a) Cherokee Reservation (b) State of Franklin (c) Province of Pisgah

7. When colonial delegates gathered in 1776 to sign the Declaration of Independence, there were three Tar Heels who put their names on that historic document. Which one of the following North Carolinians picked up the quill on that fateful day? (a) Joseph Hewes (b) Maurice Moore (c) Gasper Beaufort

8. An influential member of North Carolina's Revolutionary Convention in 1775 and later a delegate to the Continental Congress, Chowan County's Samuel Johnston lived until 1816. Though he grew up a Tar Heel, Johnston was actually born in the city of Dundee in what country?
(a) England (b) Ireland (c) Scotland

9. A Revolutionary War general, legislator, lawyer and delegate to the Continental Congress, Richard Caswell of Dobbs County (now Wayne, Lenoir and Greene counties) was also North Carolina's first state governor from 1776 to 1780. Not one to be idle, Caswell came back for another stint as governor during what years? (a) 1780-1784 (b) 1784-1787 (c) 1788-1790

10. Benjamin Hawkins (1754-1816) of Warren County was one of our state's first United States senators. During the revolution, Hawkins served on the staff of George Washington as an interpreter. What language, spoken by the colonists' closest ally, did Hawkins speak?
(a) French (b) German (c) Italian

11. Francis Nash (1720-1777), the older brother of a future North Carolina governor, was a military man who rose from lieutenant colonel to brigadier general. He was killed by a cannonball at the Battle of Germantown in October 1777. What was the name of his younger sibling, the governor of our state from 1780 to 1781? (a) Abner (b) Thomas (c) Richard

12. Settling in Granville County in 1774, Virginia native John Penn (1741-1788) would go on to sign both the Declaration of Independence and the Articles of Confederation for North Carolina. Penn died at home in what northeast Granville County town? (a) Stem (b) Creedmoor (c) Stovall

Revolutionary Places

A strategic colony during the American Revolution, North Carolina has many historic sites that date from the days when we fought for independence. Relive the excitement with this quiz.

1. The oldest house still standing in Mecklenburg County was built in 1774 and is now on the grounds of the Charlotte Museum of History. This stone dwelling was the scene of serious debate in 1775 when what patriot/owner discussed with his peers the upcoming Mecklenburg Declaration of Independence?
    (a) Leonidas Kasmer   (b) Hezekiah Alexander   (c) Marcus Francis Brendle

2. Constructed in 1773, the Alston House near Sanford is a State Historic Site. The spot where Whigs and Tories clashed in 1780-81, this dwelling was also the home of North Carolina governor Benjamin Williams (1799-1802, 1807-08). What other popular name is the Alston House called?
    (a) White House   (b) Rock House   (c) House in the Horseshoe

3. The final resting place of several veterans of the Battle of Kings Mountain, Goshen Cemetery near Belmont in Gaston County is said to have been the first cemetery west of the Catawba River. In addition to the Kings Mountain boys, several other Revolutionary period graves can be found in this plot just a half mile from what college?   (a) Belmont Abbey College   (b) Gaston College   (c) Kings College

4. From 1781-1785 Gilbert Town near Rutherfordton was the seat of Rutherford County. During the American Revolution, an impetuous British officer camped near Gilbert Town issued a rude ultimatum to the local patriots demanding they cease resisting the crown. Name this brash British leader who was killed just a short time later at Kings Mountain.
    (a) Nathaniel Greene   (b) David Caldwell   (c) Patrick Ferguson

5. A marker on Highway 421 in Chatham County pinpoints the site where an important source of munitions for North Carolina patriots was once located. The furnace for Wilcox Iron Works stood about 100 yards southeast of the road near what Chatham community that was named for a US president's home?
    (a) Arlington   (b) Ingleside   (c) Mount Vernon Springs

6. One of North Carolina's signers of the Declaration of Independence, William Hooper currently lies buried at Guilford Courthouse National Military Park. Hooper was first interred in what Orange County town that was not only his home, but also was the site for the Third Provincial Congress in 1775?
    (a) Hillsborough   (b) Caldwell   (c) Carr

7. During the revolution, many Scots Highlanders who were crown sympathizers met at a Presbyterian church near Lillington in Harnett County. Although the present church on Highway 27 was erected in 1895, the first went up in 1757 and was given what delicious name?
    (a) Catfish Church   (b) Barbecue Church   (c) Angel Cake Church

8. Fought on February 27, 1776, the Battle of Moores Creek Bridge was a patriot victory and is said to have prevented an impending British invasion of the South. The site of the battle, now Moores Creek National Military Park, is located 25 miles northwest of Wilmington near what town?
    (a) Currie   (b) Delco   (c) Bolivia

9. The Edenton Tea Party, a gathering of more than 50 ladies of the town on October 25, 1774, in support of American independence, has been called the "earliest known instance of political activity on the part of women in the American colonies." In Edenton today, the site is marked by a large, bronze teapot mounted on what?   (a) ship anchor   (b) Revolutionary War cannon   (c) cast iron oven

10. The site where several of Lord Cornwallis' troops were buried during the revolution, Old English Cemetery in Rowan County, was granted to the city in 1770 by the British government. In what Rowan town, also the site of a national cemetery, is this graveyard located?
    (a) China Grove   (b) Badin   (c) Salisbury

A Nation Divided

Ever since the showing of the PBS documentary "The Civil War" widespread interest in that terrible conflict has been rekindled. See how much you know about North Carolina's Civil War history by trying your hand at the questions below.

1. Many North Carolinians, including the 28th Regiment's Major Samuel Stowe of Gaston County, fell as casualties during Pickett's charge at the Battle of Gettysburg. What was the date of Pickett's charge? (a) July 1, 1863   (b) July 2, 1863   (c) July 3, 1863

2. Named for Richard Caswell, the first governor of North Carolina, Fort Caswell was occupied by state troops in January 1861 but abandoned by Confederates in January 1865. Which coastal town is nearest Fort Caswell?   (a) Southport   (b) Sunset Beach   (c) Holden Beach

3. Though popular support for secession wasn't unanimous in North Carolina, when did the Tar Heel State leave the Union?   (a) April 15, 1861   (b) May 20, 1861   (c) June 6, 1861

4. Who was governor of North Carolina when the Civil War began?
   (a) Donald Barnes White   (b) Irvin H. Brendle   (c) John W. Ellis

5. What famous Union ironclad ship—sunk in a gale off Cape Hatteras in 1862—was photographed in 1990 by scuba divers?   (a) *USS Monitor*   (b) *USS Michigan*   (c) *USS Potomac*

6. Which Rowan County town had the dubious honor of holding a large prisoner-of-war camp during the Civil War?   (a) Rockwell   (b) Salisbury   (c) China Grove

7. Which town held a Confederate Navy Yard now occupied by an urban civic center?
   (a) Charlotte   (b) Elizabeth City   (c) Morehead City

8. Running the Union naval blockade was risky but necessary, and potentially profitable. What North Carolina town was the chief port for this activity?
   (a) Washington   (b) Wilmington   (c) New Bern

9. Name the coastal Carolina fort known as the "Gibraltar of the South."
   (a) Fort Fisher   (b) Fort Macon   (c) Fort Hatteras

10. Before he became governor, Zebulon Vance was briefly an officer in the Confederate Army. What rank did he hold as leader of the 26th North Carolina Regiment?
    (a) General   (b) Colonel   (c) Major

11. Pettigrew Hospital was the first Confederate military hospital constructed in North Carolina. Where was it located?   (a) Goldsboro   (b) Raleigh   (c) Fayetteville

12. Twenty thousand Rebels fought three times that many Yankees in March 1865 at the largest land battle ever engaged on North Carolina soil. What was that battle called?
    (a) Battle of Asheville   (b) Battle of Winston-Salem   (c) Battle of Bentonville

13. Former storekeeper William Thomas organized Cherokee Indians as highly successful troops for the Confederate cause. What were these fighters called?
    (a) Thomas' Highland Legion   (b) Thomas' Mountain Fusiliers   (c) Braves of the Confederacy

History Marks The Spot

North Carolina has more than its share of Civil War history, and most of it is properly marked by historical markers for us to enjoy. To see how well you know your Tar Heel Civil War history, give the following quiz a try.

1. Historical highway marker 044 near Lowesville, in Lincoln County, stands near the site where Thomas Jonathan Jackson married Anna Morrison in 1857. In the Civil War, Thomas would become famous. Who would he be known as?
    (a) Stonewall Jackson   (b) Cannonball Jackson   (c) Action Jackson

2. Many highway historical markers trace this redheaded Union Army leader's path across Civil War North Carolina. Name this man, also known for his "March to the Sea."
    (a) Andrew Helton   (b) A.P. Hill   (c) William T. Sherman

3. The inscription on historical marker L3 along North Tryon Street in Charlotte states that the last full meeting of the Confederate Cabinet took place nearby. Who was the Confederate President in attendance?
    (a) Leroy Davis   (b) Jefferson Davis   (c) John C. Calhoun

4. A special highway historical marker on the University of North Carolina campus in Buncombe County marks earthworks from a Civil War battle in April 1865. What city is the location of the campus, earthworks and marker?   (a) Tryon   (b) Sylva   (c) Asheville

5. Name the Union General whose victory in 1862 is commemorated on highway marker C11 in James City as the Battle of New Bern, and whose whisker style is still popular today.
    (a) General Van Dyke   (b) General Burnside   (c) General Moustache

6. At the intersection of State Roads 1313 and 1314 in Durham County, a historical highway marker indicates the spot where the Confederate Army in North Carolina surrendered on April 26, 1865. What Rebel General faced this task?   (a) Joseph E. Johnston   (b) P.G.T. Beauregard   (c) J.E.B. Stuart

7. The historical highway marker on US 301 in Halifax tells of the outfitting of the Confederate ship Albemarle there in 1864. What type of ship was the Albemarle?
    (a) cotton barge   (b) submarine   (c) ironclad

8. Historic marker D56 on Third Street in Wilmington marks an early home of Confederate Attorney General and Secretary of War and State Judah P. Benjamin. What was Judah's ancestry?
    (a) Jewish   (b) Italian   (c) Lithuanian

9. The special highway map marker on US 64 in Washington County tells of the recapture of a nearby town in April 1864 by Confederate forces. Name this strategic town on the Roanoke River.
    (a) Sparta   (b) Plymouth   (c) Hiddenite

10. Near Buxton, on the Outer Banks, is historic marker B50, dedicated to the remains of a Union ship lying offshore. That ship battled the Confederate ship Merrimac in the first clash of ironclads. What was its name?   (a) *USS Midway*   (b) *USS Enterprise*   (c) *USS Monitor*

11. Map and historic highway markers recall the Civil War battle for Fort Macon in Carteret County. Its capture gave the Union Navy a deepwater port in Beaufort. What is Fort Macon made of?
    (a) sandbags   (b) bricks   (c) logs

12. In Waynesville, highway marker P10 tells of the May 6, 1865, surrender of the last pocket of Confederates in North Carolina. Name those brave troops' general. He had the same name as one of our recent governors.   (a) James Martin   (b) Jesse Helms   (c) James Long

Put On Those Tar Heel
Civil War Thinking Caps

During the Civil War, North Carolina contributed 125,000 troops in more than 80 regiments to the cause for Southern independence. Dust off those history books, and remember the tales great-grandpappy told, for the answers to this quiz.

1. The 6th Regiment of NC troops saw many battles, including the Confederate victory at Bull Run. This regiment was organized in May 1861 at a town then called Company Shops. What modern Alamance County city now occupies that site? (a) Burlington (b) Snow Camp (c) Kimesville

2. Eventually becoming part of the hard-fighting 16th NC Regiment, many volunteers in Gaston County signed up for army life at a town then called Brevard Station. What is the present day name of Brevard Station? (a) Lowell (b) McAdenville (c) Stanley

3. Raised in the North Carolina mountains, the 58th Regiment took part in the September 1863 Confederate victory at Chickamauga. Chickamauga was further immortalized in a short story by what famous Asheville writer? (a) Horace Greeley (b) Thomas Wolfe (c) Ernest Hemingway

4. After leaving boot camp at Raleigh in early 1862, the 52nd NC Regiment spent time in Kinston, then went by rail to become part of the Army of Northern Virginia. What Confederate general was in overall charge of that heroic throng? (a) Robert E. Lee (b) John Bell Hood (c) Jubal Early

5. Organized at Salisbury in July 1862, the 57th NC Regiment had its first action just six months later at the Battle of Fredericksburg. In what state did that win over General Burnside's Yankees take place? (a) Maryland (b) Virginia (c) Pennsylvania

6. In May 1863 Confederates achieved a stunning tactical coup at the Battle of Chancellorsville. This triumph proved costly, however, when men of the 18th NC Regiment accidentally shot and mortally wounded what great Southern leader? (a) Stonewall Jackson (b) Jefferson Davis (c) J.E.B. Stuart

7. Raised on Bald Head Island in December 1863 from several veteran coastal units, the 40th NC Regiment would one year later participate in the defense of the world's largest earthen fort near Wilmington. What is the name of that fort? (a) Fort Wagner (b) Fort Monroe (c) Fort Fisher

8. An artillery outfit, the 10th NC Regiment took part in the largest battle ever held on North Carolina soil at Bentonville March 19-21, 1865. What Confederate general commanded the troops at that fight? (a) D.H. Hill (b) Joseph E. Johnston (c) Calvinius McGuirt

9. At the Battle of Antietam, September 17, 1862, Company C of the 14th NC Regiment had all 45 men either wounded or killed. The Battle of Antietam is generally known by what name in the South? (a) Battle of Sharpsburg (b) Battle of Maryland (c) Battle of Northern Invasion

10. Members of the 26th NC Regiment had an unusual comrade in the form of one "Sam" Blalock. Though Sam wore a uniform, and was treated as one of the boys, what was different about "him?"
    (a) Sam was a woman, Malinda Blalock (b) Sam was the colonel's dog
    (c) Sam was the regimental goat

11. The 26th Regiment held another less-lighthearted distinction. At Gettysburg, it had 86 killed and 502 wounded, thereby losing more men than any unit in any battle on either side in the entire war. What Union general witnessed the high tide of the Confederacy, and the tragic bravery of the 26th, at Gettysburg? (a) George Meade (b) William Rosecrans (c) William T. Sherman

Regimental Nicknames From A Tar Heel Perspective

The Civil War saw more than 70 Confederate regiments raised in North Carolina. As colorful as the Rebels who manned them were, the monikers that our state's troops gave their military companies were full of flash. Match the tags and the teams in this quiz on Tar Heel regimental nicknames.

1. Organized at Troy in Montgomery County in March 1862, Company F of the 44th Regiment saw action in eastern North Carolina as well as Virginia. Never a group to hide in a wooden horse, Company F went by what name? (a) Hellenistic Heathens (b) Trojan Regulators (c) Grecian Grapplers

2. Company K of the 26th Regiment NC Troops signed up in Wadesboro on July 1861, and was trained at Camp Carolina in Wake County. This Confederate crowd named itself after what river that flowed through its native Anson County?
   (a) Pee Dee Wildcats (b) Lumber River Yankee Lashers (c) Rocky River Ruffians

3. Another 26th NC Troops outfit was Company B from Union County. This group was in the thick of the fighting at Gettysburg and lost several men. Company B used the surname of a former United States president known as "Old Hickory" to form what title of their own?
   (a) Monroe Marauders (b) Waxhaw Washington Warriors (c) Waxhaw Jackson Guards

4. Company E of the 29th North Carolina saw fighting at Chickamauga and other areas in the Civil War's western theater. Mountain men from the hills and dales beyond Asheville formed Company E, which was named after what county whose seat is Waynesville?
   (a) Haywood Fire Shooters (b) Henderson Heroes (c) Polk County Patriots

5. Raised in Burke and Catawba counties in Octboer 1861, Company K of the 35th Regiment took part in the Seven Days' battle in 1862. Not men who depended on their hairstyles to gain strength, Company K nonetheless chose what name?
   (a) Burke and Catawba Beehives (b) Burke and Catawba Crewcuts (c) Burke and Catawba Sampsons

6. Company D of the 27th NC was Lenoir County's first Confederate volunteer unit and consisted of 59 men. Company D was known by what nickname that reflected both an area near Lenoir County and a championship Georgia baseball team of the 20th century?
   (a) Tuckahoe Braves (b) Sand Hill Crackers (c) Woodington Peaches

7. Heroes at the Battle of Sharpsburg in September 1862, Company E, 30th Regiment NC Troops had originally formed up in the Duplin County town of Teachey. Company E named itself after its home county and what important Tar Heel pine product?
   (a) Duplin Pineknots (b) Duplin Resin Raisers (c) Duplin Turpentine Boys

8. The skilled horsemen of Company K, 1st Regiment, trained at Camp Woodfin near Asheville in July 1861 before going into action. Eventually fighting in 94 battles, Company K chose what name after the North Carolina mountain area that is today a national forest?
   (a) Blue Ridge Bandits (b) Nantahala Rangers (c) Fontana Furies

9. When mustered in at Smithfield in May 1861, Company E, 14th Regiment NC Volunteers, was 83 men strong. Though Tar Heels rather than Texans did the fighting, Company E, nonetheless adopted what nickname that might be associated with the Confederacy's westernmost state?
   (a) Longhorn Legion (b) Lone Star Boys (c) Carolina Cowboys

10. Tyrrell County men strode forth in May 1861 to sign up for Confederate service in what would become the 32nd Regiment NC Troops. Commanded by Edmund Brabble of Currituck County, the Tyrrell contingent of the 32nd went by what nickname that was inspired by native Tar Heel grapes and a North Carolina river of the same name? (a) Scuppernong Grays (b) Concord Cadets (c) Chablis Chargers

11. One of five Confederate companies raised in Rutherford County in 1861, Company B of the 34th Regiment NC Troops took part in the 1863 Battle of Chancellorsville. No doubt delivering many a sting to the Federals, Company B went by what nickname?
    (a) Rutherford Rascals (b) Forest City Foragers (c) Sandy Run Yellow Jackets

12. Cited for bravery at the Battle of Malvern Hill in July 1861, this company took its name from what Tar Heel waterway that flows through the heart of Chatham?
    (a) Haw River Boys (b) Meherrin River Musketeers (c) Waccamaw River Warriors

13. Company A of the 22nd Regiment NC Troops was unique in that four brothers from a family named Deal all served in that unit. Seeing action at battles such as Cold Harbor, the Deals and their comrades in Company A went by what nickname that reflected their home county seated by Lenoir?
    (a) Catawba Cavaliers (b) Caldwell Rough and Ready Boys (c) Wilkes Wild Bunch

39

Sherman's March

Federal forces commanded by General William T. Sherman entered the Old North State in March 1865 and began a series of battles that helped end the Civil War. Aim for the correct answers to this quiz on Sherman's march through North Carolina.

1. After leaving South Carolina in late February 1865, Sherman's troops began marching to the Tar Heel State with the eventual goal of linking up with Union forces in Virginia. One wing of Sherman's army crossed what river between Hamlet and Wadesboro to enter North Carolina?
   (a) Pee Dee River   (b) Tyger River   (c) Catawba River

2. By the time General Sherman's troops entered North Carolina, they had been cut off from their supply bases in Savannah, Georgia for weeks. What North Carolina seaport city, known as the "lifeline of the Confederacy," did Sherman hope to use as a depot for provisioning his soldiers?
   (a) New Bern   (b) Washington   (c) Wilmington

3. March 8, 1865, witnessed the arrival of both wings of Sherman's army in North Carolina. On that date, men of the Fifteenth Corps camped five miles west of Laurinburg at what town, now on US Highway 74 just southeast of Old Hundred?   (a) Red Springs   (b) Laurel Hill   (c) Masons Cross

4. On March 11, 1865, elements of Sherman's army reached Fayetteville. A major objective was the former Federal arsenal that had provided thousands of rifles and other ordnance for the Confederacy. By the time Federal troops had arrived, much of the arsenal's machinery had been moved to what coal-mining town?   (a) Bombay   (b) Egypt   (c) Shanghai

5. By March 15, 1865, Sherman had his entire army across the Cape Fear River in North Carolina and was aiming for Goldsboro. Opposing him on the Confederate side was what general whose earlier injuries at the battle of Seven Pines, Virginia in May 1861, had moved Robert E. Lee into command of the South's forces in the Old Dominion?
   (a) Joseph Johnston   (b) Stonewall Jackson   (c) Richard "Baldy" Ewell

6. The largest battle ever fought on Tar Heel soil took place during March 19-21, 1865, between 25,000 Confederates and 60,000 of Sherman's Union soldiers. The 6,000-acre Bentonville Battlefield is now a North Carolina Historic Site located off US Highway 701 in what county seated by Smithfield?
   (a) Richmond County   (b) Johnston County   (c) Sampson County

7. In a humorous incident during Sherman's march through North Carolina, Union cavalry leader General Judson Kilpatrick and a lady companion were surprised in bed near the Solemn Grove community by attacking Confederate horsemen. This dawn skirmish, in which Kilpatrick barely escaped capture, has come to be known as the battle of what?
   (a) Kilpatrick's Pants   (b) The Rude Awakening   (c) Hell on the Wabash

8. Four years to the day after Charleston's Fort Sumter surrendered to the Confederacy, Sherman's troops, near Smithfield, received the electrifying news that Robert E. Lee had capitulated to General Ulysses S. Grant several days before. On what date in April 1865 did Sherman's men hear that report?
   (a) April 1, 1865   (b) April 12, 1865   (c) April 15, 1865

9. With Federal infantry approaching Raleigh, Governor Zebulon Vance wrote a letter to Sherman requesting an interview to determine how a suspension of hostilities might be arranged. A former soldier himself, Vance had earlier in the war been colonel of what regiment?
   (a) 26th North Carolina   (b) 28th North Carolina   (c) 49th North Carolina

10. Although Union soldiers occupied Raleigh, some shots still were fired in the area. Two miles west of Raleigh on Hillsboro Road, Sherman's cavalry under Kilpatrick had a sharp fight with horsemen in gray. This skirmish was followed by another shoot-out 10 miles farther west near what town north of Cary?   (a) Rolesville   (b) Morrisville   (c) Eagle Rock

Tar Heel Officers Offered
Inspiration In Civil War

Though generals get the glory, soldiers below them carry out the missions. Bravely leading their men during the Civil War, Tar Heel officers were an inspiration. With this in mind, rally 'round the right answers to this quiz on these stalwart souls.

1. At Petersburg in 1864, Lieutenant A.E. Brown of the 49th NC Regiment was involved in one of the oddest stories of the Civil War when a mini-ball hit the Bible he had in his pocket and came to a stop directly at Jeremiah 46:14. What lifesaving words for Lieutenant Brown were these?
(a) "Arise and fly" (b) "Thou hast delivered me" (c) "Stand ye fast, and prepare"

2. Less fortunate was Second Lieutenant William Hale of the 35th NC Regiment. By losing his life at New Bern in 1862, he became the first person from Catawba County to die in the war. Name the town in that county where Hale volunteered. (a) Hickory (b) Morganton (c) Shelby

3. Also from Catawba County was Second Lieutenant Robert Cobb of the 23rd NC Regiment. A born leader, Lieutenant Cobb would later head the Western North Carolina Railroad. What town (the seat of Catawba County) was he from? (a) Forest City (b) Newton (c) Startown

4. Captain Thomas Brem was a member of the 9th NC Regiment of Confederate artillery, which was raised in Mecklenburg County. In May 1875 this Civil War veteran found that his ordnance experience came in handy when he was put in charge of fireworks for the centennial celebration of what document?
(a) US Constitution (b) Mecklenburg Declaration of Independence (c) Halifax Resolves

5. A clerk before the Civil War, Captain Thomas Mulloy of the 7th NC Regiment rose to that rank after joining up in August 1861 as a private. Foreign-born, Mulloy came from what land known as the "emerald isle?" (a) Ireland (b) Nova Scotia (c) Isle of Man

6. An able laddie, Major Murdock McLaughlin McRae was a member of a group—Company K of the 38th NC Regiment—that had the greatest percentage of Highland Scots names on its rolls than of any unit in the Rebel army. From what county, the site of present-day Pope Air Force Base, did this unique group march to war? (a) Sampson County (b) Scotland County (c) Cumberland County

7. A prominent Anson County citizen before and after the Civil War, Colonel Risden Tyler Bennett of the 14th NC Regiment helped establish the first library in 1905 in what town, the county seat of Anson?
(a) Wadesboro (b) Morven (c) Polkton

8. Colonel William Cowles was a hard-riding member of the 1st NC Cavalry CSA who was twice wounded. After the war, he practiced law in Wilkesboro, never forgetting his upbringing near Hamptonville in what neighboring county? (a) Alexander County (b) Iredell County (c) Yadkin County

9. A physician before the Civil War, Captain Oliver P. Gardner of Company I, 38th NC Regiment was well respected by his Cleveland County troops. In addition to being a fine officer, he was also the father of future Governor O. Max Gardner. What years did his son serve in that office?
(a) 1880-1888 (b) 1910-1914 (c) 1929-1933

10. In addition to being the first man in Rutherford County to graduate from the University of North Carolina at Chapel Hill, William Lewis Twitty would go on to bravely serve as Captain of Company C, 1st Battalion CSA during the Civil War. A native of the soil, Twitty had been raised in Rutherford County on the banks of what river? (a) Catawba River (b) Pee Dee River (c) Broad River

Reconstruction In North Carolina

Following the Civil War, North Carolina and the rest of the former Confederacy went through a time of social and political trial known as the Reconstruction Era. From carpetbaggers to Klansmen, the answers to this quiz will take you back to those days when our state rejoined the Union.

1. Though North Carolinas was considered a "conquered province" beginning with the Civil War's end in 1865, it was not until 1867 that the Reconstruction Era officially began. What years are considered to be the span of Reconstruction? (a) 1867-1880 (b) 1867-1877 (c) 1867-1869

2. The 17th president of the United States had to deal not only with the problems of Reconstruction, but also with the prospect of his own impeachment. Name this tormented Tar Heel, a native of Raleigh.
    (a) James Buchanan (b) James K. Polk (c) Andrew Johnson

3. From March 1867 to July 1868, North Carolina was under Union military rule. The Federal officer who was initially in charge of this situation was General Daniel Sickles. Before he hopped on down to oversee things in the Tar Heel State, Sickles had lost a leg in 1863 at what Pennsylvania battle?
    (a) Gettysburg (b) Shiloh (c) Seven Pines

4. The 13th Amendment to the United States Constitution freed more than 350,000 North Carolina slaves. The Reconstruction government set up a special agency to help these people with food, shelter, clothing and education during the period 1865-1868. Name this program.
    (a) Afro-Relief (b) Freedmen's Bureau (c) US Department of Health, Education and Welfare

5. Before Reconstruction, no black could serve on a jury in North Carolina. In 1867 former slave Joseph Grimes become the first of his race to do so when he served as a Superior Court juror in what Tar Heel county whose seat is Greenville? (a) Green County (b) Pitt County (c) Chowan County

6. During Reconstruction, North Carolina and her Southern sister states were often the destination of unscrupulous Northerners who came to take political and financial advantage of the unsettled conditions here. Named for the type of luggage they carried, what were these rascals called?
    (a) samsonites (b) dufflebags (c) carpetbaggers

7. A product of Reconstruction, the Ku Klux Klan began in Tennessee. In 1868 the first KKK notice appeared in North Carolina. The first leader of the KKK in our state was Chapel Hill resident Colonel William Saunders. As KKK leader, what title did Saunders have?
    (a) Grand Lizard (b) Grand Dragon (c) Kingfish

8. In 1866 Congress tried to force North Carolina and the other Southern states to ratify a Constitutional amendment granting citizenship to blacks but also denying former Confederates the right to hold office. As it was first written, Tar Heels legislators rejected what amendment? (a) 14th (b) 15th (c) 16th

9. The North Carolina beginnings of one of our nation's two current major political parties took place during a March 1867 convention in Raleigh. Name this party, whose Reconstruction origins included scalawags, freed slaves and carpetbaggers. (a) Democrats (b) Republicans (c) Independents

10. Appointed by President Andrew Johnson as "provisional governor" of North Carolina in 1865, William Holden was finally elected to that office in 1868. After three years of Reconstruction arguing and intrigue, Holden became the only Tar Heel governor to suffer what political catastrophe?
    (a) impeachment (b) censure (c) income tax auditing

11. According to contemporary accounts, Reconstruction days in Charlotte went by with relative harmony between the local population and occupying Federal troops. The first Union officer to oversee Charlotte was Colonel Willard Warner of what state whose capital is Columbus.
    (a) Indiana (b) Michigan (c) Ohio

12. At a convention dominated by Republicans, delegates met in post-Civil War Raleigh to adopt a new state constitution that among other things abolished slavery and extended the governor's term from two to four years. Seven years after leaving the Union, when was the new document voted in?
    (a) 1867 (b) 1868 (c) 1869

13. A delegate to the Constitutional Convention, state senator and later congressman, John A. Hyman was one of the most influential blacks during North Carolina's Reconstruction years. Hyman was born a slave in 1840 in what county bordered on the east by Halifax County?
    (a) Warren County (b) Caswell County (c) Person County

42

The Corps Of Civilians

The New Deal Administration of President Franklin Delano Roosevelt brought with it many government programs to help dig our country out of the Great Depression in the 1930s. The Civilian Conservation Corps (CCC) was the first such relief agency created. Approximately 300,000 men between the ages of 17 and 28 found jobs within the Corps, working on such projects as flood control, reforestation and roadbuilding. Twenty-seven thousand of them were enrolled in the dozens of CCC camps in North Carolina.

Read November 1992's Tar Heel Memories piece by Norman Vick on his time in the CCC on page 13, and then take the following quiz to test your knowledge of the CCC program.

1. The Civilian Conservation Corps gave many Depression-era North Carolinians hope, work and a little money. What year did the CCC begin? (a) 1930 (b) 1933 (c) 1939

2. Speaking of money, just how much salary did the CCC give the thousands of young North Carolina men who joined it each month? (a) $30 (b) $100 (c) $203

3. By the time of its disbandment in 1942, how many men from North Carolina had actually worked for the CCC? (a) 5,000 (b) 10,000 (c) 60,000

4. Scattered from mountains to the coast, CCC work camps dotted the NC landscape. How many CCC camps were eventually built in our state? (a) more than 60 (b) more than 100 (c) 35

5. CCC workers, in an attempt to control soil erosion, helped introduce a plant that now drapes the landscape of not only North Carolina, but the entire South. What is this plant, also known as "mile a minute?"
    (a) morning glory (b) pokeweed (c) kudzu

6. Jacks of all trades, CCC workers were called upon to perform many conservation jobs, not the least of which included helping battle a raging forest fire on North Carolina's tallest mountain in 1939. What mountain did the CCC help save? (a) Mount Pisgah (b) Mount Mitchell (c) Black Mountain

7. With more than 250 miles of its length in North Carolina, this highway attracts thousands of visitors to our mountains each year. Many of its miles, overlooks and tunnels were constructed by the CCC. What roadway is this? (a) Smoky Mountains Highway (b) Blue Ridge Parkway (c) Foothills Scenic Drive

8. Hacking many miles of trails and overlooks for nature lovers in the Joyce Kilmer Memorial Forest, CCC workers assured that generations to come would enjoy the woods. What North Carolina county is Joyce Kilmer Memorial Forest located in? (a) Graham (b) Polk (c) Ashe

9. CCC workers lived in camps often named for famous folks. At Smokemont there was a camp named for William Thomas, a man who organized Indians as Confederate troops. What tribe did these brave Native Americans come from? (a) Catawba (b) Pasquotank (c) Cherokee

10. Name the hiking trail that stretches from Maine to Georgia, has its highest point at Clingmans Dome in North Carolina and is dotted with shelters built by the CCC.
    (a) Appalachian Trail (b) East Coast Trail (c) Blue Ridge Excursion Trail

11. CCC men worked many hours to construct a popular campground near a mountain pass on the Haywood County and Transylvania County line. What gap in Western North Carolina is this campground near?
    (a) Bald Creek Gap (b) Deal Gap (c) Frying Pan Gap

12. CCC Company No. 1216 had a camp located in Swain County, not far from Deep Creek. What town near the camp is not only a county seat, but was also a popular socializing spot for the workers?
    (a) Franklin (b) Bryson City (c) Robbinsville

13. The US Forest Service operated a CCC camp near the biggest town in McDowell County on Buck Creek. What town might this be? (a) Marion (b) Old Fort (c) Ridgecrest

North Carolina's Role In World War II

From the home front to battles in faraway places, North Carolinians did their part to achieve victory in World War II. Put an old Glenn Miller album on the stereo and you'll be "In The Mood" to take this quiz on those valiant days more than 50 years ago.

1. During World War II more than one million North Carolinians were registered for service by their local draft boards. After deferments for various reasons were granted, how many Tar Heels were actually inducted into the armed forces during the war?   (a) 700,000   (b) 362,000   (c) 500,000

2. Naval vessels in World War II carrying names relating to our state numbered 41. The grandest of these ships was the battleship *USS North Carolina*. Now anchored at Wilmington as a floating museum and memorial, the *North Carolina* was given what nickname during its war years?
(a) Showboat   (b) New Ironsides   (c) Tar Heel Hammer

3. High in the skies over World War II Europe, Greensboro's Major George Preddy shot down 26 German planes. Today, a portion of Interstate 85 in Greensboro is named in honor of George and his brother, First Lieutenant William R. Preddy. What type of fighter plane did these two Tar Heel aviators fly?
(a) Hawker Hurricane   (b) B24 Liberator   (c) P51 Mustang

4. The greatest destruction North Carolina suffered during World War II came not at the hands of the enemy but as the result of an ammunition truck accident that set off 30,000 pounds of explosives. It happened near the town of Selma. Name the county where this blast took place in March 1942.
(a) Johnston County   (b) Pender County   (c) Dare County

5. Named for one of North Carolina's most beloved governors, the Liberty ship *Zebulon B. Vance* was the first vessel of this type launched at Wilmington during the war years. What was the primary task of the 243 Liberty ships constructed?   (a) minesweeping   (b) cargo shipping   (c) destroyer escort

6. As part of a national program, many Tar Heels planted supplemental vegetable gardens while World War II was in progress. During 1944 alone, North Carolinians canned 28 million quarts of vegetables. What was the name given to these gardens?
(a) Uncle Sam's Vegetable Patch   (b) Allied Acres   (c) Victory Gardens

7. From 1941 to 1943 German U-boats sank many vessels off the coast of our state. Though the government tried to keep the sinkings secret, coastal residents could often see burning ships on the horizon. What nickname was given to the waters off North Carolina during this perilous time?
(a) "Iron Bottom Sound"   (b) "Torpedo Junction"   (c) "Submarine Alley"

8. When World War II came, North Carolina saw the construction or expansion of approximately 20 major military installations within its borders. What base near Fayetteville held upwards of 100,000 men and was the world's largest artillery post?   (a) Fort Bragg   (b) Fort Butner   (c) Fort Macon

9. Asheville native Robert K. Morgan and his B-17 bomber achieved aviation immortality in World War II by being the first to fly 25 combat missions. Name the famous "flying fortress" that Morgan and his crew dodged Messerschmitts in.   (a) *Asheville Argonaut*   (b) *Mountain Maid*   (c) *Memphis Belle*

10. Comprised mainly of soldiers from North Carolina, South Carolina and Tennessee, the US Army's 30th Division hit the beach on D-Day and didn't slow down until V-E Day. The 30th was called the "Old Hickory Division" in reference to what American President born near Waxhaw.
(a) Andrew Jackson   (b) James K. Polk   (c) Andrew Johnson

11. Named Camp Lejeune after World War II Marine Commandant Major General John A. Lejeune, the base in Onslow County was the second-largest Marine facility in the nation. As well as humans, many K-9 dogs were trained at Lejeune during World War II. What name was given to these four-legged "dogfaces?"   (a) "Hell's Hyenas"   (b) "Hounds from Hades"   (c) "Devil Dogs"

12. To boost the morale of those serving in uniform during World War II, more than 100 USO clubs in 47 communities were operated in North Carolina. One of the largest facilities of this type was at Aberdeen near Pinehurst, where nearly 500,000 servicemen got a dose of Tar Heel hospitality. What did the letters USO stand for?
(a) United States Organization   (b) Unlimited Service opportunities   (c) United Service Organizations

Preserving Our History

With an active Historic Preservation Foundation, more than two dozen State Historic Sites and scores of preservation societies across the state, North Carolina can be proud of its efforts to maintain its historic homes, buildings and other important structures.

How much do you know about the preservation movement here?

1. Which North Carolina agency is most directly involved with historic preservation?
    (a) Department of Cultural Resources (b) Department of Commerce
    (c) Department of Historical Research

2. A Georgian-Federal style house built around 1890 is the centerpiece of Latta Plantation Park near Charlotte. Name the river that flows nearby.
    (a) Pee Dee River (b) Salauda River (c) Catawba River

3. Architectural preservation is alive and well in Bath, North Carolina's oldest town and a one-time haven for pirates. Which of these seadogs once called Bath home?
    (a) Bluebeard (b) Captain Hook (c) Blackbeard

4. Built in 1838, the estate called Connemara near Flat Rock was once the home of what famous writer?
    (a) Thomas Wolfe (b) Ernest Hemmingway (c) Carl Sandburg

5. Those seeking examples of preserved pioneer dwellings and out-buildings will have plenty to view at the Pioneer Farmstead. What highway, running between Cherokee and Gatlinburg, Tennessee, takes you to this attraction? (a) US 441 (b) Interstate 40 (c) NC 16

6. Just off I-40 near Asheville, the magnificent Biltmore House awes thousands of visitors annually. Who built the house, once the largest private residence in the country?
    (a) Cornelius Vanderbilt (b) George Washington Vanderbilt (c) Worthington Biltmore III

7. More than 90 restored buildings from the 18th and 19th centuries are the core of Old Salem, North Carolina's answer to Colonial Williamsburg. What county is Old Salem in?
    (a) Stokes County (b) Wake County (c) Forsyth County

8. Built in the 1700s, Orton Plantation on the Cape Fear River was once famous for its rice crop. These days, visitors flock there to see the gorgeous azaleas, camellias and the restored mansion. What Tar Heel city, on the Cape Fear, is nearest Orton? (a) Wilmington (b) Tin City (c) Burgaw

9. Visitors to Edenton can take a self-guided tour through the historic district. Restored dwellings include the James Iredell House (1773) and the Cupola House (1725). What body of water is Edenton on?
    (a) Pamlico Sound (b) Albemarle Sound (c) Neuse River

10. Proud of its railroading history, Hamlet saw fit to preserve its architecturally unique depot, built in 1900. What railroad company was the depot built for?
    (a) Southern Railway Company (b) Piedmont and Northern Railroad (c) Seaboard Air Line

11. With a historic district that's second to none, New Bern had a grand day April 8, 1959, when a certain palace opened to the public after an extensive reconstruction. What palace was this?
    (a) Tryon Palace (b) Crystal Palace (c) Pamlico Palace

12. Our own North Carolina Executive Mansion had an overhaul that restored the place to its former 19th century beauty. On what street in Raleigh will you find this fine symbol of our state?
    (a) North Salisbury Street (b) North Blount Street (c) West Edenton Street

Tar Heel State Historic Sites

Ever aware of its heritage, North Carolina has more than a dozen state historic sites. Travel the length and breadth of Tar Heel territory as you search for the correct answers to this quiz.

1. Town Creek Indian Mound Historic Site highlights a reconstructed 16th-century Native American ceremonial center. Just off NC Highway 273 near Mt. Gilead in Montgomery County, Town Creek is just a few miles south of what state park?
(a) Morrow Mountain State Park   (b) South Mountains State Park   (c) Medoc Mountain State Park

2. North Carolina's only frontier fort during the mid-1700s, Fort Dobbs State Historic Site was named after Royal Governor Arthur Dobbs. Just a quick trip north of Charlotte near the intersection of interstates 77 and 40, Fort Dobbs is located in what city?   (a) Gastonia   (b) Rockingham   (c) Statesville

3. Once a thriving center of business and politics, Brunswick Town State Historic Site saw its heyday before the American Revolution. About nine miles north of Southport off NC 133, Brunswick Town's excavated ruins sit near what river?   (a) Green River   (b) Cape Fear River   (c) Meherrin River

4. Not too many miles southeast of Brunswick Town are the remains of what was once the largest fort of its type in the world. Fort Fisher State Historic Site honors that Civil War bastion that finally fell in January 1865. What type of material was Fort Fisher made of?
(a) palmetto logs   (b) sand   (c) handmade bricks

5. Also known as the NC Transportation Museum, Spencer Shops State Historic Site in Spencer near Salisbury recently completed a major renovation of its facilities. Though many types of Tar Heel transport are on display, what type of locomotion is Spencer Shops main drawing card?
(a) railroading   (b) trucking   (c) flying

6. Often called North Carolina's most loved governor, Zeb Vance is honored by having a state historic site at his birthplace near Weaverville. Located five miles east of US 17/23 on Reems Creek Road, Vance's former house is what type of structure?
(a) French Renaissance chateau   (b) Neo Classic plantation home   (c) Log cabin

7. The 11th President of the United States was born in Mecklenburg County on November 2, 1795. A state historic site near Pineville recreates the farm that was this president's homeplace. Who was this great Tar Heel?   (a) Martin Van Buren   (b) James K. Polk   (c) Andrew Jackson

8. Reed Gold Mine State Historic Site sits on land where in 1799 young Conrad Reed discovered a 28-pound chunk of gold. Visitors can make their way to Reed Gold Mine 14 miles south of Concord for panning or touring by following Highway 601 or NC 200 in what county?
(a) Cabarrus County   (b) Randolph County   (c) Mecklenburg County

9. A state historic site, the boarding house at 48 Spruce Street in Asheville where author Thomas Wolfe grew up was opened to the public in 1949. In addition to his famous work, *Look Homeward, Angel,* Wolfe also penned what book?
(a) *The Old Man and the Sea*   (b) *The Hills Beyond*   (c) *The Great Gatsby*

10. The largest surrender of Confederate troops at the end of the Civil War occurred on April 26, 1865, near Durham at the farm of James Bennett. Now a state historic site, Bennett Place saw what two generals meet for that capitulation?   (a) Johnston and Sherman   (b) Lee and Grant   (c) Longstreet and Meade

11. The 1759 home of colonial North Carolina Attorney General James Iredell's house is a state historic site located in Edenton. In addition to his duties as attorney general, Iredell later served on the US Supreme Court after his appointment by what Virginia-born President?
(a) Rutherford B. Hayes   (b) Andrew Johns   (c) George Washington

12. Visitors to Kinston can view both the Richard Caswell Memorial as well as the *CSS Neuse* State Historic Site. One of two ironclad gunboats constructed in North Carolina during the Civil War, the *Neuse* was named after what Kinston geographical feature?   (a) a river   (b) a mountain   (c) a valley

North Carolina People

Cherokee Indian Reservation

Tar Heel Greats

The list of North Carolina men and women who have left their mark on the arts, education, business, and sports could fill volumes. Marvel at the many talented folks our state has produced as you guess the answers to this quiz on Tar Heel greats.

1. In 1903, New Bern drugstore owner Caleb Bradham made soft drink history when he was granted a patent for Pepsi-Cola. Prior to giving his brew the Pepsi name, Bradham had used what moniker for his fizzy quaff?   (a) New Bern Nog   (b) Brad's Drink   (c) Coastal Cola

2. The first woman to serve in North Carolina's state legislature also had the distinction of having been Asheville's first female attorney. Name this pioneering Buncombe County woman who took her General Assembly seat in 1921.   (a) Lillian Exum Clement   (b) Taylor L. Presley   (c) Sallie Walker Stockard

3. A Guilford County attorney, Henry E. Frye made history on November 5, 1968, when he became the first African-American in the 20th century elected to the North Carolina General Assembly. In 1983, Frye would also gain distinction by being the first black to attain what legal profession post?
    (a) NC Attorney General   (b) US Supreme Court Justice   (c) NC Supreme Court Associate Justice

4. North Carolina's leading business, the tobacco industry was put into high gear when James B. Duke of Durham organized the American Tobacco Company in 1890. James had learned the tobacco trade from his father, who went by what name?   (a) Washington Duke   (b) "Bull" Duke   (c) Joe "Camel" Duke

5. In August 1983, William Thornton became the first North Carolinian in outer space when he took part in a *Challenger* shuttle mission. Thornton hailed from what Duplin County town three miles south of Calypso?   (a) Pink Hill   (b) Chinquapin   (c) Faison

6. Recently a member of the world champion Chicago Bulls, Michael Jordan has been lauded by many as the greatest basketball player of all time. Before he led the University of North Carolina to a national championship in 1982, Jordan had played basketball at what Wilmington high school?
    (a) Laney High School   (b) Garinger High School   (c) Lakeside High School

7. One of our state's most famous writers, Thomas Wolfe wrote novels and stories that often reflected his younger days as a boy growing up in Asheville. Now a state historic site, the boarding house Wolfe's mother ran is located on what Asheville street?
    (a) Grovewood Road   (b) Market Street   (c) Macon Street

8. Said to be the most popular politician in North Carolina history, Zebulon Vance led our state through the Civil War years, then went on to serve in the US Senate. Early in the war, Vance was a colonel in what regiment later said to have been "furthest at Gettysburg"?
    (a) 49th Regiment NC Troops   (b) 16th Regiment NC Troops   (c) 26th Regiment NC Troops

9. A top Hollywood star during the 1940s and '50s, Ava Gardner is likely the most glamorous actress to ever come out of North Carolina. Although Gardner called Grabtown home, a museum chronicling her life and career is located in what Johnston County city?   (a) Pine Level   (b) Elevation   (c) Smithfield

10. The crew of Asheville airman Robert Morgan's B-17 bomber became the first to complete 25 missions over German-held territory in Europe in one of World War II's most publicized feats. Name Morgan's airplane, now housed in a special hangar near the Mississippi River.
    (a) *Tar Heel Gal*   (b) *Cripes a Mighty*   (c) *Memphis Belle*

North Carolina's Early Explorers

In Spanish jackboots or English pantaloons, early explorers of North Carolina found our state to be a vast wilderness rich in natural resources. As they crossed the Tar Heel landscape in search of wealth or elbow room, take a guess at the correct answers to this quiz on these brave souls and their exploits.

1. In 1524 Giovanni da Verrazzano became the first recorded European to reach what is now the North Carolina shore. As he looked across the Outer Banks to Pamlico Sound, Verrazzano entertained the decidedly mistaken notion that he was seeing what ocean?
   (a) Indian Ocean   (b) Arctic Ocean   (c) Pacific Ocean

2. July 1526 saw the Spaniard Luis Vasquez de Ayllon and 500 followers attempt settlement on Tar Heel terrain. Before retreating to disastrous circumstances in South Carolina, he had abandoned a site on what coastal North Carolina river he called Rio Jordan?
   (a) Cape Fear River   (b) Tar River   (c) Uwharrie River

3. Tramping from Florida to western North Carolina and beyond during 1539-1540, an expeditionary force of more than 700 Spaniards is said to have passed near present-day Highlands, Franklin and Asheville. What man, whose name would later grace, of all things, an automobile, led this throng?
   (a) Juan Plymouth   (b) Hernando de Soto   (c) Jesus de Chevrolet

4. In 1558 a group of shipwrecked Spanish sailors was rescued by Native Americans in this state. Said to have made a boat by lashing canoes together and using their clothes for sails, the Spanish beat a hasty retreat for Florida from what river that cleaves Beaufort County in twain?
   (a) White Oak River   (b) Pamlico River   (c) Chowan River

5. The year 1566 witnessed a group of wayward Spaniards led by Pedro de Coronas briefly exploring the Currituck County region. Finding no Indians or treasure, Coronas and his men went back to the West Indies. What body of water, projecting into Virginia and Maryland, did these men think they were exploring?   (a) Hudson Bay   (b) Tampa Bay   (c) Chesapeake Bay

6. In one of the last Spanish attempts to colonize North Carolina, a 1561 expedition led by Angel de Vilafane tramped up from the Gulf Coast and traveled all the way to the easternmost point in our state. What point of land did Angel and his boys reach?   (a) Cape Hatteras   (b) Sunset Beach   (c) Calabash

7. The first English excursions into the Tar Heel State began in 1584. With the blessing of Queen Elizabeth I, a fellow who would become known as the "Father of English America" dispatched two ships to scout our shores for colony sites. What was his name?
   (a) Sir Walter Raleigh   (b) Lord Carnarvon   (c) The Duke of Earl

8. Following a route that stretched from England to the West Indies and then up the American coast via the Gulf Stream, a 1584 expedition finally reached North Carolina after a 67-day sail. On July 4, 1584, English sailors steered their ships into what sound, said to be the largest in the world?
   (a) Albemarle Sound   (b) Pamlico Sound   (c) Core Sound

9. Led by Sir Richard Grenville and Ralph Lane, the English attempted a permanent settlement of North Carolina at Roanoke Island in 1585. Beset with problems from the start, this colony was abandoned the next year when the occupants gladly hitched a ride back to England with what famous buccaneer?
   (a) Edward Teach   (b) Stede Bonnet   (c) Sir Francis Drake

10. One of history's greatest mysteries is the fate of John White's 1587 Roanoke Island settlement known now as the Lost Colony. It has to this day defied explanation. Before they vanished, White's colonists carved what immortal word into a tree?   (a) Croatoan   (b) Manteo   (c) Ocracoke

11. Coming into North Carolina from Virginia in 1650, Edward Bland led an expedition that reported favorably on the "Indian Corne" and sugar cane he had seen growing here. One of the rivers Bland explored while visiting our state flows from the Virginia line into Albemarle Sound. Name this body of water.   (a) Pungo River   (b) Chowan River   (c) Alligator River

12. In 1662 Virginian George Durant added his family to the list of people exploring the Albemarle region of our state. Building a home on the peninsula between the Perquimans and Little rivers, Durant gave the spot what name?   (a) Durants Neck   (b) Durants Tongue   (c) Pointe Durant

North Carolina's Wonderful Women

From hearth to headquarters, the women of North Carolina have long been the steady foundation upon which our state is built. When picking the answers to this quiz on famous Tar Heel women, don't forget the countless unsung heroines in our past and present.

1. Our country's fourth first lady, Dolley Payne Madison, was born in 1768 in Guilford County. Gracious and charming, Dolley was once called "the most popular person in the nation." What US president was Dolley's husband? (a) John Madison (b) Andrew Madison (c) James Madison

2. The first woman to practice medicine in North Carolina, Annie Lowrie Alexander, obtained her medical license in Maryland, then returned to her native Mecklenburg County in 1887 to begin treating patients. What north Mecklenburg town was Annie from? (a) Pineville (b) Cornelius (c) Matthews

3. Wife of US Senator and presidential candidate Bob Dole, Elizabeth Hanford Dole of Salisbury has made a political mark of her own. What cabinet position did she hold during President Ronald Reagan's administration? (a) secretary of labor (b) secretary of commerce (c) secretary of energy

4. A lady whose achievements in the legal profession are legendary, Susie Sharp of Rocky Mount held positions that included first female city attorney in North Carolina and the first female superior court judge in our state in 170 years. In 1974 Sharp was elected to what exalted office?
(a) NC attorney general (b) chief justice of the NC Supreme Court (c) chief NC prosecutor

5. With her songs and speeches, labor organizer and union martyr Ella May Wiggins of Gastonia attracted widespread attention before her assassination during a strike in 1929. What Gaston County mill was the scene of this violent outburst of labor unrest that made national headlines?
(a) Stowe Mills (b) Piedmont Mill (c) Loray Mill

6. Though many members of the legal profession balked at the idea, self-taught Tabitha Ann Holton passed the North Carolina Bar exam in 1878, making her the first female lawyer in our state. What county, seated by Greensboro, was Tabitha's home? (a) Guilford (b) Rowan (c) Wake

7. The grandchild of former slaves, Charlotte Hawkins Brown (1883-1961) was instrumental in furthering the educational opportunities of blacks in North Carolina with her Palmer Memorial Institute. Today a state historic site marks the site of Brown's school in what Guilford County town?
(a) Osceola (b) Sedalia (c) Gilmer

8. The image of Wilmington-born Anna McNeill Whistler (1804-1881) has been one of the most universally recognized faces in the world since her son James created his famous artwork of it. What artistic medium does the immortal "Whistler's Mother" take? (a) marble sculpture (b) collage (c) painting

9. Originally from Lowesville in Lincoln County, the widow of Stonewall Jackson eventually moved into a house on Trade Street in Charlotte that became a shrine for aging Confederate veterans. The daughter of the first president of Davidson College, what was Mrs. Jackson's maiden name?
(a) Josephine Hill (b) Mary Anna Morrison (c) Eugenia Morrison

10. Another North Carolina lady who made Confederate history was Rebecca Winborne. In early 1861 Orren Smith is thought to have designed the first Confederate flag and enlisted Rebecca's help in sewing it. Her first prototype measured 12-by-15 inches and was done using flour sacks. What town, the seat of Franklin County, was Rebecca's home and the birthplace of the "stars and bars?"
(a) Louisburg (b) Elberon (c) Justice

11. One of North Carolina's most colorful Revolutionary War patriots, Penelope Barker (1728-1796) organized a tealess "tea party" with 50 other women on October 25, 1774, to protest the Tea Act. Penning a letter to the British Parliament, Barker and her friends made the English newspapers. In what coastal North Carolina town did this "tea party" take place? (a) Bath (b) Wilmington (c) Edenton

12. In 1920, Buncombe County voters elected the first woman to serve in the North Carolina legislature by a landslide margin of 10,368 votes to her opponent's mere 14. Nicknamed "Brother Exum" by her fellow legislators, what was this pace-setting Tar Heel politician's real name?
(a) Charlotte Exum (b) Lillian Exum Clement (c) Ann Pamela Exum

North Carolina's African-Americans

Throughout North Carolina's long history, African-Americans have contributed much to our state in the sciences, arts and education. This quiz will cast more light on a few of those talented and hard-working individuals who have too often labored in the shadows.

1. Born in 1854 in Elizabeth City, Joseph C. Price began his working life as a buggy boy, went on to become a minister and eventually rose to the presidency of Livingstone College. In 1893 Price died of Bright's Disease in what Rowan County town? (a) Cleveland (b) Salisbury (c) Albemarle

2. Hiram Revels (1822-1901) was a Fayetteville native who later moved to Mississippi. Revels became the first black to be elected to the United States Senate in 1870. What famous Mississippi Confederate once held the seat Revels occupied? (a) Jefferson Davis (b) Thomas Bragg (c) Harlan Sanders

3. Born a slave in 1849, Warren Coleman later became a wealthy merchant and landowner. The year 1897 saw Coleman open the first black-owned textile mill in the United States in what Cabarrus County town? (a) Harrisburg (b) Rockwell (c) Concord

4. A former slave who would eventually graduate from Shaw University, Henry Cheatham served NC in the US Congress from 1889 to 1893. In 1897, Cheatham was appointed register of deeds in Washington, DC, by what president? (a) Theodore Roosevelt (b) William McKinley (c) Woodrow Wilson

5. Pastor Calvin Brown (1859-1936) was an important black educator who founded Chowan Academy at Winton in 1886. What northeastern North Carolina county was the home for Brown's influential school?
(a) Hertford County (b) Bertie County (c) Dare County

6. Once known as "Freedom Hill," the Edgecombe County town of Princeville rightly claims to be the oldest city chartered by blacks in America. Turner Prince (1843-1912) gave his name to the community when it was incorporated in 1885 on the banks of what river?
(a) Catawba River (b) Neuse River (c) Tar River

7. Born on the North Carolina coast in 1837, Andrew Cartwright was a black religious leader who founded many churches. In 1876, Cartwright went to West Africa where he served as an AME Zion Church missionary in what country? (a) Liberia (b) Ethiopia (c) Rhodesia

8. Hailing from Henderson, James Young (1858-1921) was a black legislator and newspaper editor. Young organized and commanded the 3rd North Carolina Infantry Regiment in 1898 while what war was in progress? (a) World War I (b) Spanish-American War (c) Mexican-American War

9. James H. Harris (1832-1891) was born in Granville County and served in the Union Army as a colonel. Active in political affairs after the Civil War, Harris attended the Second North Carolina Constitutional Convention in what year? (a) 1866 (b) 1867 (c) 1868

10. Born free around 1760 in Virginia, Henry Evans was a cobbler who as a young man turned to the ministry. After settling in Fayetteville to live and preach, Evans personally constructed the very first church in that town. What was the denomination? (a) AME Zion (b) Methodist (c) Free Will Baptist

11. In the Caswell County town of Blanch in 1839, a slave named Stephen Slade accidentally discovered a way to cure tobacco that gave the leaf a distinctive hue. Revolutionizing the tobacco industry, what color did Slade's process turn the leaf? (a) yellow (b) orange (c) brown

12. Orginally from Pennsylvania, James W. Hood held a number of preaching positions up north before coming to our state in 1863. In addition to his ministerial duties, Hood was also one of the founders of what black college located in Salisbury?
(a) Johnson C. Smith University (b) Shaw University (c) Livingstone College

13. Though he began life as a slave near Warrenton in 1840, John Adams Hyman would serve as the first black congressman from North Carolina from 1875 to 1877. Today, a marker to Hyman is located on South Main Street in Warrenton. What highway is this? (a) US 401 (b) US 264 (c) NC 211

A Potpourri Of Political Trivia

In November 1992 the citizens of North Carolina elected a new governor, Jim Hunt, who became the first governor in our state history to serve three terms. How familiar are you with the accomplishments of our past governors? Did you know that our first governor was born in 1530 in Northhamptonshire, England? Take the following quiz to see how familiar you are with the former governors of our state.

1. Our first governor was appointed by Sir Walter Raleigh. His group of colonists settled on Roanoke Island in 1585, but returned to England in 1586 due to lack of food and hostile natives. Name this governor. (a) Ralph Lane (b) Captain John Smith (c) John White

2. This governor was a druggist by trade and served one year—1677. He took advantage of his job and the colonists revolted in an uprising known as "Culpepper's Rebellion." Who was this man?
(a) John Thomas (b) Thomas Miller (c) John York

3. Serving from 1765 to 1771, this governor is noted for constructing a building in New Bern that served as the governor's home and the state capital. Can you name him?
(a) William Tryon (b) John Forsyth (c) William Smith

4. The first governor to be elected by the people of North Carolina, he was elected governor twice and was a constitutional delegate. Who was he? (a) Richard Caswell (b) Washington Irwin (c) Paul York

5. During this governor's term, Chapel Hill was selected as the sight for the state university and the town of Raleigh was selected as the location for the state capital. He died after being wounded in a duel on September 5, 1802. His son was later elected governor. Who might this son be?
(a) Nathaniel Greene (b) Richard Dobbs Spaight Jr. (c) William Peyton

6. Known for his military capabilities during the Revolution, he was a Federalist and known as the "Father of the University of North Carolina." A county was named in his memory in 1836. Name this man.
(a) William Greene (b) Thomas Williams (c) William Richardson Davie

7. Born in Chowan County, he served in the War of 1812. A United States Senator, his home was located in Edenton. A county was named in his honor in 1788. Who are we talking about?
(a) James Iredell Jr. (b) Thomas Blount (c) Andrew Jones

8. This governor was serving when the Civil War began and our state passed the ordinance of secession on May 20, 1861. Who was this Rowan County native?
(a) Braxton Bragg (b) Charles White (c) John Willis Ellis

9. A native of Buncombe County, he served our state during the Civil War. He later served as a United States Senator. Can you name the man many people consider to be our state's most popular governor?
(a) Zebulon B. Vance (b) William Ellis (c) Jay Forsyth

10. A lawyer, he is remembered as our "education governor." During his term, 3,459 schoolhouses were built. Who was this man? (a) John Thurston (b) Charles B. Aycock (c) Melville Green

11. This governor is remembered for his interest and increased funding for mental institutions. The school year was lengthened to nine months during his term of office. Name him.
(a) William Lenoir (b) Benjamin Lincoln (c) Joseph M. Broughton

12. This governor's son later served as governor. A native of Alamance County, he initiated the "Go Forward" program. Who was this man who was the first governor "in the family?"
(a) William Kerr Scott (b) Robert Scott (c) Scott Kerr

13. He was our state's governor from 1961-1965 and its US Senator from 1987-1992. He was defeated November 1992 for re-election to the Senate. Who is this man who served as president of Duke University for 16 years? (a) John York (b) Terry Sanford (c) Bob Long

Tar Heel Politicos Past And Present

Often colorful and outspoken, North Carolina politicians savor a good debate as much as a barbecue fund-raiser. Cast your vote for the correct answers to this quiz on Tar Heel officeholders from the past and present.

1. A darling to some and a bit of a devil to others, Republican Senator Jesse Helms has represented North Carolina in the United States Senate since 1972. A former Raleigh radio and television personality, Helms was born in 1921 in what Union County town? (a) Indian Trail (b) Waxhaw (c) Monroe

2. Representing North Carolina in the United States Congress throughout the 1950s and 1960s, Charles R. Jonas was named "Politician of the Year" in 1962. What city, the seat of Lincoln County, was Jonas' home? (a) Boger City (b) Lincolnton (c) Cat Square

3. Describing himself as a "simple country lawyer," Senator Sam J. Ervin Jr. became a national folk hero with his witty and probing questions during the Watergate hearings that led to the resignation of President Richard Nixon. In 1974 Ervin retired to his home in what Burke County town?
   (a) Upper Fork (b) Silver Creek (c) Morganton

4. Voted North Carolina's "Man of the Year" in 1959, Governor Luther Hodges was one of our state's most dynamic governors during his term of office. Thinking of the Tar Heel State's future, Hodges was a vigorous proponent of what technological enclave located between Durham, Chapel Hill and Raleigh?
   (a) Research Triangle Park (b) Global Transpark (c) NC Computer Center

5. A lady of great political savvy, Republican Sue Myrick has served as the US Representative from North Carolina's 9th District. Before her 1994 victory over Democrat Rory Black, Myrick had held what municipal post?
   (a) mayor of Charlotte (b) New Hanover County commissioner (c) Raleigh city councilwoman

6. Born in Berlin, Germany, during the regime of Hitler, Ruth E. Cook went on to survive a five-year separation from her parents when she was 10 years old. A true heroine, Cook joined the ranks of the more than 100 women who have served in the General Assembly with her election to that body in 1975 from Wake County. What is Cook's party affiliation? (a) Republican (b) Democrat (c) Independent

7. The first North Carolina chief executive to claim the title "Good Roads Governor," Cameron Morrison was a clever politician with a colorful personality. A native of Richmond County, Morrison began his career as mayor of what town there? (a) Rockingham (b) Wolf Pit (c) Wadesboro

8. A founding father of North Carolina State University, publisher of *The Progressive Farmer* magazine and an influential member of the General Assembly, Leonidas L. Polk (1837-1892) was a political dynamo. What Anson County town incorporated in 1875 bears Polk's name?
   (a) Polkville (b) Polkburg (c) Polkton

9. In 1885, Thomas Dixon Jr. of Cleveland County set a precedent of sorts when he took his seat in the General Assembly four days before reaching voting age. Dixon's real claim to fame would come later with the publication in 1905 of what book that became the basis for the film *Birth of a Nation*?
   (a) *The Southerner* (b) *The Clansman* (c) *Abe in Illinois*

10. During the mid-1800s, former General Assembly member and Superintendent of Common Schools Calvin Wiley built what was called the best school system in the South for our state. An author, educator, politician and minister, Wiley called what Guilford County town home?
    (a) Julian (b) Osceola (c) Greensboro

11. Born in Washington, North Carolina, in 1862, Josephus Daniels was a journalist and later owner of the Raleigh *News and Observer*. He made a name for himself in national politics. A staunch Democrat, Daniels held what post during both terms of President Woodrow Wilson?
    (a) secretary of the Navy (b) attorney general (c) secretary of the Interior

12. A native of Sampson County, Marion Butler used his influence in both the North Carolina and US Senates to help further education, military preparedness and farmers. One of Butler's greatest accomplishments was the passage of his bill sponsoring what was known as "R.F.D." What does this acronym stand for? (a) Recycle For Democracy (b) Rural Free Delivery (c) Railroad Fast Delivery

Tar Heel Mountains Rich With Writers

With a literary tradition as long as its mountains are tall, Western North Carolina has produced some of the most gifted authors ever to put a pen to paper. Remember what your English teachers taught you, and what your heart has led you to read, and you'll be on the right path for this quiz.

1. Regarded by many to be the king of Western North Carolina writers, Thomas Wolfe profoundly influenced the world of serious literature. In what mountain city was Wolfe born?
(a) Bryson City   (b) Asheville   (c) Etowah

2. For generations poets have flourished in our North Carolina hills. Name the Buncombe County bard who was not only our Civil War governor, but tried his hand at poesy with a ditty called "The Little Patched Trousers."   (a) Zebulon Vance   (b) Marcus Clayton Brendle   (c) Wallace Stevens

3. O. Henry, the turn of the century author famous for his short stories, is buried in Asheville. His wife Sara Coleman was a writer as well. What town just north of Asheville did Sara hail from?
(a) Oteen   (b) Montreat   (c) Weaverville

4. Asheville native John Ehle is not only a distinguished author, but also helped establish the North Carolina School of the Arts. Which one of the following novels by Ehle was made into a hit movie in 1989?
(a) *The Winter People*   (b) *Kingstree Island*   (c) *Beyond the Hills*

5. Wilma Dykeman also hails from Asheville and has written nearly 20 books. Her first work took its title from what river that flows near her hometown?
(a) The French Broad   (b) Cane River   (c) The Rocky Bottom

6. John Parris began his writing career as a news correspondent. In 1958 he won the Thomas Wolfe Memorial Award. What mountain town, the seat of Jackson County, is the birthplace of Mr. Parris?
(a) Mars Hill   (b) Sylva   (c) Green Creek

7. Arthur T. Abernethy not only wrote 53 books, but also served as mayor of Blue Ridge foothills town of Rutherford College. In 1948, Governor R. Gregg Cherry named Abernethy to what unique post?
(a) 1st North Carolina State Novelist   (b) 1st North Carolina State Storyteller
(c) 1st North Carolina State Poet Laureate

8. James Larkin Pearson began reciting poetry at age 4. Before he died in 1981 at the age of 101, Pearson had been named North Carolina State Poet Laureate. He was also publisher of a newspaper. What Wilkes County mountain foothills area, straight south of Wilkesboro on NC 16 was Pearson from?
(a) Mulberry   (b) Moravian Falls   (c) Halls Mill

9. Veteran writer Fred Chappell has received many awards for his work, including the North Carolina Award in Literature. A true son of the high country, Chappell grew up in what fragrant Haywood County town on the Pigeon River?   (a) Canton   (b) East Laport   (c) Saunook

10. Yet another Asheville-born author, Gail Godwin has penned her way to the top of the literary world. Which one of the following million-selling novels is Godwin's?
(a) *Raney*   (b) *Walking Across Egypt*   (c) *A Mother and Two Daughters*

11. A North Carolina writer specializing in award-winning books for young adults, Sue Ellen Bridgers calls our Tar Heel hills home. At what mountain college, located in Cullowhee, did Bridgers receive her degree?   (a) Appalachian State University   (b) Western Carolina University   (c) Moses Cone College

12. Mid-19th century North Carolina writer Christian Reid was actually a woman named Frances Tiernan. Published in 1876, one of her novels about the mountains gave the region a nickname still in use. What is it?   (a) The Land of the Sky   (b) Hill After Hill   (c) The Peaks of Perfection

Show Business Tar Heel Style

No matter what the entertainment medium, Tar Heel stars have traditionally shined. Turn your attention to center stage and see if you can pick the correct answers to this lineup of North Carolina tunesmiths and troupers.

1. Dating back to the mid-1950s, the rather risque band that Doug Clark and his brother John formed in Chapel Hill has long been a favorite of the fraternity crowd. Still playing hit tunes such as "Roly Poly," Doug Clark's band goes by what name? (a) Hot Nuts (b) Hot Potatoes (c) Hot Times

2. One of seven people to receive a North Carolina Folk Heritage Award for 1995, Richard "Big Boy" Henry is an internationally acclaimed blues musician. What "Down East" town, the seat of Carteret County, is "Big Boy" from? (a) Davis (b) Harlowe (c) Beaufort

3. One of Hollywood's most promising actresses, Charlotte-born Sharon Lawrence studied journalism at the University of North Carolina at Chapel Hill before heading to Tinseltown. Name the highly rated ABC television series in which Lawrence plays an assistant district attorney named Sylvia Costas. (a) "Dragnet" (b) "Cops" (c) "NYPD Blue"

4. Entertaining and enthralling air show audiences nationwide with her death-defying aerial stunts, Georgia "Tiny" Thompson became the first woman to parachute from an airplane at Los Angeles' Griffith Field in 1913. Name the North Carolina town in Vance County on US Highway 1 that gave "Tiny" to the skies. (a) Henderson (b) Townsville (c) Wise

5. Though he was born in Clinton, South Carolina, Arthur "Guitar Boogie" Smith hosted a radio and TV country music variety show on Charlotte's WBT for more than two decades with his lively group, the "Crackerjacks." One of Arthur's biggest hits, "Dueling Banjos," was used as the theme for what movie written by James Dickey? (a) *White Water* (b) *Cannonball Run* (c) *Deliverance*

6. Born in Brevard, Lauretta Aiken (1894-1975) blazed new ground by becoming the first black comedienne to achieve celebrity status. For many years Lauretta was a regular on the "Ed Sullivan Show," where she went by what name? (a) "Jokin" Jocelyn Brice (b) "Moms" Mabley (c) Fantastic Fanny Foxx

7. Gastonia native Maria Howell developed her nationally known jazz singing voice in the church choir. In 1985, Howell got her big break by being chosen to sing in what Steven Spielberg film that starred Oprah Winfrey and Danny Glover? (a) *The Color Purple* (b) *E.T.* (c) *Porgy and Bess*

8. Glamourous film star Ava Gardner was an actress who put North Carolina on the map. Born on Christmas Eve in 1922, Gardner declared in her book, *Ava: My Story,* that she was not born in Smithfield (where there is a museum in her honor), but in what community? (a) Brodgen (b) Grabtown (c) Pine Level

9. John Coltrane (1926-1967) of Hamlet has been referred to as the most popular and influential jazz entertainer of the 1960s. More than a musician, Coltrane was also a highly accomplished composer. What musical instrument was Coltrane's vehicle to musical superstardom? (a) trumpet (b) clarinet (c) saxophone

10. From his early acting days at Manteo in *The Lost Colony* outdoor drama, North Carolina's own Andy Griffith went on to achieve entertainment immortality as sheriff of the television town of Mayberry. Born in 1926 and still going strong, Griffith was given what name at birth? (a) Thomas Johnathan (b) William Samuel (c) Marcus Bryan

11. Recipient of the Country Music Association Male Vocalist of the Year award in 1974, Ronnie Milsap overcame visual impairment and gave up a career in law to pursue his love of jazz, blues and country music. A success story based on talent and determination, Milsap hails from what Tar Heel town, the seat of Graham County? (a) Robbinsville (b) Yellow Creek (c) Cheoah

12. Daytime drama fans will recognize Gaston County's Eileen Fulton from her many years as a conniving femme fatale on the soap opera "As The World Turns." What is the name of the character Fulton plays that so many viewers love to hate? (a) Judith (b) Nancy (c) Lisa

Tuneful Tar Heels

From "waltz kings" to "country balladeers," more that a few musical legends have claimed roots in the Tar Heel State over the years. How well do you know them?

1. A longtime star on WBTV, this singing cowboy and his horse, Calico, entertained two generations of "Little Rascals" lovers. Who was he? (a) Fred Kirby (b) Gene Autry (c) Todd Hagans

2. This bluegrass music legend was born in Cleveland County in 1924. He was part of the duo that composed the theme song for the TV hit "The Beverly Hillbillies." Who is he?
(a) Jim "Banjo" Crawley (b) Willy "Po Boy" McIntosh (c) Earl Scruggs

3. Name the Charlotte resident who composed the hit "Dueling Banjos" for the movie *Deliverance*.
(a) Loonis McGlohon (b) Arthur Smith (c) "Cousin" Ralph Smith

4. Born in Deep Gap in 1923, this folk music legend is blind and goes by the nickname "Doc." What is his given name? (a) Will Watson (b) Thomas Watson (c) Arthel Watson

5. The 1965 tune "I Washed My Hands In Muddy Water" was a big hit for this Tabor City native who is named for a Confederate hero. What name do they share?
(a) Stonewall Jackson (b) Jeb Stuart (c) P.G.T. Beauregard

6. Name the Charlotte music group that was voiced most popular trio at the International Country Music Awards in Peterburough, England. (a) The Moody Brothers (b) Spongetones (c) Sonny Ledford

7. Born blind in Robbinsville, this country balladeer was named by the Country Music Association as Male Vocalist of the Year in 1974. Who is he? (a) Tommy Tune (b) Ronnie Milsap (c) Pete Best

8. With classic country hits such as "Abilene" and "Tobacco Road" to his credit, this Durham native began his music career with a Salvation Army band.
(a) Johnny Paycheck (b) Billy Loudermilk (c) John D. Loudermilk

9. Name the Cherokee native who sold 3 million copies of his country music blockbuster "Shenandoah Waltz." He was given the title "Hillbilly Waltz King" for this achievement.
(a) Clyde Moody (b) D.V. Wiggins (c) Dwight "C.B." Frady

10. Charlotte used to be a nationally known music recording center. The famous Bill Monroe, who is credited with inventing bluegrass music, visited one of the city's largest studios in 1936 and made several recordings. What was the name of the building where the studio was located?
(a) Plyler Building (b) The Radio Building (c) Jefferson-Pilot Studios

11. During the 1920s one of the most popular string bands playing was the NC Ramblers. Their hits included "Don't Let Your Deal Go Down." Name the Alamance County native who was the group's banjo player and leader. (a) Claude B. Casey (b) Levi Ledbetter (c) Charlie Poole

12. Daughter of a Mount Airy tobacco farmer, this country music songstress attended High Point Teachers College before embarking on a music career that included a number one hit titled "The Happiest Girl In The Whole USA." Name her. (a) Donna Fargo (b) Stella Mae Putnam (c) Lou Ann Thomas

North Carolina Indian Tribes

North Carolina Indian people continue to contribute to our state's culture. Explore the history of Tar Heel tribes and leaders as you answer the questions to this quiz.

1. Historically, North Carolina Native American tribes are classed in three linguistic families—Algonquian, Iroquoian, and Siouan. At the time of the first European contact with Indians in our state by Giovanni da Verrazzano in 1524, how many major tribes called North Carolina home?   (a) 12   (b) 20   (c) 30

2. In 1584, English explorers Philip Amadas and Arthur Barlowe explored North Carolina's coast and made contact with native peoples there. When they returned to England to report their findings, two Indians went with them. Named Wanchese and Manteo, these Tar Heel Native Americans would one day give their names to towns on what island?
   (a) Ocracoke Island   (b) Roanoke Island   (c) Hatteras Island

3. Town Creek Indian Mound State Historic Site is one of North Carolina's most unusual and interesting locations. Used as a temple mound, mortuary, and ceremonial gathering place by Indian tribes as far back as the 1500s, Town Creek is located in what county near the Pee Dee River?
   (a) Union County   (b) Chatham County   (c) Montgomery County

4. After many decades of tension, war between whites and Indians broke out in North Carolina in 1711. Although several tribes took part in this conflict, the majority of Native American warriors came from what tribe led by a chief known as "King Hancock?"
   (a) Chowan Indians   (b) Tuscarora Indians   (c) Lumbee Indians

5. Part of the Iroquoian group of American Indians, the Cherokee tribe is said to have more than 50 spellings of its name. What North Carolina portion of this tribe calls Qualla Reservation in our Tar Heel mountains home?   (a) Eastern Band of the Cherokee Indians   (b) Southern Cherokee Band
   (c) Mountain Band of the Cherokees

6. During the federal government's removal of Cherokees from their native lands in the 1830s, a hero named Tsali sacrificed his life so other members of the tribe could go free. Today, a state historical marker telling Tsali's story stands in Swain County's seat. What is the town's name?
   (a) Dillsboro   (b) Junaluska   (c) Bryson City

7. When the Civil War erupted in 1861, many Cherokee tribesmen joined the Confederate Army. One very famous regiment from North Carolina was the 69th, which became known as the Thomas Legion. What was the name of the white businessman and friend to the Indians who organized this regiment and became their colonel?   (a) John Thomas   (b) Thomas Tallis   (c) William Thomas

8. The modern-day town of Cherokee is one of North Carolina's most popular tourist attractions; the town saw the opening of Harrah's Cherokee Casino in 1998. What is the name of the woman who is principal chief of the Cherokees and who is keeping a close eye on the effect that gaming has on her people?
   (a) Joyce Dugan   (b) Ollie Brendle   (c) Leslie Rankin

9. Once the largest and most powerful of the Siouan tribes who lived in the Carolinas, the Catawba Indians still reside in the Southern Piedmont. In North Carolina, a town, a river, and a county are all called Catawba after this tribe whose name may have come from what Choctaw word?
   (a) Calawa   (b) Katapa   (c) Cawawa

10. Centuries before herbal medicine and teas became popular in white communities, North Carolina Indians were making use of plants indigenous to our state. A popular medicine as well as trade item for early Indians was tea made from the plant *Ilex vomitoria,* which still grows along our coast and is called what?   (a) Yaupon   (b) Spanish Moss   (c) Mesquite

Tales From Tar Heel Tribes

North Carolina Indian legends are as fascinating today as when they were first told years ago. See the world through the eyes of Indian storytellers with the correct answers to this quiz.

1. Numbers have often played an important part in North Carolina and other Indian legends. The Cherokee believe their sacred figure represents the number of clans, heavens, sacred trees, and major religious ceremonies in their world. What numeral holds this much power in the Cherokee world?
   (a) Seven   (b) Five   (c) Ten

2. Northeastern North Carolina Indians tell a story about a curse placed on the plantation of a Revolutionary War general after he mistreated a young brave. The William Baker Plantation, circa 1775, was located about six miles north of this Gates County seat.   (a) Drum Hill   (b) Huntsville   (c) Gatesville

3. According to legend, a certain Cherokee chief, who had developed a fondness for rum, fell into a deep sleep in which he had a vision warning him of the dangers of alcohol. Name the chief who made his tribe swear off liquor for 20 years after his revelation.
   (a) Chief Qualla   (b) Chief Junaluska   (c) Chief Nantahala

4. A North Carolina tribe once known as the Pomeioc spoke of a spirit known as the "Good Twin," who sent them seeds of a special apple tree by a magic goose. This tribe lived on the shores of our state's largest natural lake. Can you name it?   (a) Lake Mattamuskeet   (b) Lake Norman   (c) Phelps Lake

5. The beautiful daughter of Cherokee leader Osseo is the subject of a heartbreaking North Carolina Indian love story. Tricked into spurning her true love Kwasind, Princess Starlight saw him borne back to her on winds after he despondently threw himself off what Watauga County promontory known for its upward gusts?   (a) Blowing Rock   (b) Clingmans Dome   (c) Chimney Rock

6. The Tuscarora tribe of North Carolina has a legend about a gift called the "Three Sisters" that came from their god Tarenhiawagen. The staff of early Indian life, these "sisters" were actually what three staple crops that were planted together?
   (a) corn, tobacco, beans   (b) corn, beans, squash   (c) beans, yams, collard greens

7. Dating back to the Tuscarora War of 1711, the legend of Indian Gallows concerns a young warrior who died by hanging rather than continuing a star-crossed love affair with a white girl. Formed by two giant oaks, the Indian Gallows was in what county crossed by the Cashie River?
   (a) Greene County   (b) Craven County   (c) Bertie County

8. English explorers to our state's coast observed how indigenous people used the yaupon for medicinal purposes. Legend says a sick Indian fell into a trance and awoke with a magic yaupon growing at his head. Still used for medicine today, yaupon also is known by what name?
   (a) Caffena-tree   (b) Roanoke bush   (c) Croatan tree

9. From Harnett County comes the saga of the son of a Tuscarora chief and his forbidden Catawba sweetheart. Today, the spot where the young warrior and his chosen rendezvoused is in what state park near Lillington?
   (a) William B. Umstead State Park   (b) Crowders Mountain State Park   (c) Raven Rock State Park

10. A very popular bird-watching spot, the 15-square-mile lake in Columbus County was formed, say local Indians, when a maiden named "Keeper of the Wild Flowers" died and fell into the earth after her tribe was destroyed by invaders. What lake is named for the maiden's tribe?
    (a) Lake Junaluska   (b) Lake Waccamaw   (c) Lake Pocosin

11. Many Cherokee stories refer to a great flood like the one recounted in the Old Testament. One tale describes how the spirits told the animals and trees to stay awake for seven nights waiting for the rain. Of the trees, only the evergreens, similar to what species, were vigilant and permitted to keep their "hair" in winter?   (a) holly   (b) hemlock   (c) sassafras

Natural History
and
Phenomenon

Wildflowers

Flower Power

Home to more than 3,000 species of flowering plants, our state hosts patch after patch of budding beauty. Test your horticultural know-how with this quiz on Tar Heel wildflowers.

1. Sometimes growing to three feet in length, the arching stems of *Polygonatum biflorum* are festooned with small, bell-shaped white flowers. Found in North Carolina's deciduous forests, which plant is named after a wise biblical figure?   (a) Joshua's lily   (b) Solomon's seal   (c) David's flute

2. The leathery, evergreen leaves of the Spanish bayonet plant are accented during May and June in North Carolina with a cluster of creamy flowers reaching six feet in height. A native of our coastal plain, Spanish bayonet also goes by what name?   (a) Mesquite   (b) Guava   (c) Yucca

3. Frequently found in showy clumps along North Carolina roadsides, *Saponaria officinalis* goes by the common name of bouncing Bet. Flowering from May until the first frost, bouncing Bet has what other name reflective of the texture of its crushed stems?   (a) Soapwort   (b) Toadflax   (c) Silkystem

4. Often used as a symbol of Dixie, the magnolia tree reaches the natural northern limit of its range in North Carolina. Featuring fragrant flowers up to 112 inches across that bloom from May to June, the magnolia also goes by what other colloquial name?
   (a) Plantation tree   (b) Redwood of the South   (c) Bull bay

5. Appearing in North Carolina bogs, wet pine barrens, and swamp margins as a shrub or tree, poison sumac shows small green flowers during May and June as well as colorful foliage in the fall. What other name is attributed to this plant, whose leaves can cause severe allergic reactions?
   (a) Firewood   (b) Thunderwood   (c) Lightningbush

6. Small, melon-shaped fruits about two inches long and lacy, pink blooms are prominent features of the passion flower. A native perennial to our state, *Passiflora incarnata* also goes by what name that comes from the sound its fruit makes when squeezed?   (a) Maypops   (b) Crackerballs   (c) Snapdragon

7. With its large clusters of tiny, white flowers, Queen Anne's lace is a familiar sight in North Carolina fields and along roadsides. Blooming from May to September, this native Tar Heel wildflower also has what name reflective of its significant root structure?
   (a) Beet flower   (b) Peanut plant   (c) Wild carrot

8. A glabrous annual standing as high as three feet, *Nicandra physalodes* is a North Carolina wildflower with pinkish blooms composed of a corolla of five fused petals. Found mainly in our mountain counties, this plant is originally from South America and goes by what name that includes a nation whose capital is Lima?   (a) Apple of Peru   (b) Cone of Columbia   (c) Fruit of the Falklands

9. The bright blue flowers of *Cichorium intybus* are a familiar sight along many North Carolina roadsides and fields. An introduced species, the roots of this weedy plant can be dried, then ground up and used as a substitute for coffee. Name this wildflower that blooms from June until October.
   (a) Chicory   (b) Chick weed   (c) Chicarillum

10. Called coneflower by some, the wildflower *Rudbeckia hirta* has a dark brown center surrounded by two- to three-inch bright orange petals. Growing in nearly every Tar Heel county, this native species also goes by what feminine-sounding name?
    (a) Bouncing Betty   (b) Jumping Jill   (c) Black-eyed Susan

11. Spatterdock is a native North Carolina wildflower whose yellow flowers are about two inches wide and characterized by a prominent stigma. Found at ponds, rivers, and swamps throughout the Piedmont and coastal plain, *Nuphar luteum* also has what bovine-sounding common name?
    (a) Bull plant   (b) Cow lily   (c) Milkweed

Native Plants Plentiful In North Carolina

No matter whether they're growing in the coastal plains' sandy soil, the Piedmont's red clay or along a Great Smoky Mountains' slope, many unique plants are native to our state. See if you can boost your botanical bent with this quiz.

1. A member of the holly family, the yaupon tree takes its name from the Catawba Indian word for "small tree." Name the product still made in Eastern North Carolina from this evergreen.
    (a) yaupon stew   (b) yaupon tea   (c) yaupon jam

2. The largest natural garden of rhododendrons in the world is located high atop Roan Mountain near Bakersville in Mitchell County. What unique variety of this beautiful flowering shrub is to be found there? (a) Catawba rhododendron (b) red rhododendron (c) Cherokee rhododendron

3. Found exclusively in a seven-county area of our North Carolina mountains, the blooms of the lovely pinkshell azalea may be best seen on the Blue Ridge Parkway near Mount Pisgah and also just south of Cashiers. What highway would you take from Cashiers to view this special plant?
    (a) US 29   (b) NC 321   (c) NC 107

4. The carnivorous Venus flytrap is one of the most unusual plants in the world. Nowhere on the globe does this insect-eating oddity grow except within a 75-mile radius of what North Carolina county seat?
    (a) Wilmington   (b) Swan Quarter   (c) Windsor

5. Some plants in North Carolina are unique for their size. Near Robbinsville there is an example of a certain tree that at 118 feet tall is listed on the National Register of Champion Trees. Famous also for honey, what type of tree is this? (a) poplar   (b) sourwood   (c) sweet birch

6. A member of the pea family, Devil's Shoestrings root was used by the Cherokees in our mountains to stun fish in the water for capture. Pioneers later gave this plant what name when they fed it to goats to stimulate milk production? (a) goat's rue   (b) goatpep   (c) nannyweed

7. Once worth more than its weight in gold, "sang," as the North Carolina mountain folk call it, is a special plant in our state that the Chinese and many others believe has qualities as an aphrodisiac. What is the full name of sang? (a) ginseng   (b) sangfroid   (c) sanguine

8. Synonymous with coastal Carolina scenes of live oaks, cypress swamps and plantations, Spanish moss is oddly enough related to the pineapple. The ability to grow on other structures without roots of its own makes Spanish moss what type of plant? (a) neophyte (b) parasite (c) epiphyte

9. Strange cone-like projections armed with spines give the Southern prickly ash tree one of its names. What other moniker, which reflects the medicinal properties of its bark used since earliest time, is this tree known by? (a) headache tree   (b) toothache tree   (c) heartburn tree

10. Made famous in a popular 1969 song by Tony Joe White, the tender young leaves of what roadside plant may be picked and eaten once they've been boiled and then sauteed in a bacon grease?
    (a) poke sallet   (b) Rose of Sharon   (c) Veronica

11. Native to the coastal woodlands of North Carolina, deer-tongue is avidly sought in summer for harvest by locals who sell several million pounds annually to a certain industry. Having a very distinct odor of vanilla, deer-tongue is used in the curing of what product?
    (a) ham   (b) smoked turkey   (c) tobacco

12. A very rare native plant in our state is the Indian Plantain, also known as Rugel's Ragwort. Since this plant is found only in the Great Smoky Mountains National Park, which one of the counties below would not have examples in evidence. (a) Catawba County (b) Swain County (c) Haywood County

13. In Piedmont and mountain bogs, the heady aroma of the skunk cabbage plant helps draw flies to itself as a means of pollination. Many folks know skunk cabbage by what other name?
    (a) stinkweed   (b) Polecat bush   (c) swamp cabbage

Coastal Carolina Flora And Fauna

The Tar Heel coast is an ecosytem rich in plant and animal diversity. From the hundreds of species that call our shore and backwaters home, see if you can identify those that appear in this quiz.

1. The darling of Hatteras surf-casters, the red drum is also our state fish. The world record for this fighter is more than 90 pounds and was taken at Avon. What do fishermen call the smaller specimens of this prize quarry? (a) drumettes   (b) puppy drum   (c) porgies

2. Synonymous with visions of the Old South and a common sight in our state's coastal areas, Spanish moss is a plant that has no roots of its own. What tropical plant is a close relative of Spanish moss? (a) pineapple   (b) banana   (c) coconut

3. Burying its eggs along the Atlantic Coast as far north as Ocracoke Inlet, the loggerhead turtle is the most commonly seen sea turtle in North Carolina. How much can a loggerhead weigh? (a) 50 pounds   (b) 100 pounds   (c) up to 500 pounds

4. Small and silvery, there is one species that is the most important commercial fish caught in North Carolina's coastal waters. A factory for the extraction of oil from this little fish was first built on Harkers Island in 1865. Name the species. (a) stickleback   (b) menhaden   (c) shad

5. Preferring to spend most of its time in coastal trees and bushes, there is a type of chameleon-like lizard in our state that is the only species here able to change color. What is the name of this skittish creature? (a) Carolina anole   (b) Carolina mudpuppy   (c) ground skink

6. Sometimes called the "fish eagle," there is a bird of prey often seen along Tar Heel coastal waterways that is mostly white on its belly with a brownish black. What is the name of this large bird whose diet consists entirely of fish? (a) gannet   (b) skua gull   (c) osprey

7. Vital to the stabilization of sand dunes on our beaches, there is a native grass on the Tar Heel coast that can grow up to 6 feet tall. Though many tourists would like to take some of it home for decoration, pulling this plant is strictly taboo. What wheat-like growth is this? (a) sea oats   (b) sea rye   (c) beach farina

8. Referred to as "choppers" by North Carolina's coastal anglers, there is a sleek, bloodthirsty type of gamefish that blitzes our shore in spring and fall. Name this species, said to be pound for pound more vicious than a shark. (a) cobia   (b) tarpon   (c) bluefish

9. Though its scientific name, "Ilex vomitoria," may not sound very appetizing, there is a member of the holly family that grows on our coast and whose leaves are made into tea. What is the name of this evergreen shrub? (a) yaupon   (b) sweetflag   (c) indigobush

10. Another Tar Heel coastal evergreen often seen dripping with Spanish moss is a member of the oak family. Name the oak that can grow up to 80 feet tall and often lines the entrances to plantation houses. (a) pin oak   (b) white oak   (c) live oak

11. One of the most popular panfish to be found in North Carolina coastal waters takes its name from the noise it often makes when reeled in. What is the name of this silver-green and yellowish little fish that fills so many frying pans? (a) squeeler   (b) croaker   (c) moaner

12. Looking for seashells is a popular activity for visitors to our state's coast. There's a colorful and beautifully shaped shell that is abundant in our coastal waters at depths between 200 and 500 feet. Name this, the state shell of North Carolina. (a) palmetto shell   (b) olive shell   (c) Scotch Bonnet

13. Anyone who strolls our Tar Heel beaches has seen the pale little crabs that skitter into the holes they strategically place every few feet. What type of crab is this that can disappear in a flash? (a) ghost crab   (b) phantom crab   (c) mole crab

14. Empty clamshells are commonly found on the North Carolina shoreline. Some clamshells can grow several inches across and become quite thick. Pick the correct name, given by the Algonquin Indians, for our hardshell clam. (a) holehog   (b) bush hog   (c) quahog

A Bird Baffler

You don't have to be a registered member of the National Audubon Society to answer most of these questions about North Carolina birds. Of course, it might help if you lived in the "Bluebird Kingdom of the World"—or you're a W.C. Fields fan.

1. What is the official state bird of North Carolina?
   (a) Cardinal   (b) Red-tailed Hawk   (c) Eastern Kingbird

2. With several chapters in North Carolina, what organization is the largest bird-watching society in the United States? (a) John Cromlish Memorial Bird-watching Association (b) National Audubon Society (c) Birders of America

3. What North Carolina county, with Wadesboro as the county seat, claims the title "Bluebird Kingdom of the World?" (a) Scotland County   (b) Anson County   (c) Union County

4. What large, brown and white bird, sometimes called the "fish hawk," favors our coastal areas and can often be seen there snatching fish from the water?
   (a) Cooper's Hawk   (b) Sharp-shinned Hawk   (c) Osprey

5. What is the largest natural lake in North Carolina, home to thousands of geese, swans and ducks?
   (a) Pungo Lake   (b) Lake Norman   (c) Lake Mattamuskeet

6. The population of this wily bird was once depleted but is again on the rise. Benjamin Franklin wanted it to be our official national bird? (a) Wild Turkey   (b) Rough-legged Hawk   (c) King Eider

7. Though traditionally a harbinger of spring, what red-breasted member of the thrush family can be seen hopping across North Carolina lawns during all but the worst weather?
   (a) American Robin   (b) Wood Thrush   (c) Brown Thrasher

8. What small duck, considered by many to be our most colorful duck, inhabits the lowland areas of North Carolina, where it finds the swamps and hollow trees it prefers for nesting?
   (a) Loon   (b) Wood Duck   (c) Peking Duck

9. Feathery tufts on the head of North Carolina's largest owl give it what name?
   (a) Great Horned Owl   (b) Barred Owl   (c) Saw-whet Owl

10. Name this North Carolina country favorite, whose voice ranges from gentle warbles to a cat's meow?
    (a) Blue Jay   (b) Rusty Blackbird   (c) Mockingbird

11. No Tar Heel cornfield would be complete without some of these glossy and raucous rascals, said by some to be the smartest of birds? (a) Crow   (b) Bobolink   (c) Magpie

12. A popular visitor to bird feeders throughout North Carolina, what black-capped little bird was immortalized by W.C. Fields in his famous saying, "Ah, my little___?
    (a) Wren   (b) Sparrow   (c) Chickadee

13. Many North Carolina birders offer thistle seeds to attract this yellow and black species. Name the little bird known as the "wild canary." (a) Goldfinch   (b) Pine Warbler   (c) Golden-crowned Kinglet

14. Just 100 of these birds were imported from Europe and released in New York's Central Park in 1890. Now, countless swarms drive out more desirable species. Name this bird, the bane of Tar Heel bird lovers and freshly washed cars. (a) Ovenbird   (b) Starling   (c) Chipping Sparrow

A Tar Heel Quiz For The Birds

North Carolina's diverse geography means that more than 400 species of birds have been spotted residing in or visiting our state. Train your sights on the correct answers to this quiz on Tar Heel bird-watching hot spots.

1. In recent years the bald eagle has made a comeback in North Carolina. Originally made by Carolina Aluminum in 1917, what lake on the Yadkin River in Montgomery and Stanly counties is an excellent place to go eagle-watching? (a) Lake Tillery (b) Badin Lake (c) Lake James

2. The Mount Pisgah area of Buncombe and Haywood counties offers hikers a variety of nesting and migratory birds to watch. Of special interest are the displays of aerial expertise by what type of bird of prey formerly called the duck hawk? (a) merlin (b) caracara (c) peregrine falcon

3. Located near Southern Pines, the Weymouth Woods Sandhills Nature Preserve is a 400-acre tract of longleaf pine and hardwood forest where the endangered red-cockaded woodpecker may be observed. What county is home for this unique Tar Heel ecosystem?
   (a) Moore County (b) Bladen County (c) Montgomery County

4. Called the best area for observing shorebirds in North Carolina, Pea Island National Wildlife Refuge extends from just below Oregon Inlet to near Rodanthe on the Outer Banks. What sliver of highway provides access to the Banks and the Pea Island refuge? (a) NC 94 (b) US 70 (c) NC 12

5. Craggy Gardens Recreation Area is a 700-acre tract of forest and rhododendrons where bird-watchers can spot species such as the solitary vireo and chestnut-sided warbler. Located in Buncombe County, Craggy Gardens is nearest which one of the following towns? (a) Oteen (b) Canto (c) Jupiter

6. Doughton Park near mile marker 248 on the Blue Ridge Parkway is named for Robert Lee "Muley Bob" Doughton, a North Carolina ninth district congressman from 1911 to 1953 who was also chairman of the House Ways and Means Committee for 18 years. Birds galore frequent Doughton Park, including scarlet tanagers, ovenbirds and what fowl named by Ben Franklin to be our national bird?
   (a) kestrel (b) great horned owl (c) wild turkey

7. Marsh birds, including the secretive American bittern, await the discerning birder's binoculars at Cedar Island National Wildlife Refuge. From Ocracoke Island, what type of transportation is available to Cedar Island? (a) toll bridge (b) ferry boat (c) PBY Catalina airport

8. Buzzards may not be beautiful, but hikers who want to see many of them riding air currents like ballet dancers upon the wind will do well to trek to the top of Crowders Mountain. One of our most popular state parks, Crowders is in what county?
   (a) Mecklenburg County (b) Rowan County (c) Gaston County

9. Warbling vireo, yellow-breasted chat and Indigo bunting are just a few of the wide variety of bird species that may be seen from shore or canoe on the second-oldest river on the globe. Name this wild waterway that flows from northwestern North Carolina into West Virginia.
   (a) New River (b) French Broad River (c) Pacolet River

10. Lake Phelps in Pettigrew State Park in Washington County is a prime wintering and observation area for tundra swan, Canada geese, ruddy duck and the rare lapland longspur. Also a great fishing spot, Lake Phelps encompasses how many acres? (a) 5,000 (b) 16,600 (c) 20,000

11. With upwards of 150,000 swans, geese and other waterfowl in residence, Tar Heel winter bird-watching can't be beat at Lake Mattamuskeet. Covering 30,000 acres, and with a maximum depth of five feet, this wildlife haven is in what coastal county? (a) Hyde County (b) Dare County (c) Tyrrell County

12. Located 24 miles north of Winston-Salem, Pilot Mountain is a 1,500-foot thrust of quartzite that has been a landmark for travelers since early times. Birders who visit Pilot Mountain will find one of the few nesting grounds in the Piedmont for what species, the subject of a poem by Edgar Allan Poe?
    (a) whippoorwill (b) mockingbird (c) raven

13. Interlaced with challenging hiking trails and populated with exciting bird species like the golden eagle, Northern goshawk and Alder flycatcher, Shining Rock Wilderness in western North Carolina was established in 1964. What county is home to Shining Rock and its birds?
    (a) Ashe County (b) Haywood County (c) Buncombe County

North Carolina's Mineral Magnificence

Thanks to our state's unique geological and geographical makeup, North Carolina is considered by many to be a rockhound's heaven. Sharpen up those picks and shovels, and leave no stone unturned as you dig out the answers to this quiz.

1. Thanks to the incredible variety of rock and mineral types found in North Carolina, our state has been given the nickname "Nature's Sample Case." About how many different types of rocks and minerals do we boast?   (a) 100   (b) 200   (c) 300

2. Showcasing North Carolina's mineral wealth is a museum at milepost 331 on the Blue Ridge Parkway near Spruce Pine. What is the name of this facility?
   (a) Museum of NC Minerals   (b) NC Rock Center   (c) Mineral and Gemstone Museum of NC

3. Coal is not a mineral resource usually associated with North Carolina, but much bituminous coal was nonetheless once extracted from the Deep River Coal Field near Sanford. What mine in that field took its name from an ancient nation?   (a) Persian Mine   (b) Egypt Mine   (c) Chinese Mine

4. The lightest metal known, lithium, is used in many products, including grease and storage batteries. Since lithium deposits were first discovered in our state in 1879, what rank has North Carolina risen to in its production of the metal?   (a) 1st in the South   (b) 2nd in the nation   (c) 1st in the world

5. Granite is an important North Carolina mineral resource as evidenced by the fact that the North Carolina Granite Corporation operates the world's largest open-face granite mine in what Surry County town?
   (a) Mount Airy   (b) Lumberton   (c) Mount Pilot

6. Iron ore is also an abundant mineral in many areas of North Carolina. Identify the Lincoln County community located on NC 27 that took its name from the many iron foundries located there between 1770 and 1880.   (a) Ironville   (b) Ironburg   (c) Iron Station

7. Feldspar is the most abundant mineral in the earth's crust and was first mined in North Carolina near Spruce Pine in 1911. What other state mines more feldspar than North Carolina?
   (a) Iowa   (b) no other state   (c) Kansas

8. Topaz, an orange-brown or yellow gemstone, occurs in North Carolina on Bowlings Mountain near the little town of Stem just southwest of Oxford. What county, named for one of the Lords Proprietors, is this topaz deposit located in?   (a) Granville County   (b) Burke County   (c) Polk County

9. Western North Carolina near Mason Branch in Macon County is the only place in the United States where rhodolite, a variety of the gemstone garnet, is located. What month of the year has garnet as its birthstone?   (a) June   (b) January   (c) October

10. Gold was first discovered in North Carolina in 1799 on a farm in Cabarrus County. What once-prolific mine, now a popular museum and gold mining exhibition site, occupies that very locale?
    (a) Concord Mine   (b) Reed Gold Mine   (c) Midland Mines

11. So much gold was found in North Carolina that until 1848 we led the nation in its production. What West Coast state came along during that time and knocked us out of the golden saddle?
    (a) California   (b) Washington   (c) Oregon

12. The world's rarest gem, found only in Alexander County, is named for the New York mineralogist William Hidden, who discovered it there. What community in central Alexander County is also named for this jewel?   (a) Hiddenville   (b) Hiddenite   (c) Hiddenton

December 1993

Tar Heel Gold

Before 1850 North Carolina was the nation's leading producer of gold. See if you can strike it rich with a lode of correct answers to this quiz on the Tar Heel gold rush.

1. Gold was first discovered in North Carolina in 1799 when a 12-year-old boy named Conrad pried a 17-pound nugget out of Little Meadow Creek in what is now Cabarrus County. A state historic site, the mine that grew from Conrad's discovery goes by what name?
    (a) Reed Gold Mine   (b) Little Meadow Mine   (c) Cabarrus Mine

2. Burning up with gold fever, the 1840s Rowan County boom town of Gold Hill once had as many as 15 mines and 27 saloons in operation. Things are calmer these days in Gold Hill, which is located on what highway that runs between Rockwell and Misenheimer?   (a) NC 22   (b) US 421   (c) US 52

3. Gold-mining production in North Carolina prior to 1860 was valued at $50 million to $65 million. The gold industry in our state during this period employed up to 30,000 people annually, making it second only to what type of work in economic importance?
    (a) fishing   (b) agriculture   (c) distilling corn liquor

4. Before 1829 all the gold in the United States fashioned into coins at the US Mint in Pennsylvania was from North Carolina. Around $9 million worth of coins were struck from Tar Heel gold in what Keystone State city?   (a) Philadelphia   (b) Pittsburgh   (c) Cashtown

5. Authorized by Congress in 1835, a branch of the US Mint officially opened in Charlotte on December 4, 1837. More than $5 million worth of gold had been coined at the mint by 1860. In 1936 the mint began a new life as North Carolina's first what?   (a) casino   (b) credit union   (c) art museum

6. The first attempt at gold mining in Mecklenburg County was made by a fellow named Samuel McComb in 1825 . McComb's mine was located under what street near present present-day uptown Charlotte?
    (a) West Morehead Street   (b) Biltmore Avenue   (c) New Bern Avenue

7. The first gold dollar minted in the United States was produced in North Carolina by German immigrant Christopher Bechtler Sr. In 1832 Bechtler began producing the gold pieces from his shop in what Piedmont county seated by Rutherfordton?
    (a) Polk County   (b) Rutherford County   (c) Cleveland County

8. In 1901 a distinguished visitor made his way to the Charlotte Mint to conduct experiments for extracting gold from Tar Heel ore by using electricity. Name this inventive wizard whose credits include the phonograph and electric light.   (a) Samuel Morse   (b) Henry Ford   (c) Thomas Edison

9. Only a sunken depression in the forest remains of what was once the W.V. Smith Gold Mine in eastern Gaston County. Played out around the turn of the century, the Smith Mine is located in what textile community on US 74 between Charlotte and Gastonia?
    (a) Crowders Mountain   (b) Ellenboro   (c) Belmont

10. The first American discovery of gold veins in quartz rock was said to have been by North Carolinian Tobias Barringer in 1828. Barringer found his golden cornucopia along the banks of Long Creek in what county whose seat is Albemarle?   (a) Stanly County   (b) Moore County   (c) Anson County

11. Mines with colorful titles such as Copperhead and Dark Springs operated in the Montgomery County community of Eldorado during North Carolina's golden heyday. Located on NC 109 in the Uwharrie National Forest, the name Eldorado means what?
    (a) Golden Forests   (b) City of Gold   (c) Nugget Valley

12. The most important gold-producing geological feature in our state is called the Carolina Slate Belt. Varying in width from 25 miles to 70 miles, this band of gold-bearing rock stretches from Union County northeast across the Piedmont into what county seated by Roxboro?
    (a) Person County   (b) Caswell County   (c) Stokes County

13. The most important gold works in eastern North Carolina, the Portis Mine produced millions of dollars worth of flakes. Operated from 1838 to the 1930s, Portis Mine was located near present-day Centerville in what county that also includes the towns of Justice and Alert?
    (a) Bertie County   (b) Gates County   (c) Franklin County

The Answers Are Blowin' In The Wind

North Carolina has been ravaged over the years by a variety of tropical storms and hurricanes. From Hazel to Hugo, Tar Heel residents have learned to cope with dangerous weather. To test your knowledge of all the storms we've endured, try the following quiz.

1. Well deserving of the title "Mother of All Hurricanes," Hazel has been called the most destructive hurricane in North Carolina history. What year did Hazel ravage our coast?
   (a) 1950   (b) 1954   (c) 1952

2. In the early morning hours of September 22, 1989, as winds and rain lashed the Piedmont the center of Hurricane Hugo passed just west of Charlotte. What is the center of a hurricane called?
   (a) eye   (b) ear   (c) throat

3. Hurricane Hugo has the dubious distinction of being listed in the *Guinness Book of Records* as being the most costly hurricane in United States history. How many dollars worth of damage did Hugo cause?
   (a) $100 million   (b) $1 billion   (c) $7 billion

4. In the same year that the Mecklenburg Declaration of Independence was signed, a hurricane not only wiped the town of Bar, North Carolina, off the map, but also killed more people on the East Coast than any previous storm. What was the year?   (a) 1776   (b) 1775   (c) 1780

5. In early September 1846, Hatteras and Oregon Inlets were punched on the Outer Banks by a raging hurricane. What sound were the inlets formed in?
   (a) Pamlico Sound   (b) Albemarle Sound   (c) Bogue Sound

6. Imagine a friend tells you that they are thinking of going fishing off Morehead City, but have seen hurricane warning flags go up. What do hurricane warning flags look like?
   (a) blue stripe on white background   (b) yellow circle on green background
   (c) black square in center of red background

7. Causing much beach erosion in North Carolina, winds from a hurricane rotate in a certain direction in the Northern Hemisphere due to the "Coriolus Effect." What is that direction?
   (a) clockwise   (b) counterclockwise   (c) sideways

8. Packing 135 mph winds, Hurricane Diana came ashore September 13, 1984, near Carolina Beach. What North Carolina county did this take place in?
   (a) New Hanover County   (b) Hyde County   (c) Dare County

9. What North Carolina government agency is dedicated to the effective and timely response to disasters, and would be in charge of emergency planning if a hurricane struck our state?
   (a) Marine Affairs Office   (b) Environment, Health and Natural Resources Department
   (c) Division of Emergency Management

10. During Jim Hunt's governorship, Hurricane David not only raked the Caribbean, but did a pretty good job of shaking the bushes in North Carolina as well. What year did David pay North Carolina a call?
    (a) 1985   (b) 1979   (c) 1975

11. Ordinarily providing some of North Carolina's finest beach weather, what months also lie squarely in what is called "hurricane season?"
    (a) August and September   (b) March and April   (c) May and June

12. Though many nor'easters and gales blow at the North Carolina coast each year, storm winds must reach a certain speed to be considered a full-blown hurricane. What is that windspeed?
    (a) 50 mph   (b) 60 mph   (c) 74 mph or more

Arts and Leisure

Richard Petty Museum, Level Cross

Try To Tackle This

It's time once again for Monday night football games, roars from high-school stadiums, and long-awaited homecomings.

When fans across the state get ready for a new season of that great All-American sport, we think they ought to put their knowledge of North Carolina football to the test. Some of the questions are from fairly recent history; others go back a few years. So dust off your memory, put on your helmet and get ready for a challenge.

1. For which pro team did Wake Forest star Brian Piccolo play four seasons?
   (a) Washington Redskins (b) Chicago Bears (c) Detroit Lions

2. Name the Hendersonville native who played end for the Washington Redskins through 1963 and for the Green Bay Packers in 1965 before retiring after the 1966 season.
   (a) Walter "Bill" Anderson (b) Marcus Click (c) Gary Stewart

3. Clarence Stasavich was an outstanding coach and athletic director at two colleges in North Carolina. Name them. (a) Gardner-Webb University and UNC (b) Campbell University and ECU
   (c) Lenoir-Rhyne College and ECU

4. Who became Wake Forest's head football coach in March 1981?
   (a) Al Groh (b) Ron Massey (c) Dom Capers

5. Which football play was UNC the first to use, during a game with Georgia in Atlanta on October 26, 1895? (a) Lateral pass (b) Quarterback sneak (c) The first forward pass

6. In which 1981 bowl game did North Carolina defeat Arkansas 31-27?
   (a) Rose Bowl (b) Gater Bowl (c) Orange Bowl

7. What Wilmington native became the 11th quarterback in NFL history to gain more than 25,000 yards passing? (a) Roman "Gabe" Gabriel (b) Marcus Brendle (c) Gary "Go-Go" Rankin

8. Name five football greats whose jerseys have been retired at UNC.
   (a) Johnny Unitas, Cy Young, Joe Theisman, Knute Rockne, Art Weiner
   (b) Charlie "Choo-Choo" Justice, Cotton Sutherland, Art Weiner, Andy Bershak, George Barclay
   (c) Roman Gabriel, Sonny Jurgensen, Lawrence Taylor, John Baker, Jim Thorpe

9. Name the Duke University tackle who was the first North Carolinian to be honored as an All-American.
   (a) Joe Crawford (b) R.L. "Pineknot" Helton (c) Fred E. "Freddie" Crawford

10. Which North Carolina State halfback played for the Pittsburgh Steelers, Boston Patriots, New York Titans and the New York Jets? (a) Richard Christy (b) Joe Christy (c) Christy Key

11. What was the nickname given to Jack Merritt, UNC's star fullback in 1922?
    (a) "Jumpin' Jack" (b) "The Battering Ram" (c) "Jack B. Nimble"

12. Name the former East Carolina University football coach who left Greenville in 1979, coached one year at the University of Wyoming, and went on to be head coach at Auburn University.
    (a) Mike Ditka (b) Pat Dye (c) Joe Gibbs

13. Which UNC athletic business manager appropriated $25 to buy the school's first mascot?
    (a) Charlie Woollen (b) Dwayne Hastings (c) William Friday

14. Which UNC player caught a record 52 passes in 1949?
    (a) Art Shoemaker (b) Art Weiner (c) Bill Weiner

15. What team did UNC play in the 1983 Peach Bowl? (a) Georgia Tech (b) VMI (c) Florida State

Gridiron Greatness In The Tar Heel State

Autumn's crisp air has football fans and players alike in North Carolina geared up for pigskin action. See how many points you can score on this quiz about our state's gridiron greatness.

1. Though a freewheeling form of football had been played in North Carolina for many years, the first "scientific" game took place at the State Fairgrounds in Raleigh on Thanksgiving Day in 1888. Trinity College faced off against what other school that day?
    (a) University of North Carolina   (b) Rutgers University   (c) Clemson University

2. The first meeting of black inter-collegiate football teams was just four years later in 1892 when Livingstone College battled a team from Biddle Institute. The game was played at Livingstone College which is still located in what North Carolina city?   (a) Greensboro   (b) Wadesboro   (c) Salisbury

3. History has had its effect upon North Carolina football, as in 1942 when fear of Japanese bombing raids forced the Rose Bowl to be moved from pasadena, California, to what Tar Heel town?
    (a) Durham   (b) Wilmington   (c) Asheville

4. Perhaps the most celebrated University of North Carolina football player of all time, Charlie "Choo-Choo" Justice wore what number on his jersey during his days as a Tar Heel sports sensation in the 1940s?   (a) 43   (b) 17   (c) 22

5. Another great player from UNC, linebacker Lawrence Taylor, went on to a career in pro football. In 1987 Taylor spearheaded what National Football League team to a Super Bowl triumph?
    (a) Atlanta Falcons   (b) New York Giants   (c) Green Bay Packers

6. During the 1930s the great Clarence Parker was a football star at Duke University. Later, Clarence would be elected the NFL's Most Valuable Player of 1940. What was Parker's well-known nickname?
    (a) "Ace"   (b) "Crazy Legs"   (c) "Flying Flea"

7. A member of the NFL Hall of Fame from our state is Wilmington native Sonny Jurgensen. During the 1960s and '70s what pro team did Sonny quarterback to many exciting wins?
    (a) Atlanta Falcons   (b) Kansas City Chiefs   (c) Washington Redskins

8. A football contemporary and fellow Wilmingtonian of Jurgensen, Roman Gabriel played quarterback for the Los Angeles Rams and the Philadelphia Eagles. At what North Carolina college did Gabriel advance his football career?
    (a) Mars Hill College   (b) Pembroke State University   (c) NC State University

9. Pulling their own "Three-peat," the Duke Blue Devils captured ACC football championships in 1960, '61 and '62. Exactly what does the acronym "ACC" stand for?   (a) Atlantic Coast Conference
    (b) American College Conference   (c) Atlantic Confederation of Conferences

10. When Greenville's East Carolina University Pirates football team takes to the turf for a home game, they battle their foes at what on-campus stadium?
    (a) Ficklen Stadium   (b) Lombardi Stadium   (c) Pitt Stadium

11. This former Elizabeth City State University star was once part of the feared "Doomsday Defense" of the Dallas Cowboys during the 1970s. Who is this defensive lineman?
    (a) Doug Wilkerson   (b) Joe Greene   (c) Jethro Pugh

12. Nestled deep in our mountains near the Blue Ridge Parkway, Western Carolina University in Cullowhee is one place where fans of that school's Catamounts football team enjoy great viewing on and off the gridiron. What team colors do those Catamounts proudly sport?
    (a) purple and teal   (b) yellow and black   (c) purple and gold

"What It Was Was Football"

It's autumn and time for the Old North State's annual pigskin frenzy. Go for a win with the answers to this quiz on football in North Carolina.

1. Thanksgiving Day in 1888 saw the first modern game of football played in North Carolina. Held at the Raleigh Fairgrounds, the tussle saw Trinity College defeat what school?
(a) University of Alabama (b) Davidson College (c) University of North Carolina

2. A black intercollegiate football team first played in North Carolina in 1892. Biddle Institute (now Johnson C. Smith University) was defeated 4-0 by what school based in Salisbury?
(a) Livingstone College (b) Saint Augustine's College (c) North Carolina A&T

3. Early college football in North Carolina had its detractors as well as supporters. Citing, among other reasons, an "undermining of student morals," UNC, Trinity College, and what Baptist college dropped the game for a while? (a) Belmont Abbey College (b) Wake Forest College (c) Davidson College

4. In 1942 a famous college football bowl game had to be moved from its home in California to North Carolina for fear of a Japanese air raid. Name this bowl game that was held for one year only in Durham. (a) Orange Bowl (b) Sugar Bowl (c) Rose Bowl

5. Coached by Carl Snavely, UNC football in the post-World War II era is legendary. In 1946, UNC racked up an 8-1-1 season before losing 20-10 in the Sugar Bowl to what team in the Tar Heels' first post-season bowl game? (a) Georgia (b) Alabama (c) Auburn

6. Instrumental in UNC's post-war football glory was All-American Charlie "Choo-Choo" Justice of Asheville. Said by some to be the most famous athlete in North Carolina, Justice narrowly missed being awarded what prize in 1948 and 1949?
(a) Cy Young Award (b) Heisman Trophy (c) ACC Most Valuable Player

7. A member of the NFL Hall of Fame, former Washington Redskins star quarterback Sonny Jurgensen is a North Carolina native. With more than 225 pro touchdown passes to his credit, Sonny hailed from what Tar Heel port city? (a) Morehead City (b) Oriental (c) Wilmington

8. In 1969, North Carolina-born Roman Gabriel became the first Atlantic Coast Conference football player to be named NFL Most Valuable Player. From 1962-1977 Gabriel played for what two teams?
(a) Los Angeles Rams, Chicago Bears (b) Los Angeles Rams, Philadelphia Eagles
(c) Atlanta Falcons, New Orleans Saints

9. On October 14, 1951, two TV stations in our state carried the first Washington Redskins game broadcast to North Carolina. Viewers saw the Redskins take a 45-0 whipping from the Cleveland Browns on Greensboro's WFMY-TV and on what Charlotte station? (a) WCCB-TV (b) WSOC-TV (c) WBTV

10. Named NFL Rookie of the Year and Defensive Player of the Year in 1981, former UNC football star Lawrence Taylor was also a league Most Valuable Player. What team did Taylor lead to Super Bowl triumph in 1986? (a) New York Giants (b) New York Jets (c) Buffalo Bills

11. The Duke University Blue Devils have many football superlatives to their credit including a Southern Conference Championship in 1952. Shifting to the Atlantic Coast Conference, Duke won championships in what three consecutive years? (a) 1955, 1956, 1957 (b) 1960, 1961, 1962 (c) 1980, 1981, 1982

12. The East Carolina Pirates' colorful football history includes Clarence Stasavich as coach during the 1960s and several bowl victories. During 1964 and 1965, the Pirates defeated Massachusetts and Maine two years running in what post-season bowl game?
(a) Hula Bowl (b) Rose Bowl (c) Tangerine Bowl

13. Perhaps the Carolina Panthers' biggest victory of the 1995 season came when they defeated the reigning Super Bowl champs on their own field. With a 13-7 victory that set the football world on its ear, the Panthers won over what team? (a) San Francisco 49ers (b) Atlanta Falcons (c) Washington Redskins

North Carolina Roundball Roundup

Basketball may not have been invented in North Carolina, but the fanatical following the sport receives in our state might lead some to believe that it was. To prepare for the pro and college basketball seasons, whet your appetite for hoops with this Tar Heel basketball quiz.

1. The first intercollegiate basketball game in North Carolina took place on February 6, 1906, when Guilford College beat Wake Forest College 26-19. What Tar Heel town is the home of Guilford College? (a) Greensboro (b) Shelby (c) Oxford

2. A North Carolina State University basketball coaching legend, Everett Case, began his career at that school in 1946. Highlights of Case's tenure as coach included 156 victories in Reynolds Coliseum and election to the Basketball Hall of Fame. In what year did Everett Case pass away? (a) 1975 (b) 1961 (c) 1966

3. Under the leadership of coach Frank McGuire, the 1957 University of North Carolina basketball team crowned its season with a triple-overtime win over Kansas for the national championship. What nickname did the starters for that incredible Tar Heel team go by? (a) Tar Heel Terminators (b) Flaming Five (c) UNC Invincibles

4. An outstanding basketball player during his high school days in Durham, Horace Albert McKinney would go on to coach the Wake Forest College team to many thrilling wins. What name did Horace prefer to go by? (a) Bones (b) Babe (c) Baldy

5. From 1949 to 1960 a very popular basketball tournament was held annually just after Christmas in Raleigh's Reynolds Coliseum. Name this tournament that was created by Everett Case and pitted top national teams against North Carolina's "Big Four" schools. (a) Southern Classic (b) Carolina Classic (c) Dixie Classic

6. A Pittsburgh native whose 17-year basketball coaching career included stints at Clemson, North Carolina State and Appalachian State, Press Maravich was also the father of a famous National Basketball Association basketball star. What was the name of the junior Maravich? (a) "Passin'" Paul (b) "Pistol" Pete (c) "Shootin'" Sam

7. Cedric Maxwell led the University of North Carolina at Charlotte 49ers on a Cinderella run to the 1977 NCAA Final Four in Atlanta. What Southern culinary favorite was the 6-foot-8 center nicknamed after? (a) Livermush (b) Cornbread (c) Grits

8. In January 1953, St. Augustine's College's Clarence Burks scored a record-setting 69 points when he led his team to a victory over St. Paul's of Virginia. What North Carolina city is the home of St. Augustine's College? (a) Raleigh (b) Boone (c) Wilmington

9. Before he succumbed to cancer in 1993, North Carolina State basketball coach Jim Valvano led his team to the 1983 national championship. Known for his wit and determination, Valvano was originally from what metropolis? (a) Chicago (b) New York (c) Los Angeles

10. Davidson College in Mecklenburg County has a basketball heritage that stretches back to 1909 and includes such legendary coaches as Lefty Driesell. What type of animal does Davidson use for its team's nickname? (a) Panther (b) Lion (c) Wildcat

11. A former star with the Charlotte Hornets of the National Basketball Association, Tyrone "Muggsy" Bogues was known for speed and daring during his Atlantic Coast Conference playing days at Wake Forest in the mid-1980s. A giant among men in many ways, how tall does Muggsy stand? (a) 5 feet 3 (b) 5 feet 7 (c) 6 feet 2

12. After many attempts, University of North Carolina basketball coach Dean Smith won his first national basketball championship in 1982 with a triumph over Georgetown in the NCAA finals. How many trips to the championship game did it take Smith to win the title? (a) 6 (b) 4 (c) 3

13. In the late 1960s, the first black player to make the University of North Carolina varsity basketball team took to the hardwood. Who was this 6-foot-6 All-American from New York who was also voted All-Atlantic Coast Conference three times? (a) William Baxter (b) Bill Chamberlain (c) Charlie Scott

It's Tee Time

OK, North Carolina golfers, here's your chance to brush up on the game and you don't even have to pick up a club. (Sorry, no handicaps allowed.)

1. North Carolina native Raymond Floyd was victorious in the 1976 Masters and the 1986 US Open golf tournaments. What Tar Heel city is he from? (a) Durham (b) Asheville (c) Fayetteville

2. At 747 yards, the longest par 6 golf hole in the world can be played in North Carolina. Which club claims it? (a) Cullasaja Club (b) Black Mountain Golf Club (c) Forest Oaks Country Club

3. The town of Pinehurst is known worldwide for its golf. What year did James Walker Tufts turn 5,000 acres of scrub into this resort community? (a) 1895 (b) 1900 (c) 1910

4. Which golf course at Pinehurst is the site of the PGA World Golf Hall of Fame?
(a) No. 4 (b) No. 6 (c) No. 2

5. Which gentleman, with hundreds of golf courses already to his credit, designed the first course at Pinehurst in 1898? (a) James McFadden (b) Donald Ross (c) Bud Peters

6. This former Wake Forest student and team golfer won the Masters Tournament four times. Who is he?
(a) Ben Hogan (b) Arnold Palmer (c) Byron Nelson

7. Name the Western North Carolina golf course that has an elevation of 5,000 feet and claims to be the highest link east of the Rockies.
(a) Linville Ridge (b) Kenmure Golf Club (c) Lake Toxaway Country Club

8. Which US President hosted the opening of the PGA World Golf Hall of Fame in Pinehurst?
(a) Richard Nixon (b) Gerald Ford (c) Jimmy Carter

9. Name the North Carolina island, accessible only by ferry, that prohibits cars but boasts a George Cobb-designed golf course. (a) Bald Head Island (b) Emerald Isle (c) Ocean Isle Beach

10. Right next to Asheville's famous Grove Park Inn, the Grove Park Country Club was originally known as the Asheville Country Club. What year did it open? (a) 1909 (b) 1915 (c) 1921

11. The 1974 PGA championship was held at the Tanglewood Championship Course in Clemmons. Who won that event? (a) Lee Trevino (b) Gary Player (c) Ben Crenshaw

12. Forest Oaks Country Club has hosted the Greater Greensboro Open for many years, but it wasn't always the event's site. What year did the tournament move to Forest Oaks?
(a) 1969 (b) 1973 (c) 1977

13. March 1938 saw the playing of the first Greater Greensboro Open. Who won that event?
(a) Sam Snead (b) Bobby Locke (c) Walter Hagen

14. Collegiate golf is a popular team sport in North Carolina. Which college won the 1986 NCAA Golf Championship? (a) Duke University (b) Wake Forest University (c) Davidson College

15. Playing in the Greater Greensboro Open, Charlie Sifford became the first black golfer to compete in a PGA Tour event in the South. What year was that GGO? (a) 1970 (b) 1961 (c) 1965

Golf Is More Than Just A Game In NC

It's not by pure accident that North Carolina is home to the World Golf Hall of Fame in Pinehurst. Our state has a rich history in the gentleman's game. We're home to some of the world's most challenging courses, prestigious tournaments and talented golfers. How much do you know about the sport here?

1. North Carolina has earned the nickname "Golf State, USA." About how many golf courses grace our Tar Heel landscape?   (a) 175   (b) 400   (c) 1,000

2. Golf and its related industries mean big business for North Carolina. Approximately how many dollars does the sport pump into the state economy each year?
   (a) $20 billion   (b) $10 million   (c) $2 million

3. The PGA World Golf Hall of Fame in Pinehurst inducted longtime pro Chi Chi Rodriguez into its hallowed halls in 1992. Name the island, about 1,400 miles south of Pinehurst, where Chi Chi grew up.
   (a) Bermuda   (b) Australia   (c) Puerto Rico

4. In 1985, Nancy Lopez set an LPGA record low score of 268 for 72 holes at the Henredon Classic golf tournament. What North Carolina town hosted that event?   (a) Hickory   (b) Waxhaw   (c) High Point

5. Famed golf-course designer Tom Fazio skillfully blended the Wade Hampton Golf Club into the Blue Ridge hills near Cashiers. What was Wade Hampton's claim to fame?   (a) He shot a hole-in-one on opening day.   (b) He was a Confederate general.   (c) He built the clubhouse.

6. On June 18, 1981, James Lee Thorpe of Person County became the first black man to lead a US Open by posting a first round score of 66. What town in Person County is Jim from?
   (a) Roxboro   (b) Olive Hill   (c) Flat River

7. Now surrounded by Charlotte development, Myers Park Country Club's rolling links still retain a bit of the rural look the course had when it was laid out in the 1920s. The first clubhouse there was unusual. What had that building been previously?
   (a) Military school office   (b) Corset factory   (c) Donkey barn

8. Pinehurst hosted the first serious athletic competition for women in North Carolina with its North-South Amateur Golf Tournament. What was the year?   (a) 1863   (b) 1903   (c) 1937

9. Blue Ridge Country Club in Linville Falls not only offers beautiful scenery, but also a Lee Trevino-designed golf course. What National Forest is adjacent to the links?
   (a) Croatan National Forest   (b) Madge White National Forest   (c) Pisgah National Forest

10. In Charlotte on June 23, 1991, Orville Moody shot a 207 to squeak by Dick Hendrickson as victor by a mere stroke and won the tournament there. What was this contest called?
    (a) Paine Webber Invitational   (b) Mecklenburg Open   (c) Charlotte Masters Tournament

11. Curtis Strange, former Wake Forest University All-American golfer, won more than $1 million prize money in 1988. What famous Wake Forest golf team coach helped Curtis, and many others, achieve success?   (a) Phillip Cherry   (b) Bill Brice   (c) Jesse Haddock

12. He was a six-time winner of The Masters and nicknamed the "Golden Bear." He also designed the course at Elk River Club in Banner Elk. Who is this legendary golfer?
    (a) Mack White   (b) Jack Nicklaus   (c) John Dempsey

13. Three miles from the main club house, the Pinehurst No. 6 golf course has been characterized as tight and demanding. In what year did Tom and George Fazio build this challenging course?
    (a) 1980   (b) 1955   (c) 1947

Par For The Course

With the splendor and variety of this Tar Heel institution, nothing could be finer than golf in North Carolina. Take your best swing at the answers to this quiz.

1. Opened in 1996, Currituck Club at Corolla on the Outer Banks features a par-72 course with 6,800 yards of championship play. Situated on NC Highway 12, Currituck Club was once known for what other type of sporting activity that saw locals as well as celebrities like Babe Ruth try their luck at?
   (a) Horse racing   (b) Waterfowl hunting   (c) Crabbing

2. Constant winds are a factor that tests the skills of golfers at Goose Creek Golf and Country Club in Grandy. A par-72 course that has nearly 6,200 feet in total playing yardage, Goose Creek is located near the Currituck Bridge on what highway that runs from Coinjock on down to Mamie?
   (a) NC 34   (b) NC 94   (c) US 158

3. Located in Durham on NC Highway 751, the Duke University Golf Club was designed by Robert Trent Jones in 1957. In 1993, the links were reworked by Rees Jones. The Duke University Golf Club is part of what country club named for a member of the Duke family?
   (a) George B. Duke Golf and Country Club   (b) Doris Duke Golf and Country Club
   (c) Washington Duke Golf and Country Club

4. Finley Golf Course in Chapel Hill is UNC's golf course of choice. With 6,580 yards of championship play, Finley first opened in 1950. What famous Wilmington-born basketball star took up golf as a student at UNC under the eye of Davis Love III?
   (a) Michael Jordan   (b) James Worthy   (c) Brad Daugherty

5. In operation for more than 20 years, Keith Hills Country Club in Buies Creek is a par-72, Dan Maples designed course that has what some have called the largest practice facility in North Carolina. Keith Hills is located adjacent to what college whose mascot is a camel?
   (a) Gardner-Webb University   (b) Campbell University   (c) Wingate University

6. With its rolling, wooded landscape, Pine Needles Resort in Southern Pines has been in business since 1927. A Donald Ross designed, par-71 golf course, these links have seen many rounds of championship play, including what tournament in 1996?
   (a) US Men's Open   (b) US Amateur Invitational   (c) US Women's Open

7. The Wilmington area has many fine golf courses, including Echo Farms Golf and Country Club. Designed by George Hamm and opened in 1974, Echo Farms has a tricky par-5 eighth hole that combines a dogleg and water hazard. Before it became a golf course, what type of agricultural endeavor took place at Echo Farms?   (a) dairy farm   (b) tobacco farm   (c) peanut farm

8. Opened in 1965, Sea Scape Golf Club at Kitty Hawk is the second oldest golf course on the Outer Banks. With five par-5 holes, and much of its playing yardage in woods or on dunes, this Art Wall designed course is styled in the tradition of what country known as the birthplace of golf?
   (a) Ireland   (b) Scotland   (c) Germany

9. Said by many that its third hole is one of the finest par-4s in the world, Linville Golf Club opened its Donald Ross designed links in 1924. An earlier course that dated back to 1892 had brought golf to Linville and went by what name that is similar to a popular Clemmons golf and recreation area?
   (a) Reynolds Park   (b) Tanglewood   (c) Vanderbilt Acres

10. A golf-oriented complex in the Sandhills, Pinehurst Hotel & Country Club offers seven magnificent courses that beckon to duffers around the world. Which of these seven wonders is a perennial on lists of the nation's 10 best courses?   (a) Pinehurst No. 7   (b) Pinehurst No. 2   (c) Pinehurst No. 4

Batter Up!

The crack of the bat, the roar of the crowd, the taste of peanuts and Cracker Jack; there's no mistaking minor-league baseball season in North Carolina.

If you're new to this All-American spectator sport, try reading the article by Scott Smith first, on page 16 of *The State* July 1991 issue. Then step up to the bat and give this quiz your best shot.

1. What minor league do the Gastonia Rangers compete in?
    (a) South Atlantic League   (b) Textile League   (c) Piedmont League

2. Who starred in the 1988 movie *Bull Durham,* based on Durham's minor-league baseball team?
    (a) Mark Harmon   (b) Tom Cruise   (c) Kevin Costner

3. The original Charlotte Hornets were a popular minor-league baseball team. What major-league team were they a farm team for?
    (a) New York Yankees   (b) Minnesota Twins   (c) Boston Red Sox

4. Though the Queen City's present baseball team is the Charlotte Knights, their home field is just across the border in South Carolina. What town hosts them?
    (a) Rock Hill   (b) Fort Mill   (c) York

5. Beginning with five North Carolina teams and one from Virginia, Judge William G. Bramham organized a baseball league that lasted from 1920 to 1955. What was it called?
    (a) Piedmont League   (b) Middle Atlantic League   (c) Tar Heel League

6. Home of the Charlotte Hornets baseball team for many years, this stadium burned down in 1986. What was its original name?
    (a) Magnolia Avenue Park   (b) Charlotte Field   (c) Clark Griffith Park

7. Besides Durham and Kinston, which of the following Tar Heel towns also has a Class A Carolina League team?   (a) Hendersonville   (b) Winston-Salem   (c) Pilot Mountain

8. The proud town of Zebulon built a new stadium for its baseball team. What is the team's name?   (a) Mudcats   (b) Bull Frogs   (c) Salamanders

9. During the 1940s, Durham was the headquarters for the governing body of minor-league baseball. What is the name of that organization?   (a) Association of Minor League Baseball Clubs
    (b) American Baseball Organization   (c) National Association of Professional Baseball Leagues

10. Donning new, more conservative uniforms for the 1991 season, the Charlotte Knights will forsake the controversial black ones they wore in 1990. Who designed those trendy suits?
    (a) Ralph Lauren   (b) Alexander Julian   (c) Bill Blass

11. What year were the Asheville Tourists champions of the South Atlantic League?
    (a) 1928   (b) 1925   (c) 1930

12. The Charlotte Hornets baseball team took the Southern League championship in 1969 with a double-header win over what rival?   (a) Greenville   (b) Birmingham   (c) Raleigh

13. Early in his career Babe Ruth socked an unforgettable homer out of this minor-league stadium in Asheville.   (a) McCormick Field   (b) Biltmore Stadium   (c) Avery Park

14. What major-league team is the Charlotte Knights a farm team for?
    (a) Atlanta Braves   (b) Chicago Cubs   (c) Texas Rangers

15. The first-organized baseball league in North Carolina was formed in 1902. What town took the first championship pennant?   (a) Fayetteville   (b) Durham   (c) Raleigh

Who's On First?

Step up to the plate and take a swing at the correct answers to this quiz on Tar Heel baseball greats.

1. The first North Carolinian to play professional baseball was Benjamin Rippay, whose career lasted from 1876 until 1888. Rippay, who played under the name Charles Wesley Jones, was a native of what county seated by Graham? (a) Wake County (b) Guilford County (c) Alamance County

2. One of the greatest Olympic athletes of all time played professional minor league baseball in North Carolina for Rocky Mount and Fayetteville in 1909 and 1910. Name this Native American from Pennsylvania who won the decathlon at the 1912 Olympics.
(a) Cy Young (b) Jim Thorpe (c) Gary Stewart

3. East Bend native Ernie Shore has been credited as the only pitcher to throw a no-hitter in relief when he retired 26 batters on June 23, 1917, as a replacement for his Boston Red Sox teammate who had been ejected. What player, whose first and middle names were George Herman, did Shore relieve?
(a) George Herman Ruth (b) George Herman Aaron (c) George Herman Mantle

4. Prevented from playing in the segregated major baseball leagues during the 1930s and 1940s, many black baseball players displayed their talents in the Negro Leagues. Rocky Mount native and Baseball Hall of Fame member Walter "Buck" Leonard was so good that he was often compared with which great New York Yankee? (a) Ernie Banks (b) Dizzy Dean (c) Lou Gehrig

5. Founded in 1920, the Piedmont League brought pro baseball to many towns in North Carolina and Virginia. What Piedmont League player for High Point lead the association four times in batting and was named after a famous pioneer who once lived on the Yadkin River?
(a) Dan Boone (b) Kit Carson (c) Davy Crockett

6. Charlotte has long had minor league baseball teams as part of its history. Playing at stadiums like Griffith Park, standouts such as Minnie Mendoza and Tony Oliva thrilled fans of the Hornets and O's. What former Charlotte player went on to compete in more consecutive big-league games (2,632) than anyone else? (a) Yogi Berra (b) Todd Hagans (c) Cal Ripken, Jr.

7. North Carolina native Tony Cloninger made history on July 3, 1966, by hitting two grand slam homers against San Francisco pitchers Bob Priddy and Ray Sadecki. Playing as an Atlanta Brave, Cloninger became the first player of what position to accomplish this feat?
(a) Catcher (b) Pitcher (c) Left Fielder

8. A native of Roxboro, Enos Slaughter's baseball career as a major league outfielder during the 1940s and 1950s led him to the National Baseball Hall of Fame. A colorful character, Slaughter went by what nickname reflective of his rural North Carolina upbringing?
(a) "Farmhand" (b) "Plowboy" (c) "Country"

9. During his 20-year career from 1952-1972, relief pitcher Hoyt Wilhelm of Huntersville threw in more than 1,000 games. What type of pitch was Wilhelm most noted for?
(a) Knuckleball (b) Eightball (c) Highball

10. Winner of 300 professional baseball games and two Cy Young Awards, North Carolinian Gaylord Perry is the younger brother of Jim Perry who was also awarded the Cy Young laurels. What Tar Heel town that is the seat of Martin County did both Gaylord and Jim call home?
(a) Williamston (b) Beargrass (c) Goose Nest

11. A native of Hertford, the late Jim Hunter had an exemplary career as a pitcher for the New York Yankees and Oakland Athletics in the 1960s and 1970s. During his pitching days, Hunter won more than 220 regular season and five World Series games under what nickname?
(a) "Redfish" (b) "Catfish" (c) "Mudcat"

Fishing For Answers

Fishing is a year-round sport in the Tar Heel State, but in spring and summer especially, enthusiasts start cranking up.

Put your insider's knowledge of this pastime to the test by attempting the questions below. Even if you're not much of an angler, you'll learn enough to impress your friends who are.

1. What location is not only one of the most heavily fished spots on the NC coast but considered by many as the surfcaster's mecca?   (a) Corncake Inlet   (b) Cape Point at Cape Hatteras   (c) Holden Beach

2. A saltwater fisherman tells you he is going to the coast to catch some speckled trout, but first he needs to check his chuggers and poppers. What are chuggers and poppers?
   (a) Refreshments   (b) Lead weights   (c) Top-water, floating fishing lures

3. Britisher John Holden teaches coastal surfcasters a unique method of casting that allows baits to be tossed several hundred feet past the breakers. What is the casting method called?
   (a) Power-pendulum or English casting   (b) "Limey Toss"   (c) "Holden's Haul"

4. David G. Deuel caught the world's record red drum on November 7, 1984, in the surf near Avon. How much did the whopper weigh, give or take a few pounds?   (a) 60 lbs.   (b) 70 lbs.   (c) 94 lbs. 2 oz.

5. What is a "Hatteras heaver?"
   (a) large wave   (b) a strong, 10-foot-long saltwater casting rod   (c) seasick fisherman

6. You are fishing in the surf, when suddenly the water is alive with mullet trying to escape a school of predators. "Big choppers!" another fisherman calls, as he clips a Hopkins spoon onto his line and casts out. What is a chopper?   (a) large bluefish   (b) tuna   (c) barracuda

7. Give at least one of the three names that our state saltwater fish, the red drum, goes by.
   (a) quahog, spot, angelfish   (b) croaker, toadfish, puffer   (c) puppy drum, redfish, spottail

8. Local coastal fishermen sometimes call that slender fish known as the whiting by a nickname less than dignified to our Old Dominion neighbors. What is that nickname?
   (a) Virginia mullet   (b) Skinny Virginny   (c) Richmond Throwback

9. A prize bait for all types of coastal rod-and-reel fishing is the killifish. What are some other names for this bait?   (a) Sardine Sandwich, Skank, Mudger   (b) Killi Catfish, Gaffer, Little Minnie
   (c) Mummichog, Chog, Gudgeon

10. Fishing from an Outer Banks pier, you land a big gamefish. If it should be considered for record status, what organizations would certify your catch?   (a) Oriental International Record Keepers
    (b) International Game Fishing Association   (c) Swan Quarter Fish and Game Association

11. What North Carolina town is renowned for its annual Shad Festival, held in April?
    (a) Grifton   (b) Ocracoke   (c) New Bern

12. The site of some excellent surf fishing, Corncake Inlet is located just below what Civil War fort?
    (a) Fort Macon   (b) Fort Anderson   (c) Fort Fisher

13. If you reeled in a Fat Albert, what would you have caught?   (a) little tunny   (b) cobia   (c) triggerfish

14. According to state law, what is the minimum length for a flounder to be considered a "keeper"?
    (a) 10 inches   (b) 12 inches   (c) 13 inches

15. Crystal Pier at Wrightsville Beach was built near the wreck of what Confederate ship?
    (a) *Fanny and Jenny*   (b) *CSS Albemarle*   (c) *CSS Housatonic*

Coastal Piers And Fishing

Pier and surf fishing on the North Carolina coast must surely rank as one of life's most sublime and exciting endeavors. Cast your line for the correct answers to this quiz.

1. Catching everything from croaker to king mackerel, North Carolina pier fishermen are a special breed who enjoy the taste of salt air and a sharp tug on their line. How many ocean fishing piers in our state are licensed by the Division of Marine Fisheries for the period 1998-1999?
   (a) 15 piers   (b) 20 piers   (c) 24 piers

2. The fishing pier currently at Kure Beach near Fort Fisher is nearly 600 feet long. Many years ago there was a pier at Kure that was one of the few of its type anywhere. Of what sort of material was this original Kure Beach fishing pier constructed?   (a) concrete   (b) steel   (c) railroad ties

3. In 1997 North Carolina recreational fishermen harvested more than 8,600 of the state's official saltwater fish. Totaling about 40,000 pounds in weight, these stout surf fighters go by what name?
   (a) Red Drum   (b) Bluefish   (c) Sheepshead

4. With close to 1.5 million harvested annually by recreational saltwater anglers in North Carolina, there is a certain species of fish that, though small, is unusually tasty. From pier and surf, countless lines are baited with worms and cast for what type of fish whose distinctive black marking gives it its name?
   (a) Striper   (b) Spot   (c) Pinfish

5. With more than 4.7 million pounds caught and kept by North Carolina saltwater anglers in 1997, a type of fish known as the "chicken of the sea" is a popular species found off the Tar Heel coast. Name this quarry that can grow to 500 pounds of hard-fighting muscle.
   (a) Porgies   (b) Jacks   (c) Yellowfin tuna

6. Swansboro in Onslow County is the site of a popular fishing pier that projects 576 feet from shore. This pier takes its name from what nearby inlet that is formed close to the end of White Oak River?
   (a) Bogue Inlet   (b) Corncake Inlet   (c) Oregon Inlet

7. Powerful and fast, cobia is a species of saltwater fish that gives Tar Heel fishermen a run for their money. The North Carolina state record cobia was caught in 1988 and weighed 103 pounds. Besides crabeater, what other name is the cobia known by?   (a) Torpedo   (b) Subchaser   (c) Lemonfish

8. With nearly 10,000 harvested from piers and offshore reefs by North Carolina fishermen in 1997, grouper is one of the tastiest species in the sea. Fishermen have given grouper many colorful nicknames including black, gag, scamp, and what other moniker that describes one species' color?
   (a) Orange   (b) Red   (c) Blue

9. Sunset Beach Fishing Pier on Sunset Beach gives anglers 745 feet of space to try their luck. To get to Sunset Beach and its pier, visitors must first cross over the Intracoastal Waterway by what unusual type of bridge?   (a) Covered bridge   (b) Cantilever bridge   (c) Pivoting drawbridge

10. Located at Carolina Beach on Lake Park Boulevard, Golden Sands Motel/Center Pier is the shortest ocean fishing pier licensed by the Division of Marine Fisheries. Short in length but big in action, Center Pier is how long?   (a) 20 feet   (b) 100 feet   (c) 150 feet

11. Five ocean fishing piers are licensed to operate in and around Atlantic Beach, including Triple S Fishing Pier, which at 940 feet is the longest pier on the Tar Heel coast. When fishermen decide to give their rods a rest, attractions in the Atlantic Beach area include Fort Macon and a natural area named for what "bully" US president?   (a) Theodore Roosevelt   (b) Franklin Roosevelt   (c) Andrew Jackson

Testing Tar Heel Slopes

North Carolina has long been a popular state for snow skiing. We were the first Southern state to introduce the sport in 1939, and in 1990 the ski industry pumped more than $55 million into our economy.

See how much you know about Tar Heel slopes by trying your hand at the questions below.

1. In the history of recreational snow skiing in NC, Cataloochee holds what distinction?
    (a) first ski resort to open in NC   (b) first ski lift   (c) steepest slopes in NC

2. Considered by many to be the "granddaddy" of snow skiing in the state, what Maggie Valley resident was drawing plans for slopes as early as 1939? (a) Hugh Morton (b) Tom Alexander (c) Jules Morros

3. One of the first professional ski instructors to arrive in NC, Austrian Sepp Kober had formerly coached what two countries' Winter Olympic teams?
    (a) Germany and Italy   (b) Sweden and Denmark   (c) Norway and Spain

4. Rick Coker was founding president of the NC Ski Areas Association in what year?
    (a) 1960   (b) 1965   (c) 1977

5. When did Hound Ears Lodge and Club first open?   (a) 1950   (b) 1959   (c) 1964

6. Seven Devils was the High Country's third slope to open. When did it begin operation?
    (a) 1966-67   (b) 1970-71   (c) 1975-76

7. The NC Legislature passed what ski-related act in 1981?
    (a) Skier Safety Act   (b) Ski Instructor's License   (c) Ski Slope operator's Act

8. Green Berets, Navy Seals and Sunday school groups have all taken instruction at what NC ski school?
    (a) Ski Bivouac School   (b) French-Swiss Ski College   (c) Avalanche Academy

9. What world-famous skier visited the slopes of NC one week before the 1972 Winter Olympics in Japan? (a) Francois Mitterand   (b) Jean Claude Killy   (c) Wolfgang Schultz

10. Winter Olympics of another type were hosted for the first time by Jim Cottrell. What was unique about them? (a) Southern Ski Olympics   (b) Highcountry Handicapped Games
    (c) Southeastern Winter Special Olympics

11. Commonly called cross-country skiing, what is the more correct term for this winter sport?
    (a) Nordic skiing   (b) Ski-Trekking   (c) Snow Hiking

12. Artificial snow has saved many a Carolina ski trip. What company is generally credited with pioneering snow-making technology? (a) General Electric   (b) Snow Concepts   (c) Larchmont Engineering

13. 1978 saw the South's first cross-country ski center open. What was the location?
    (a) Beech Mountain   (b) Sugar Mountain   (c) Hounds Ears

14. Skiers enjoyed the area's first chair lift at what slope?
    (a) Maggie Valley   (b) Hound Ears   (c) Banner Elk

15. What town claims to be the "Ski Capital of the South?"   (a) Boone   (b) Banner Elk   (c) Highlands

16. What is the name of the cross-country ski trail that tops out on Mount Mitchell at 6,684 feet?
    (a) Black Mountain Crest Trail   (b) Skyline Drive   (c) Mile High Meadow

17. What NC ski resort boasts slopes with the biggest vertical drop of any in the South? How many feet is the vertical drop there? (a) Kill Devil Hill, 2,000 foot drop   (b) Sugar Mountain, 1,200 foot drop
    (c) Cold Mountain Resort, 1,000 foot drop

Hitting The Slopes

For nearly 40 years now, the North Carolina mountains have provided snow skiers with thrilling action and entertainment. Glide on down the slopes of Tar Heel snow skiing with the answers to this quiz.

1. North Carolina's first ski resort was started by ranch owner Tom Alexander after he made a visit to the slopes at Hot Springs, Virginia. Starting with a tow made out of rope and a lot of faith, Alexander launched his Cataloochee Ski Area in what year?   (a) 1959   (b) 1962   (c) 1965

2. Located on Fie Top Mountain, Cataloochee is still going strong with nine slopes, night skiing, and snowboarding available. Not far from the Smoky Mountains and Blue Ridge Parkway, Cataloochee Ski Resort is in what valley?   (a) Maggie Valley   (b) Happy Valley   (c) Swiss Valley

3. Although snowfall in North Carolina can sometimes be capricious, automatic snowmaking machinery often picks up where nature leaves off. In what month of 1997 did a Tar Heel ski resort experience the latest seasonal closing to that date?   (a) March   (b) April   (c) May

4. Sugar Mountain near Banner Elk features a 1,200-foot vertical drop and 18 slopes for its patrons to enjoy. Carrying all those skiers are eight lifts, including two of the longest in North Carolina. About how many people per hour can these lifts transport to the top?   (a) 4,000   (b) 6,000   (c) 8,000

5. The highest ski resort in eastern North America, Ski Beech at Beech Mountain has 14 slopes and nine lifts. What elevation above sea level marks the top of this popular destination for skiers?
    (a) 6,000 feet   (b) 5,506 feet   (c) 4,800 feet

6. Wolf Laurel Ski Resort features 54 acres of skiable terrain, 14 runs, and 100 percent snowmaking capability. About 20 miles north of Asheville, Wolf Laurel is located near what town?
    (a) Mars Hill   (b) Black Mountain   (c) Trust

7. Located near Banner Elk, Hawksnest Resort at Seven Devils has 13 colorfully named runs. Skiers will find plenty of thrills as they glide down hills with names like "Sock-em-Dog," "Merlin," and what moniker like that of an airplane fighter pilot?   (a) Red Baron   (b) Top Gun   (c) Ace

8. Snow skiing has had a major impact on the North Carolina economy. According to figures gathered by Dr. Rick Kirkpatrick at Appalachian State University, in 1996 $100 million were pumped into Tar Heel cash registers by about how many ski enthusiasts?   (a) 307,458   (b) 598,241   (c) 641,000

9. Just three miles from Cashiers, Sapphire Valley Ski Area has a 425-foot vertical drop, night skiing, and snowboarding areas. With 20 acres of skiable area, Sapphire Valley is located in what county?
    (a) Jackson County   (b) Cherokee County   (c) Mitchell County

10. When snowfall comes to western North Carolina, even woodland trails can become ski areas. Downhill skiing also is known as Alpine skiing; what name does cross-country skiing also go by?
    (a) Ski aerobics   (b) Nordic skiing   (c) Trail gliding

11. Ski resorts and other western North Carolina businesses depend on snow reports to help maintain profitability. Weather data for the region is collected at the NOAA National Climatic Data Center located at 37 Battery Park Avenue in what Tar Heel city?
    (a) Hendersonville   (b) Boone   (c) Asheville

Hunting Down Some Answers

With a tradition of hunting that goes back for centuries, North Carolina continues to provide its citizens with game thanks to wise wildlife management and hunters who are conscientious about their sport. Go ahead and give this quiz your best shot.

1. The North Carolina Wildlife Resources Commission primarily funds its services with money collected from the sale of hunting, fishing and trapping licenses. How much does an annual, basic, hunting license for North Carolina residents cost? (a) $10 (b) $15 (c) $25

2. Hunters using shotguns to pursue their sporting activities in North Carolina may not, according to regulations, use a weapon larger than what gauge? (a) 10 gauge (b) 20 gauge (c) 5 gauge

3. Wild boar hunters in our state are allowed to take two boars per season. You may want to watch your shots, however, as it is illegal to bag a boar weighing less than how many pounds?
    (a) 70 pounds (b) 50 pounds (c) 30 pounds

4. During the April 10-May 8 season, bearded wild turkeys are a challenging and tasty quarry for hunters in some North Carolina counties. Which one of the following weapons may not be used hunting turkeys?
    (a) shotgun (b) pistol (c) bow and arrow

5. Requiring a high degree of stealth and skill, bow-and-arrow hunting has become increasingly popular. What type of bow is not allowed in North Carolina for this hunting?
    (a) crossbow (b) longbow (c) compound bow

6. Thanks to careful management, the deer population in North Carolina is healthy and high. What are the dates for the muzzle-loading rifle deer season in the eastern counties of North Carolina?
    (a) November 10-22 (b) October 5-10 (c) September 11-29

7. Many a Tar Heel farmboy has cut his hunting teeth pursuing rabbits with a trusty .22 caliber rifle. What are the dates for rabbit hunting in North Carolina this season (1993)?
    (a) November 21-February 27 (b) December 12-January 21 (c) January 1- February 28

8. Recognizing the need for hunting safety, NC Wildlife Resources rules require hunters of certain game in the state to wear a cap or garment made of what color cloth?
    (a) lime green (b) blaze orange (c) fire-engine red

9. When they explode from their cover, quail offer hunters high-speed excitement. What was the daily bag limit for quail hunters during the October 12-February 27, 1993 season?
    (a) 12 daily (b) 8 daily (c) 10 daily

10. Certain counties in North Carolina have game laws particular to their locale. For instance, it is unlawful in Madison County to hunt what type of fox? (a) red (b) gray (c) spotted

11. Just as well for the bears who live there, hunting is prohibited at a place called Bombing Range Bear Sanctuary in what North Carolina county named for the first English child born in America?
    (a) Washington County (b) Dare County (c) Jones County

12. In the North Carolina locations where bear hunting is allowed, hunters should be aware that they are not permitted to bag a bear smaller than what size?
    (a) 5 feet tall (b) 100 pounds in weight (c) 50 pounds in weight

13. When hunting on federal lands in North Carolina, in places such as Pea Island National Wildlife Refuge, or in any national forest, what game regulations must hunters obey?
    (a) NC state regulations (b) Recreation Commission regulations (c) federal regulations

14. Gray, red and fox squirrels are all fair game for hunters in North Carolina during each species' particular season. When gunning for squirrels, hunters should remember that it is unlawful to shoot at them when...? (a) they are on the ground (b) they are in the nest (c) they are sleeping

Tar Heel Hiking Trails

With many miles of hiking trails available, North Carolina has an abundance of places for tourists or Tar Heel natives to get up close and personal with our state's natural beauty. Pull on your hiking boots and see if you can gather a rucksack load of correct answers to this quiz.

1. Often referred to simply as the "UT," there is a 34-mile-long hiking trail that runs through one of North Carolina's four national forests. What is this trail, situated deep in the Piedmont near Badin Lake? (a) Uwharrie Trail   (b) Untamed Trail   (c) Unknown Trail

2. Several hiking and nature trails await visitors to Eno River State Park, including the Eno Trace Nature Trail and its native flora and fauna information posts. Name the city, also on the Eno, that lies just east of the park.   (a) Rocky Mount   (b) Greensboro   (c) Durham

3. Starting at a parking lot four miles south of Oregon Inlet on NC Highway 12, North Pond Trail features several bird-watching observation towers as it weaves its way along the Outer Banks dunes. What refuge contains North Pond Trail?
    (a) Bodie Island Refuge   (b) Pea Island National Wildlife Refuge   (c) Cape Hatteras Bird Refuge

4. A 3,800-acre tract of virgin timber, the Joyce Kilmer Memorial Forest features several trails to hike while enjoying the sight of hemlock and poplar trees that grow up to 150 feet tall. Not far from its beginning, the Joyce Kilmer Memorial Trail crosses what rushing mountain stream?
    (a) Linville River   (b) Pigeon River   (c) Little Santeetlah Creek

5. A three-mile trail encircling Jones Lake in Bladen County near Elizabethtown passes walkers through some unique woodlands that include several types of aromatic evergreens. Jones Lake is an unusual depression and geographical oddity called what?
    (a) Carolina Bay   (b) coast plain collapse   (c) peat pit

6. The Weymouth Woods Trails consist of five walks through landscape near the golf mecca of Southern Pines. From red-cockaded woodpeckers to huge fox squirrels, there are a variety of visual delights along these trails that are located in what geographical region of our state?
    (a) foothills   (b) Sandhills   (c) maritime forest

7. Called the longest marked footpath in the world, the Appalachian Trail stretches from Maine to Georgia. The "granddaddy" of North Carolina hiking trails, the Appalachian has how many of its 2,050 miles within our state's borders?   (a) 150   (b) 175   (c) 200

8. The Tanawha Trail winds for 13.5 miles from Price Park campground to the Beacon Heights overlook in our state's Blue Ridge Mountains. An excellent choice for birding, Tanawha Trail also passes by one of the last and most spectacular links in the Blue Ridge Parkway. What is this curving bridge called?
    (a) Linn Cove Viaduct   (b) The Curve Grande   (c) Round-the-Mountain Bridge

9. A round trip of 6.6 moderately difficult miles, the Hazel Creek Trail can be reached by boats rented at a nearby marina. What Great Smoky Mountains lake, formed by the highest dam in the Eastern United States, is the location for this North Carolina boating and hiking adventure?
    (a) Lake James   (b) Fontana Lake   (c) Lake Toxaway

10. Deep Creek in Swain County has for many years been a popular spot for camping and hiking the four-mile-long Deep Creek Loop through woods made famous by author Horace Kephart. Name the town, the seat of Swain County, just down the road from Deep Creek.
    (a) Bryson City   (b) Franklin   (c) Highlands

11. Beginning at a point 19.6 miles north of Oconaluftee Visitor Center on US Highway 441 (Newfound Gap Road), the Alum Cave Bluffs Trail is a rugged yet picturesque hike that is a 10-mile round trip., From the parking lot on US 441 where it begins, this trail rises to the peak of what mountain, the third-highest in the Smokies?   (a) Mount Blanc   (b) Mount Davis   (c) Mount LeConte

12. Roan Mountain on the Tennessee-North Carolina border is a unique natural area that offers hikers several treks to choose from, including the pleasant three-mile Cloudland Trail. Another trail here is named for the blooming plant that is Roan's real drawing card. What plant is this?
    (a) White azalea   (b) Catawba rhododendron   (c) Birdfoot violet

The Appalachian Trail

The Appalachian Trail offers hikers an intimate view of our state's mountain splendor. Take a tour of this venerable path with this quiz on North Carolina's portion of the Appalachian Trail.

1. With a total length of 2,157 miles, the Appalachian Trail weaves its way through 14 states. How long is North Carolina's portion? (a) 560 miles (b) 305.1 miles (c) 265 miles

2. Since its completion in 1937, the entire length of the Appalachian Trail has been traveled by more than 3,000 people. The first North Carolinian to hike the whole trail was Joseph Marion of Winston-Salem in 1972. In 1974, Marjorie Fowler of what Chatham County town became the second Tar Heel to accomplish this feat? (a) Pittsboro (b) Carbonton (c) Siler City

3. The Appalachian Trail enters North Carolina on the Tar Heel-Georgia border at Bly Gap. With an elevation of 3,840 feet, Bly Gap is located in what county seated by the town of Hayesville? (a) Cherokee County (b) Avery County (c) Clay County

4. In a truly amazing example of bravery and determination, visually impaired Bill Erwin completed the entire Appalachian Trail in 1990 with the help of his seeing-eye dog Orient. Author of *Blind Courage,* Bill is from what Alamance County town that once went by the name of Company Shops? (a) Burlington (b) Graham (c) Faucette

5. Eighty-six miles north of where the Appalachian Trail enters North Carolina from Georgia, hikers can freshen up at Fontana Village. A walk across nearby Fontana Dam gives a breathtaking view of its lake as well as the Little Tennessee River below. Fontana Dam holds what distinction in the Eastern United States? (a) highest dam (b) oldest dam (c) most costly dam

6. Appalachian Trail hikers passing through Swain County on a clear day will find spectacular views from the 5,375-foot heights of Charlies Bunion Mountain. One of the most popular sights to see from Charlies Bunion is 6,593-foot Mount LeConte off Highway 441 between Gatlinburg, Tennessee, and what Tar Heel town? (a) Cherokee (b) Bryson City (c) Balsam

7. Just a few miles from Mount Sequoyah, Appalachian Trail hikers can veer off on a trail spur that takes them to the summit of 6,621-foot high Mount Guyot. Mount Guyot takes its name from the 19th century geographer who first mapped much of the Smoky Mountains region. What was Guyot's first name? (a) Bernard (b) Irvin (c) Arnold

8. At 3,200 feet, Spivey Gap in Buncombe County marks the 250th mile that the Appalachian Trail meanders from south to north in our state. With just 55 miles left to go before it leaves North Carolina, that trail skirts what major Buncombe thoroughfare? (a) US 19 W (b) NC 9 (c) US 64 W

9. A heaven on earth, Cloudland Rhododendron Gardens await Appalachian Trail hikers and other visitors in Mitchell County. At an elevation of 6,285 feet, what mountain in Mitchell County is the home for both great hiking and the botanical splendor that Cloudland Gardens provide? (a) Black Mountain (b) Linville Mountain (c) Roan Mountain

10. Yellow Mountain Gap near the border of Avery and Mitchell counties is a spot where the Appalachian Trail meets the Overmountain Victory Trail. Used by early settlers to march into battle during the Revolutionary War, the Overmountain Victory Trail led patriots to what site where they defeated the British? (a) Guilford Courthouse (b) Kings Mountain (c) Camden

11. Elk Park marks the spot where the Appalachian Trail leaves North Carolina and heads northwestward into Tennessee. Name the county where 3,182-foot high Elk Park offers hikers lodging, food, and even a post office. (a) Avery County (b) Ashe County (c) Watauga County

September 1998

Stock-Car Stars

From early days when rough-and-tumble jalopies roared around dirt tracks, to its modern status as one of our state's premiere attractions, stock-car racing has deep roots in North Carolina. Head for the front of the pack as you answer the questions in this quiz.

1.   The roots of today's NASCAR Winston Cup can be traced back to 1949 when 33 cars went 200 laps around a 3/4-mile dirt oval in Charlotte during the first "Strictly Stock"-class auto race. Jim Roper in a Mecklenburg Motors '49 Lincoln won that inaugural event that saw what famous Petty family member crash on lap 107?   (a) Lee Petty   (b) Richard Petty   (c) Kyle Petty

2.   A colorful chap on and off the racetrack, NASCAR legend Junior Johnson won more than 50 Grand National events during his career. Inducted into the North Carolina Sports Hall of Fame in 1982, Johnson had learned the art of fast driving as a youth on backroads near what eastern Wilkes County town that he called home?   (a) Horse Gap   (b) Boomer   (c) Ronda

3.   A household name all over the world, Richard Petty of Level Cross has 200 NASCAR Grand National victories and a total of seven championships to his credit. "King" Richard took his first Grand National victory and a whopping $800 prize at the Charlotte Fairgrounds in what year?
     (a) 1956   (b) 1960   (c) 1963

4.   One of the nation's premiere sporting facilities, Charlotte Motor Speedway near Concord draws the largest crowds of any sports facility in North Carolina. In 1967, Hollywood camera crews filmed action at the World 600 for the feature film *Speedway* starring what popular singing star and Nancy Sinatra?   (a) Fabian   (b) Elvis   (c) Donovan

5.   NASCAR two-time champion Ned Jarrett of Hickory was known as "The Gentleman" during his driving career. These days, Ned's son is following in dad's footsteps by making regular visits to the winner's circle. Name Ned's son, runner-up in the 1997 Winston Cup championship.
     (a) Dale Jarrett   (b) Jeff Jarrett   (c) A.J. Jarrett

6.   A venerable stock-car racing track is located on US Highway 1 in rural Richmond County. Name this track, whose inaugural race on October 1965 saw Curtis Turner take an 11-second win over second place Cale Yarborough.
     (a) Rockingham Raceway   (b) North Carolina Motor Speedway   (c) Richmond County Raceway

7.   Another of NASCAR's pioneers was Chevy driver "Speedy" Thompson. A marvel of consistency, Thompson finished third in Grand National racing points each year from 1956-1959. Winner of the 1960 National 400 at Charlotte Motor Speedway, Thompson hailed from what Union County town?
     (a) Monroe   (b) Indian Trail   (c) New Salem

8.   Dodge driver Bobby Isaac of Catawba won many NASCAR races during the 1960s including a scorcher at Weaverville in the 1969 Western NC 500 where he overcame a five-lap deficit to win by four laps. What year was Bobby crowned Grand National champ?   (a) 1965   (b) 1969   (c) 1970

9.   The third NASCAR Grand National champion was Tar Heel Herb Thomas who hailed from Olivia in Harnett County. Crowned in 1951, Thomas edged Georgians Fonty and Tim Flock for the honor by wheeling what brand of stock car that has the same name as a geographical feature up north?
     (a) Dodge   (b) Hudson   (c) Plymouth

10. Another NASCAR Grand National champ from North Carolina was Jim Pascal, who took his first Grand National win in 1953 at Martinsville, Virginia, after 60 previous Grand National starts. Name the Guilford County town that Pascal called home.   (a) Bruce   (b) Center Grove   (c) High Point

Start Your Engines For Tar Heel Racing Quiz

From rough-and-tumble dirt tracks to steep-banked asphalt ovals where the racers seem to go ballistic, North Carolinians have a long-running need for speed. Put your stock car memory's pedal to the metal with this quiz.

1. In 1924 what may be considered one of the "granddaddies" of North Carolina auto racing tracks, Charlotte Speedway, was constructed just south of Charlotte in Pineville. A mile and a quarter long, this nationally recognized facility was paved with what material?
    (a) gravel   (b) concrete   (c) wooden planks

2. The first Grand National stock car race was won by Jim Roper in a Lincoln on July 19, 1949. The dusty oval that this historic event took place on was just off Wilkinson Boulevard near Douglas Airport in what Tar Heel metropolis?   (a) Charlotte   (b) Raleigh   (c) Greensboro

3. A pioneer in the stock car racing industry, Junior Johnson won 50 Grand National races in his own right and is today a highly successful race team owner. In his youth, Junior honed his driving skills hauling what commodity through the Wilkes County wilds?   (a) flowers   (b) corn squeezins   (c) pizzas

4. Stock car racing superlatives can scarcely describe the incredible career of 200-race winner Richard Petty. Hailing from Level Cross in Randolph County, "King Richard" was born in what year?
    (a) 1945   (b) 1930   (c) 1937

5. Following in the footsteps of his father, Lee Petty, Richard took to the track at an early age. His first Grand National win was February 28, 1960, at the old Charlotte Fairgrounds. What make of car did Richard Petty drive to that victory?   (a) Plymouth   (b) Ford   (c) Chevy

6. Ten years after that Charlotte Fairgrounds triumph, Richard Petty would win the last Grand National stock car race to be held on a dirt track. Dubbed the Home State 200, this event was held on September 30, 1970, in what Wake County town?   (a) Garner   (b) Raleigh   (c) Willow Springs

7. Tar Heel stock car driver Buddy Baker is hard to miss at 6 feet 5 inches tall. Retired now, but with many Grand National and Winston Cup victories under his belt, Buddy is the son of what other racing legend?
    (a) Bob Baker   (b) Buster Baker   (c) Buck Baker

8. Another "chip off the old block" is the son of the late racing great Ralph Earnhardt, Winston Cup racing champ Dale Earnhardt. A fierce competitor, Dale's let-it-all-hang-out driving style has led some of his peers to give him what nickname?   (a) Ironhead   (b) Cannonball   (c) Bulletproof

9. Proving that fast cars have universal appeal, the North Carolina Motor Speedway in Rockingham saw two-time Formula One champ Jim Clark try his hand at stock cars in a 500-mile race held there in October 1967. Quite a ways from home, "wee" Jimmy hailed from what country?
    (a) Wales   (b) Scotland   (c) Australia

10. In 1960 the inaugural World 600 stock car race was held at Charlotte Motor Speedway near Harrisburg in Cabarrus County. Name the driver who piloted his Chevy to victory at the new 1.5 mile tri-oval in this premiere event.   (a) Joe Lee Johnson   (b) Tiny Lund   (c) Cotton Owens

11. In the late 1960s Hollywood crews came to Harrisburg and shot a film entitled *Speedway* that included plenty of World 600 action. What swivel-hipped singer played the starring role in that production?   (a) Buddy Holly   (b) Frankie Avalon   (c) Elvis Presley

12. North Wilkesboro Speedway has been the site of many thrilling stock car races, including the 1986 Holly Farms 400 where Darrell Waltrip gunned his Chevrolet to victory over Geoff Bodine. How long is the race track at North Wilkesboro?   (a) 1.8 miles long   (b) .625 miles long   (c) 2 miles long

13. The last Grand National stock car race to be held at Hickory Speedway on dirt was April 1967. Richard Petty pocketed $1,000 for his win at this banked oval built right beside what major North Carolina highway?   (a) US 64/70 W   (b) NC 49   (c) NC 226

14. Born on a farm near Newton in 1932, Ned Jarrett earned two national stock car championships before becoming a successful broadcast racing analyst. A credit to his home state in every respect, Jarrett was long ago given what nickname by his friends?
    (a) "The Gentleman"   (b) "Old Smoothie"   (c) "Mr. Ambassador"

Stating The Facts About Our Parks

North Carolina has 42 state parks, natural areas and recreation areas encompassing nearly 135,000 acres. Do you know which one has the highest sand dune on the East Coast? Which was named for a former North Carolina senator? Which was the site of an 11-hour battle?

1. Bordered by the Cape Fear River and the Snows Cut canal on the Intracoastal Waterway, Carolina Beach State Park has carnivorous plants and a 50-foot-high sand dune named Sugarloaf. In what county can this park be found? (a) New Hanover County (b) Beaufort County (c) Dare County

2. Located in Wayne County on land once occupied by Tuscarora and Saponi Indians, Cliffs of the Neuse State Park has an 11-acre lake, nature trails and, of course, the 90-foot cliffs for which it was named. What type of body of water is the Neuse? (a) tidal creek (b) natural springs (c) river

3. Hammocks Beach State Park offers good surf fishing and is the summer nesting ground for scores of loggerhead turtles. What 892-acre Onslow County island is home to this park?
   (a) Bobcat Island (b) Bear Island (c) Turtle Island

4. Fort Macon State Park not only has a restored fort overlooking Beaufort Inlet, but is an excellent place to study the coastal environment. What war saw an 11-hour battle rage for control of Fort Macon?
   (a) Revolutionary War (b) War of 1812 (c) Civil War

5. In 1915 the General Assembly passed a bill making Mount Mitchell State Park the first in the state. A politician named Locke Craig was instrumental in saving Mitchell from complete deforestation. What office did Craig hold? (a) Governor (b) Congressman (c) Senator

6. Hikers who enjoy Crowders Mountain State Park might be interested to know it is the remnant of a 500 million-year-old range of peaks that once dominated the area. Which of these Gaston County towns is closest to Crowders Mountain? (a) Mount Holly (b) Cramerton (c) Gastonia

7. Hang-glider pilots from all over flock to Jockey's Ridge State Park to leap off the highest sand dune in the eastern United States. What Outer Banks hamlet borders the park?
   (a) Buxton (b) Nags Head (c) Avon

8. Located on land donated by President Theodore Roosevelt's grandchildren, Theodore Roosevelt State Natural Area is a preserved barrier-island ecosystem. What county is it in?
   (a) Carteret County (b) Dare County (c) Bladen County

9. In the northwest corner of North Carolina, the New River flows through a state park named in its honor. This river, a favorite of canoeists, has a special claim to fame. Is it the...
   (a) rockiest river in North America (b) deepest river in North America (c) oldest river in North America

10. Which "Jordan" are the 13,900-acre Jordan Lake and the Jordan Lake State Recreation Area named for? (a) Michael Jordan (b) B. Everett Jordan (c) Jordan River

11. Boone's Cave State Park, on the Yadkin River in Davidson County, is located on land once frequented by what famous member of that clan?
    (a) Daniel Boone (b) Beth Boone (c) T. Boone Pickens

12. Named for James B. Duke, Lake James State Park is on Lake James, which is fed by what two rivers?
    (a) French Broad and Pigeon rivers (b) Tar and Haw rivers (c) Linville and Catawba rivers

Roughing It—Tar Heel Style

Whether your idea of outdoor accommodations revolves around an army surplus pup tent or a recreational vehicle, North Carolina has a place to set up camp. Dream of nighttime breezes in the pines as you answer the questions to this quiz on Tar Heel campgrounds.

1. Morgan's Mountain Retreat Campground offers its guests everything from hot showers to church services. Open May through October, this campground is located near what Watauga County town famous for its wayward winds and Green Park Inn? (a) Windy Gap   (b) Blowing Rock   (c) Hurricane Mountain

2. Hickory Nut Falls Family Campground has its own playground and welcomes both tent and trailer campers. This campground is located just a short distance from what popular Rutherford County tourist attraction—once the site of a celebrated annual sports car hill climb?
(a) Frog Level   (b) The Ellenboro Stretch   (c) Chimney Rock

3. Located near Billy's Seafood Market on Colington Island, Colington Park Campground on the Outer Banks can accommodate more than 50 campers. Fishing and crabbing in the waters of what Dare County sound are a popular pastime for visitors to this campground?
(a) Pamlico Sound   (b) Roanoke Sound   (c) Core Sound

4. Riverside Campground in the Beaufort County village of Belhaven features its own boat ramp and water-skiing facilities. Campers, fishermen, and skiers at Riverside can exercise their skills at what adjacent waterway? (a) Pungo River   (b) Catawba River   (c) New River

5. Just a couple of miles from Lake Norman, Cross Country Campground is located on Highway 150 in Lincoln County. What town with the same name as Colorado's capital is Cross Country near?
(a) Boulder   (b) Dallas   (c) Denver

6. Blue Ridge Foothills Family Campground offers its guests a camp store and fishing pond. Located on John's Pond Road, this campground is located in what town serving as the seat of Surry County?
(a) Mount Airy   (b) Dobson   (c) Low Gap

7. Visitors to Holly Ridge Family Campground on River Road in northern Yadkin County can enjoy hot showers along with a nature trail and playground for children. Holly Ridge Campground is located in what town, named for a famous explorer who also camped here in our state's early days?
(a) Crockett   (b) Boonville   (c) Daniel Town

8. River Bend RV Park in Transylvania County offers cool mountain breezes and plenty of shade for its patrons. Open April through October, this campground is located close to what body of water, which is the largest privately owned lake in western North Carolina?
(a) Lake Toxaway   (b) Lake James   (c) Lake Wylie

9. A member of the North Carolina Campground Owners Association, Happy Holiday RV Park and Campground is located in the heart of our state's Great Smoky Mountains. Name the Swain County tourist haven where Happy Holidays awaits your tent or RV.
(a) Bryson City   (b) Cherokee   (c) Flat Rock

10. Minutes from Green River kayaking and fishing at the base of Tryon Mountain, Silver Creek Campground has everything from a swimming pool to bait. Although its mailing address is Mill Spring, this campground is just shy of what town, which serves as Polk's county seat?
(a) Lake Adger   (b) Cooper Gap   (c) Columbus

11. Visitors to Cartoogehaye Creek Campground in Macon County may be interested to know that the site's unusual name means "corn fields" in the Cherokee language. Near what town, the seat of Macon County and a renowned gemstone center, is this campground located?
(a) Franklin   (b) Otto   (c) Gneiss

12. Open April through October, Raccoon Holler Campground in Glendale Springs has plenty of picnic tables and firewood for those outdoor feasts. Folks camping at Raccoon Holler will want to see nearby Holy Trinity Church where artist Ben Long's famous fresco depicts what Biblical scene?
(a) Noah's Ark   (b) The Last Supper   (c) The Resurrection of Christ

Taking An Artsy Look At The Tar Heel State

From the mountains to the Piedmont to the coast, there's certainly much to give inspiration to any artist who makes North Carolina his home. And we're fortunate that our state has always placed an emphasis on cultural enrichment. It's a philosophy that has produced many talented Tar Heel artists over the years. How well do you know the arts in North Carolina? Take the following quiz and find out.

1. Considered by some to be North Carolina's first artist, John White was part of an expedition sent here in 1585 to record in picture and word the flora, fauna and Native Americans of our state. In addition to his artistic skills, White also achieve notoriety as governor of what colony?
    (a) Lost Colony   (b) Colony of Georgia   (c) Colony of Rhode Island

2. Always in the forefront in supporting the arts, North Carolina state government formed what agency by executive order in 1964?
    (a) Carolina Artists Society   (b) Council On Fine Art   (c) North Carolina Arts Council

3. During the Great Depression, Raleigh became the first city in the United States to have a federal-supported arts center. What government agency made this possible?
    (a) Federal Artists Relief   (b) Federal Art Project   (c) Federal Cultural Relief Agency

4. During the governorship of Bob Scott, our state government became the first in the nation to have a cabinet-level department devoted to furthering art, the Department of Cultural Resources. What year was this department established?   (a) 1971   (b) 1968   (c) 1973

5. Still another first for North Carolina art was achieved when Winston-Salem set up the nation's first local arts council in the same year that Harry Truman was inaugurated for his second term as president. What was the year?   (a) 1950   (b) 1949   (c) 1952

6. Long a fixture on the Carolina arts scene, the Penland School of Crafts has been in operation near the North Toe River for decades. What county would that put the Penland School in?
    (a) Mitchell County   (b) Cherokee County   (c) Hyde County

7. Seagrove, in the Piedmont region of North Carolina, is an area well known by artists and collectors for the pottery and ceramics made there. Which one of these other attractions is nearest Seagrove?
    (a) Tanglewood Park   (b) Carowinds   (c) North Carolina Zoological Park

8. Former motorcycle daredevil Mel Steele is a successful artist who paints rural Carolina scenes in such detail that his work sometimes seems almost photographic. What is this popular method of painting detailed rustic scenes called?   (a) Art Rural   (b) Rural Realism   (c) Agricultural Expressionism

9. Davidson sculptor Tom Clark's fanciful imagination has led him to create a popular series of collectible statuettes depicting what type of beings?   (a) Gnomes   (b) Cats   (c) Birds

10. Numerous are the distinguished artistic alumni who attended what Buncombe County arts school that had its heyday from 1933-1956?
    (a) Asheville Art School   (b) Biltmore School Of The Arts   (c) Black Mountain College

11. Many people have seen examples of black North Carolina-born artist Selma Burke's work. Selma was responsible for the original design for Franklin Roosevelt's head on what piece of US coinage?
    (a) half-dollar   (b) dime   (c) silver dollar

12. The beautiful Folk Art Center by the Blue Ridge Parkway near Asheville not only exhibits extraordinary handicrafts, but is also home for what organization?   (a) Southern Highland Handicraft Guild
    (b) Mountain Artists Association   (c) Blue Ridge Craft Guild

The Undisputed King Of Outdoor Drama

With twice as many outdoor dramas performed each season within its borders as any other state, North Carolina may rightly proclaim itself the nation's capital of this form of entertainment. Take center stage, and go for the bravos with your answers to this quiz.

1. North Carolina is the birthplace of historic outdoor drama in the US. In 1993, how many of these entertaining and informative productions were staged in our state? (a) 20 (b) 11 (c) 5

2. The nation's first outdoor drama was written by Lillington's Paul Green. Name this work which has been performed at Manteo every year (except during World War II) since 1937.
   (a) *The Lost Colony* (b) *Graveyard of the Atlantic* (c) *Sir Walter Raleigh*

3. Proving that outdoor dramas are an essential part of the Tar Heel tourist trade, figures indicate that close to 300,000 people attended these shows in our state in 1993. What was the total economic impact for North Carolina of all these outdoor theater-goers? (a) $20 million (b) $30 million (c) $80 million

4. Keeping a finger on the pulse of outdoor drama not only in our state but across the nation, the Institute of Outdoor Drama is a research and advisory agency of UNC. What campus of the UNC system is home for the Institute? (a) Greensboro (b) Charlotte (c) Chapel Hill

5. Prolific author of more than 40 plays, Kermit Hunter wrote the story of the Cherokee Indians in his outdoor drama *Unto These Hills*. Which one of the following Native American chiefs is highlighted in this popular outdoor drama produced by the Cherokee Historical Association?
   (a) Tsali (b) Geronimo (c) Manteo

6. *Unto These Hills* has not only been acclaimed artistically, it has also been a great commercial success since its premiere in the summer of 1950. Take a guess at about how many people attended the play in 1993. (a) 25,000 (b) 40,000 (c) more than 100,000

7. Another popular outdoor drama by Kermit Hunter is *Horn in the West*. Depicting life in the Appalachians during the American Revolution, this production has as one of its main characters what famous pioneer who gave his name to the town where the play is performed?
   (a) Kit Carson (b) Daniel Boone (c) Jim Bridger

8. A moving religious passion play penned by J.T. Adams, *Worthy is the Lamb* features a symphony orchestra and more than 150 actors. *Worthy is the Lamb* is put on each summer in Swansboro near the banks of what river? (a) Cape Fear (b) French Broad (c) White Oak

9. Last year nearly 5,000 people attended performances of the outdoor drama *Song of Liberty*. The story of relationships between the races in Duplin County during the Civil War, this play is performed in what town that is the county seat of Duplin? (a) Kenansville (b) Tin City (c) Rose Hill

10. Written by Randolph Umberger and produced by Robeson Historical Drama, *Strike at the Wind* is an outdoor play that tells the story of Indian outlaw Henry Lowrie. Staged in the Robeson County town of Pembroke, *Strike at the Wind* focuses on what Native American tribe indigenous to that area?
    (a) Cherokee Indians (b) Lumbee Indians (c) Blackfoot Indians

11. Produced each summer from late June to mid-August at Snow Camp, *The Sword of Peace* tells the story of members of the Society of Friends and their belief in nonviolence during the Revolution. What is another name for the Society of Freinds? (a) Quakers (b) Amish (c) Mormons

12. Staged each June just outside the Union County town of Waxhaw, *Listen and Remember* is an outdoor drama depicting the rich history of the Waxhaw region. One of the central characters is the 7th president of the US. Who is this lanky leader? (a) Abe Lincoln (b) Thomas Jefferson (c) Andrew Jackson

13. The little town of Autryville just east of Fayetteville stages the outdoor drama *Micajah* each July to remember the Micajah Autry, who founded the hamlet. Born in 1793, Autry would later go to Texas and lose his life in 1836 at what battle? (a) Battle of Dallas (b) the Alamo (c) Battle of the Rio Grande

14. Depicting the events that led to the first declaration of independence from England by an American colony, *First for Freedom* is staged in the town of Halifax. What famous document inspired this play?
    (a) Halifax Resolves (b) Carolina Conventions (c) North Carolina Declarations

15. *From This Day Forward* is about the religious sect the Waldensians and their founding of Valdese in 1893. Name the European country that the Waldensians left to come here.
    (a) Sweden (b) Bosnia (c) Italy

Mayberry, U.S.A.

Recall the days of Sheriff Andy Taylor, zealous deputy Barney, charming Aunt Bee, and the wholesome folks in America's favorite TV town as you guess the answers to this quiz on "The Andy Griffith Show."

1. Shown for eight seasons, "The Andy Griffith Show" aired nearly 250 episodes. The first show titled "The New Housekeeper," which introduced Aunt Bee debuted on October 3 of what year?
    (a) 1959   (b) 1960   (c) 1962

2. In addition to his funny portrayal of Sheriff Andy Taylor, Tar Heel native Andy Griffith perfected the lead dramatic role in what outdoor play?
    (a) *Unto These Hills*   (b) *Strike at the Wind*   (c) *The Lost Colony*

3. Illustrating the enormous influence of the Mayberry mystique, a museum has been established in Andy Griffith's hometown. Name this Surry County community.   (a) Mount Ulla   (b) Mount Airy   (c) Sparta

4. Called the "Heart of Mayberry," the sweet character Aunt Bee nurtured everyone with whom she came in contact. New York native Frances Bavier, who played Andy's beloved aunt, retired to Siler City. In what year did she pass away, at the age of 86?   (a) 1989   (b) 1991   (c) 1992

5. On maps drawn to locate the fictional town, visitors would find Mayberry in the northern Piedmont not far south of Interstate 85. This would put Mayberry between what two major North Carolina cities?
    (a) Statesville and Winston-Salem   (b) Charlotte and Salisbury   (c) Greensboro and Raleigh

6. Some call it coincidental, others say by design, that within 30 miles of Mount Airy are three towns with names similar to three Mayberry characters: Lawsonville is teamed up with barber Floyd Lawson, Walkertown with Ellie Walker, and Crumpler with what Mayberry school teacher?
    (a) Helen Crump   (b) Judy Crumpler   (c) Darlene Crumpelman

7. Although folks in Mayberry enjoyed sitting on their porches, soaking up the small-town atmosphere, they did tune in to watch "Colonel Tim's Talent Time." What fictional Raleigh TV station broadcast this show?   (a) WBTV   (b) WALH   (c) WASG

8. Each year for the past 10 years, Mount Airy has sponsored an annual celebration called Mayberry Days. A gathering of Mayberry fans and stars, the jamboree takes place the last weekend of what month?   (a) May   (b) September   (c) November

9. Lodging in Mount Airy includes the Mayberry Motor Inn on US Highway 52 North where paraphernalia from the TV show is on exhibit. A replica of what type vehicle that Andy and Barney drove is parked outside the motel?   (a) 1963 Ford Galaxie   (b) 1960 Ford Fairlane   (c) 1962 Chevrolet Impala

10. On "The Andy Griffith Show," Mayberry had a "sister city" that was home to Aunt Bee's cousin Edgar, as well as the spot where Goober went to see the French film *La View Du Femme*. Name this town whose name is the reverse of a prominent Surry County landmark.
    (a) Mount Holly   (b) Mount Pilot   (c) Mount Taylor

11. All good things must eventually come to an end, as "The Andy Griffith Show" did with its 249th airing on March 25, 1968. Name the title of this concluding episode in which Mayberry's favorite service-station mechanic looked for love.   (a) "Gomer's Girl"   (b) "Kerley's Cutie"   (c) "A Girl for Goober"

Music Makers

From a dulcimer's sweet mountain melodies to the spirited strains of a Highland bagpipe, tap your foot to some old-time tunes as you sound out the correct answers to this quiz on North Carolina's rich folk music heritage.

1. From 1916 until 1918, internationally known musician Cecil J. Sharp toured southern Appalachia looking for the origins of folk songs. Sharp spent 14 weeks in North Carolina, where he found 559 tunes. What county, whose town of Hot Springs tallied 102 ditties alone, accounted for nearly half of these songs?
   (a) Madison County   (b) Jackson County   (c) Haywood County

2. North Carolina mountain music master Wiley Morris of Black Mountain died in 1990. Around 1940, Wiley and his brother Zeke were among the first musicians to record what song about a mountain "all covered with snow"?   (a) "Rocky Top"   (b) "Brown Mountain Lights"   (c) "On Top of Old Smoky"

3. One of North Carolina's largest folk get-togethers, Asheville's Mountain Dance and Folk Festival dates back to 1927. What Buncombe County legend, known as the "Squire of South Turkey Creek," began the festival to showcase hill country culture?
   (a) Michael Wayne Hoover   (b) Bascom Lamar Lunsford   (c) P. Wesley Grooms

4. Introduced in 1989, the North Carolina Arts Council presents several Folk Heritage Awards to outstanding folk artists. In 1998, fiddler Smith McInnis of Raeford was a recipient. What song is not only one of McInnis' favorites, but also his nickname and the name of the county in which he resides?
   (a) "The Hoke County Special"   (b) "Robeson County Rambler"   (c) "Franklin County Fireball"

5. A true North Carolina folk song legend, the late Delli Norton of Madison County lived to be more than 90 years old. Among her many accomplishments was a performance at the 1982 World's Fair in what city?   (a) Berlin   (b) Knoxville   (c) New York

6. Born in the Laurel Creek community near Beech Mountain, long-time mountain music maker Leonard Glenn was a member of Tommy Hunter's Carolina String Band in the 1950s. Besides his ability to play, Glenn has contributed to the art of folk music by making banjos and what other wood-and-metal strings folk instrument?   (a) Dulcimer   (b) Viola   (c) Ukulele

7. Master fiddler and fiddle maker, the late folk music talent Thomas Hunter of Madison County performed professionally by age 12 way back in 1931. A pioneer of folk music radio broadcasting, Hunter often played with Zeke and Wiley Morris on what Asheville radio station?
   (a) WWNC   (b) WBT   (c) WRAL

8. A rollicking little folk tune called "Roll on the Ground" speaks of "workin' on the railroad for a dollar a day" and "eatin' soda crackers 'til the wind blow them away." This delightful ditty also makes reference to what North Carolina city, home of the Folk Art Center?   (a) Brevard   (b) Asheville   (c) Waynesville

9. "Naomi Wise" is a folk tune that tells the tale of a maiden killed by a villainous lover named Lewis. As the song tells it, Naomi was buried in what North Carolina county in the center of our state?
   (a) Forsyth County   (b) Guilford County   (c) Randolph County

10. Composed by O.L. Coffey in 1939, the folk tune "The North Carolina Hills" lauds the beauty of our Tar Heel landscape. Coffey had plenty of hills from which to draw his musical inspiration, since he called Shulls Mill in what county home?   (a) Watauga County   (b) Burke County   (c) Polk County

11. Composed by D.W. Fletcher, this song tells of "cold corn bread" for breakfast and lice "long as a rail" in a certain Tar Heel jailhouse. Added to our folk song repertoire as early as 1890, it bemoans the harsh conditions in the jail of what city, known for its Methodist university?
    (a) Durham   (b) Winston-Salem   (c) Raleigh

The Beat Goes On

From a rousing overture to a somber nocturne, strike the right chord with correct answers to this quiz on classical music.

1. Since 1946, the North Carolina Symphony has traveled to schools around the state introducing children to classical music. Since the inception of the "Symphony Day" program, how many students have been visited by the orchestra?   (a) 3,000,000   (b) 1,000,000   (c) 250,000

2. Founded in 1972 as the Durham Boys' Choir, the North Carolina Boys' Choir was given its current name in 1983 by Governor Jim Hunt. Among its numerous performances, the choir has sung for the University of North Carolina Center for Public Television, as well as what house of worship on the Duke University campus?   (a) Duke Abbey   (b) Duke Chapel   (c) Duke Monastery

3. Based in Winston-Salem, the Piedmont Opera Theatre has performed since 1978 and has made two performances each year since 1984. Volunteers from the Triad area and students from what renowned school contribute their time and talents to this group?   (a) North Carolina School of the Arts   (b) Carolina Arts Academy   (c) North Carolina Opera Organization

4. The Carolina Chamber Symphony was founded in 1993 to perform chamber orchestra music from the 18th, 19th, and 20th centuries. In addition to concerts, the group also makes educational performances available for school children. What city, founded just after the post-Romantic music era, is home for these musicians?   (a) Charlotte   (b) Winston-Salem   (c) New Bern

5. The Brevard Music Center's roots extend back to 1936 when it was founded by James Christian Pfohl. Each summer the school hosts more than 400 students age 14 and older who study music under the tutelage of 120 instructors. Brevard Music Center is located in what county?   (a) Avery County   (b) Transylvania County   (c) Buncombe County

6. Opera Carolina in Charlotte celebrated its 50th anniversary in May 1999 with a gala gathering that featured an opera by Johann Strauss the Younger in the Belk Theatre. Name this opus whose title means "the bat."   (a) *Der Rosenkavalier*   (b) *Fra Diavolo*   (c) *Die Fledermaus*

7. The Salisbury Symphony Orchestra presented its first concert in November 1967, which was a result of collaboration between educators Dr. Samuel Duncan and Dr. Donald C. Dearborn. The orchestra played for the first time in Keppel Auditorium on what campus?   (a) Gardner-Webb University   (b) Catawba College   (c) Davidson College

8. Organized in 1964, the Western Piedmont Symphony held its first rehearsal at Lenoir-Rhyne College under the guidance of founding music director and conductor Albert Chaffoo. What Catawba County town is home base for the group?   (a) Hickory   (b) Lenoir   (c) Newton

9. One of the country's top choral groups, Bel Canto Company recently celebrated its 17th anniversary. Based in Greensboro, Bel Canto Company is led by David Pegg and has performed at many festivals including what famous Charleston, South Carolina, gathering?   (a) Carolina Choral Jam   (b) Charleston Choral Fest   (c) Spoleto Festival USA

10. North Carolina has produced many fine musicians, one of whom is Lamar Stringfield. In 1928, Stringfield won what prize for this suite "From the Southern Mountains?"   (a) Nobel Prize   (b) Carnegie Prize   (c) Pulitzer Prize

11. One of the finest violinists in North Carolina, Fritz Gearhart, holds a master's degree from the Eastman School of Music and has taught for more than seven years at the university level. Gearhart is on the staff of what institute of higher learning located in Greenville?   (a) Peace College   (b) Johnson C. Smith University   (c) East Carolina University

A 'Fair' Test Of Knowledge

The North Carolina State Fair celebrated its 125th anniversary October 16-25, 1992 at the State Fairgrounds in Raleigh. The 10-day festival of Tar Heel agriculture has become an annual affair for many of the state's families, offering a little bit of something for everyone. To test your knowledge on the Fair's first years, give the following quiz a try.

1. In antebellum Raleigh, the first North Carolina State Fair was held with the stated purpose being "a cattle show and exhibit of domestic manufactures." What year was the first North Carolina State Fair held?   (a) 1875   (b) 1853   (c) 1775

2. What was the name of the group that sponsored that initial State Fair?
   (a) North Carolina State Agricultural Society   (b) Farmers For Fairs   (c) Carolina Cattlemen

3. No doubt with the harvest schedule in mind, in what month is the North Carolina State Fair traditionally held?   (a) September   (b) October   (c) November

4. From 1873 until 1925, the NC State Fair was held at a 55-acre site on Hillsborough Street in Raleigh. Which one of these institutions of higher learning is located nearest that plot?
   (a) Peace College   (b) Wake Technical Community College   (c) North Carolina State University

5. In 1928, at a future governor's urging, the North Carolina Legislature approved a 200-acre site that to this day is still the State Fairgrounds. Who was that "fair-minded" fellow who would later be our governor from 1941-45?   (a) J. Melville Broughton   (b) Robert Cherry   (c) Oliver Gardner

6. Political speeches have long been a North Carolina State Fair tradition. In 1905, a certain "rough-riding" United States president stirred up the crowd. Who was that chief executive?
   (a) Grover Cleveland   (b) William H. Taft   (c) Theodore Roosevelt

7. In 1907, another politician, nicknamed "The Commoner," addressed the State Fair throngs. This silver-tongued orator was a three-time loser as the Democratic nominee for president. Who was he?
   (a) William Jennings Bryan   (b) Thomas Dewey   (c) Josephus Daniels

8. A large reunion of Confederate veterans gave the 1903 NC State Fair a look at many tattered gray and butternut uniforms. Who was our governor when all of those "Johnnies" got together?
   (a) Terry Sanford   (b) Charles Aycock   (c) Elwood P. Suggins

9. Two gentlemen named Ely and McCurdy thrilled the 1910 NC State Fair by displaying the first machine of what type to be seen in the city of Raleigh?   (a) motorcycle   (b) combine   (c) aeroplane

10. Instrumental in the success of the NC State Fair are the many 4-H clubs located throughout North Carolina. What do the four "H's" stand for?   (a) Happiness, Horses, Horticulture, Home
    (b) Hard work, Heart, Hogs, Hens   (c) Head, Heart, Hands, Health

11. The NC State Fair was not held in 1918 because of World War I and the outbreak of what major disease epidemic in this country?   (a) mumps   (b) influenza   (c) yellow fever

12. Hailing from Columbus County, the musically gifted twins Millie and Christine Monemia entertained folks at the first NC State Fair, toured Europe to wide acclaim, then came back home for the 1895 State Fair. What type of twins were they?   (a) Siamese   (b) identical   (c) fraternal

13. Running the NC State Fair is a big job. What North Carolina government agency oversees the State Fair?   (a) Department of Entertainment   (b) Department of Agriculture   (c) Department of Tourism

Tar Heel Celebrations

Nearly every day of the year a celebration or festival takes place somewhere in North Carolina. Join in the merrymaking as you guess the answers to this quiz on Tar Heel jamborees.

1. August is the month for square dance fans to enjoy the Mountain Dance and Folk Festival. A favorite since 1927, this annual event has been called one of the nation's top 100 festivals and takes place in what "Land of the Sky" city? (a) Bryson City (b) Asheville (c) Waynesville

2. For folks whose eyes light up at a bit of shining armor, the Carolina Renaissance Festival should fill the bill. The 1997 event spanned seven weekends during October and November in what Mecklenburg County college town? (a) Davidson (b) Mooresville (c) Wingate

3. Fried fish, fun, and hush puppies by the carload mark Gastonia's annual fall festival. Featuring everything from catfish races to face painting, this 12-year-old jamboree goes by what name?
    (a) Fish Camp Slam (b) Catfish Celebration (c) Fish Camp Jam

4. For a quarter century the Smoky Mountain Folk Festival has entertained visitors with the finest in Southern Appalachian music and dance each Labor Day weekend. What Haywood County resort is the site of this popular event? (a) Cherokee (b) Lake Junaluska (c) Cataloochee Resort

5. Traditionally held the first weekend in May, the Salter Path Clam and Scallop Festival is an excellent way to chow down on some great seafood and take in some good tunes. Don't get lost on your way to Salter Path as you travel the sandy soil of what county? (a) Craven (b) Carteret (c) New Hanover

6. December's chilly winds and sea mists don't dampen the spirits of visitors to the Core Sound Decoy Festival. Staged to benefit the core Sound Waterfowl Museum, the festival has been called the area's largest off-season event and is held on what island? (a) Harkers Island (b) Core Banks (c) Beaufort

7. Each July, for more than 30 years, revelers and dog fanciers have gathered at the picturesque Polk County town of Saluda for a festival of food, crafts, and serious hound dog howling. Name this popular celebration of the canine species. (a) Blue Tick Bash (b) Plott Hound Jamboree (c) Coon Dog Days

8. The largest town in Tyrrell County, Columbia kicks up its heels each October with a festival, parade, and church baked goods sale that can bring out as many as 5,000 folks from our state's least populous county. This celebration takes its name from what river that flows through Columbia?
    (a) Tar River Festival (b) Scuppernong River Festival (c) Alligator-Pungo Days

9. Located on the South Fork River just west of Charlotte, cotton mill town McAdenville has for 35 years celebrated Christmas by decorating every tree, house, and bush in sight with lights. Drawing 2 million visitors annually to its display, McAdenville is located in what county?
    (a) Gaston (b) Cabarrus (c) Union

10. A fantastic fleet of imaginatively decorated boats as well as a festival of arts and crafts mark the annual North Carolina Holiday Flotilla held in late November. What beach, southeast of Wilmington, is the location of this popular event? (a) Long Beach (b) Carolina Beach (c) Wrightsville Beach

Christmas In The Old North State

The Christmas season in North Carolina brings out the best our citizens have to offer in celebrations and decorations. Take a Tar Heel yuletide tour with this quiz of just a few of the many Tar Heel towns that do Christmas right.

1. "Christmas at Connemara" will include a tour of Carl Sandburg's famous home, cookies baked from Mrs. Sandburg's recipes and hot cider. What foothills town is the location for Sandburg's Connemara? (a) Flat Rock   (b) Waynesville   (c) Tryon

2. Christmas visitors to Garner will enjoy seeing that town's Greenfield Park illuminated with more than 350,000 lights. Not far from Raleigh, Garner is located in what county? (a) Orange County   (b) Johnston County   (c) Wake County

3. Located about six miles southeast of Concord in Cabarrus County, Reed Gold Mine will celebrate Christmas with 19th-century decorations and special music. What highway off US 601 will take visitors to this golden yuletide event?   (a) NC 49   (b) NC 200   (c) NC 84

4. Guilford Courthouse National Military Park near Greensboro will display 6,000 Christmas luminaria to honor soldiers who fought in this crucial battle. In what war did the Battle of Guilford Courthouse occur?   (a) Revolutionary War   (b) Civil War   (c) War of 1812

5. The coastal town of Swansboro will celebrate its Christmas season with a parade of decorated boats that will travel from Emerald Isle Bridge to Swansboro Turning Basin. What waterway will these beautiful craft take on their ride?   (a) New River   (b) Neuse River   (c) Intracoastal Waterway

6. The North Carolina Transportation Museum at Spencer will create a festive holiday mood by offering train rides with Santa, Christmas decorations and an exhibit featuring its restored 1901 private railcar "Loretto." What famous Tar Heel millionaire once owned "Loretto?"
    (a) William R. Hearst   (b) James B. Duke   (c) R.J. Reynolds

7. A recreated Confederate regimental band will perform both Christmas and Civil War music at Bennett Place State Historic Site near Durham on December 4. Costumed guides here will lead you on a tour of the site of Rebel surrender to what Yankee general?
    (a) William T. Sherman   (b) George Meade   (c) George A. Custer

8. The 1825 Malcolm Blue Farm in Moore County entertains Christmas holiday visitors with traditional food and tunes. What town, south of Pinehurst and named for a Scottish city, is the site of the Blue Farm?   (a) Dundee   (b) Glasgow   (c) Aberdeen

9. Always lovely at Christmas, Asheville's Grove Park Inn pulls out all the stops with sing-alongs, craft displays, gorgeous decorations and a gingerbread village. Still an "inn" place to be, Grove Park once hosted which one of the following famous writers?
    (a) Marcel Proust   (b) Stephen Crane   (c) F. Scott Fitzgerald

10. A textile community in Gaston County, McAdenville attracts thousands of visitors each Christmas season with its amazing array of decorations. Annually decorating 375 trees with 365,000 lights has earned McAdenville what nickname?   (a) Santaland   (b) Christmastown USA   (c) City of Santa

11. The antebellum home of the Kenan family opens its doors to Christmas visitors with music on a 1700 pianoforte, snacks, guided tours and a Confederate encampment. What Duplin County town, named after the Kenans, hosts these events?   (a) Kenansville   (b) Kenanburg   (c) Kenantown

12. The mountain town of Weaverville has a Christmas open house and candlelight tour of the restored home of our state's Civil War governor. Now a State Historic Site, this house was once the home of what great man?   (a) Oydell Ledford-Crisp   (b) Ozville Forrester   (c) Zebulon Vance

13. The Furniture Discovery Center Museum does its part to stir up the Christmas spirit with displays of decorated doll houses, miniature rooms and holiday figurines dating back to the 1490s. What Piedmont city, known as the "furniture capital of the world," is home for this unique show and museum?
    (a) Burlington   (b) High Point   (c) Concord

Agriculture, Business
and
Industry

Farmer's Market

The Business Of Banking

Charlotte may be the biggest banking town in the Carolinas, but it's not the only city in the state to benefit from that industry.

You don't have to be a banker to answer all of the following questions, but it *would* help to know a little about banking in North Carolina.

1. Which of the following has served as head of the North Carolina Banking Commission?
    (a) James Hunt   (b) Monty J. Thornburg   (c) William T. Graham

2. A pioneer among black businessmen in North Carolina, Richard B. Fitzgerald and eight other black entrepreneurs from Greensboro founded which bank in 1908?
    (a) Farmers and Mechanics National Bank   (b) Mechanics and Farmers Bank   (c) Farmers State Bank

3. Upon its completion in 1992, North Carolina National Bank's Charlotte skyscraper was the tallest building in the Southeast. How many stories tall does it stand?
    (a) 70 stories   (b) 60 stories   (c) 55 stories

4. What year did the Federal Reserve Bank of Richmond open a branch in Charlotte?
    (a) 1867   (b) 1910   (c) 1927

5. Name the Winston-Salem based bank that takes its name from an Austrian valley that belonged to a prominent Moravian family named Zinzendorf.
    (a) First Gaston Bank   (b) Wachovia Bank   (c) First Moravian Bank

6. With $1.6 million in capital, the State Bank of North Carolina began in what year?
    (a) 1810   (b) 1825   (c) 1900

7. Both founded in 1804, what were the first two banks in North Carolina?
    (a) Tar Heel Trust Co., Naval Stores National Bank   (b) Bank of New Bern, Bank of Cape Fear
    (c) Bank of Wilmington, Bank of Edenton

8. Approved by the General Assembly in 1833, the Albemarle Bank was established in what Chowan County town?   (a) Walhalla   (b) Edenton   (c) Ryland

9. What year did the Planters Bank open, and in what town?
    (a) 1850 in Gold Rock   (b) 1930 in Red Oak   (c) 1899 in Rocky Mount

10. First Union National Bank evolved from what institution founded by H.M. Victor in 1908?
    (a) Union National Bank   (b) Victor Trust and Surety Co.   (c) Charlotte Municipal Bank

11. Commercial National Bank, founded in 1874, was the predecessor of what banking giant?
    (a) Bank of the South   (b) NCNB   (c) Freedom Bank and Trust

12. What Charlotte street was the original location for the US Mint when it opened in 1837?
    (a) Graham Street   (b) West Trade Street   (c) College Street

13. The Bank of North Carolina Building located at 122 South Tryon Street, before being torn down in 1973, saw what fleeing politician on April 19, 1865?
    (a) Zeb Vance   (b) Alexander Stevens   (c) Jefferson Davis

14. What financial institution had the dubious honor of being the first major bank in North Carolina to fail as a result of the Great Depression?
    (a) Central Bank and Trust Co. of Asheville   (b) Fidelity Commercial Bank   (c) First Bank of Charlotte

15. What Gaston County bank that survived the Great Depression merged with Wachovia Bank in 1981?
    (a) First Textile Banks and Trust   (b) Bank of Belmont   (c) Catawba National Bank

North Carolina Means Business

Spearheading the economic rise of the New South, North Carolina offers a friendly climate for both business and industry. Firms from foreign lands, the Northeast and those spawned right here at home all seem to prosper in the Tar Heel State. Put your Carolina business sense to the test with this quiz.

1. Headquartered in Cherryville, Carolina Freight Corp. has had trucks plying the highways since 1932. What is the predominant color scheme of these frequently seen rigs?
   (a) brown   (b) yellow   (c) red and black

2. One of Belmont's largest employers, R.L. Stowe Mills Inc., has been a vital part of that town's economy since 1901. What type of business does R.L. Stowe Mills engage in?
   (a) textile mills   (b) carpet mills   (c) flour mills

3. Established in 1888, Belk Brothers Co. has long been a leader in the retail department store trade. What Belk was mayor of Charlotte from 1969 to 1977?   (a) Reginald Belk   (b) John Belk   (c) Sam Belk

4. Power Curbers Inc. of Salisbury manufactures large, automatic, concrete curb-making machinery. A feather in Power Curbers cap took place in 1993 when their product was chosen to lay concrete in the tunnel being built under the English Channel between France and England. What is this tunnel called?
   (a) The Chunnel   (b) The Tube   (c) Napoleon's Revenge

5. Though based in Chicago, Sara Lee Corp. is North Carolina's largest private-sector employer. Approximately how many Carolinians work for Sara Lee?   (a) 5,000   (b) 22,000   (c) 35,000

6. Radiator Specialty Co. of Charlotte makes all types of chemicals for use by professional and home mechanics. Their engine degreaser is a product familiar to anyone who has ever poked his head under a hood. What is that product's brand name?   (a) Gorp   (b) Goop   (c) Gunk

7. With hundreds of stores scattered across the Southeast, Food Lion Inc. is a true Carolina success story. Started in 1957 by Ralph Ketner, Brown Ketner and Wilson Smith, Food Lion began its rise in what town?   (a) Concord   (b) Salisbury   (c) Statesville

8. Starting with a broken spinning machine in a chicken coop in 1939, Surratt Hosiery Mill Inc. has prospered over the years to become one of Davidson County's most stable firms. Located at Jackson Hill near Denton, what highway passes in front of the busy Surratt complex?
   (a) US 74   (b) US 29   (c) NC 8

9. Waldensian Bakeries Inc. of Valdese had more than $40 million in sales in 1992. What fresh-faced lass graces the wrappers of their wholesome products?
   (a) Little Miss Sunbeam   (b) Little Miss Goodness   (c) Little Betty Bakery

10. Home to Drexel-Heritage, Henredon, Miller Desk and a host of other furniture manufacturing firms, High Point is arguably North Carolina's furniture capital. What county do furniture-seekers find High Point in?   (a) Catawba County   (b) Guilford County   (c) Davie County

11. House of Raeford Farms Inc. is based in the town of Raeford in Hoke County. Dating back to the 1920s, this company claims to have the world's largest line of what type of product?
    (a) sweet potatoes   (b) tobacco goods   (c) poultry products

12. Glaxo Holdings p.l.c., is an English pharmaceuticals firm that not only employs more than 3,000 Carolinians, but also has its US headquarters located in what unique area near Durham?
    (a) Research Triangle Park   (b) Foreign Firms Center   (c) Scientific Business Park

13. With 92 restaurants already operating in North Carolina, and another 25 slated for construction in 1993, Bojangles Corp. serves up a whole lot of good chicken and biscuits. Though its menu has diversified in recent years, what ethnic cuisine formed the backbone of Bojangles?
    (a) Tex-Mex   (b) Greek   (c) Cajun

Manufacturing In The Tar Heel State

Though North Carolina has always excelled in its agricultural endeavors, manufacturing also plays a vital role in our state's economy. Check your labels and logos, then match the answers in this quiz to the correct Tar Heel product or town that it was made in.

1. Since 1962, North Carolina has been the nation's leading producer of bricks. In operation since 1889, Isenhour Brick and Tile sells $15 million worth of Tar Heel bricks annually. Isenhour is located near the North Carolina Transportation Museum in what town? (a) East Spencer (b) Sanford (c) High Point

2. The Ecusta Division of P.H. Glatfelter Company, a paper manufacturer, is the world's largest producer of cigarette papers. What Transylvania County town near the French Broad River is home to the Ecusta mill? (a) Brevard (b) Beech Gap (c) Pisgah Forest

3. Countless miles are traveled and schoolchildren safely delivered by drivers of Thomas Built Buses. All those orange buses that ply the routes to school and back are built by Thomas in what Piedmont city? (a) Greensboro (b) High Point (c) Salisbury

4. The sprawling Lance Inc. snack food factory in Charlotte produces a wide variety of tasty treats. One of its best-known products, the little peanut butter and cheese crackers, are affectionately called what? (a) nabs (b) nobs (c) Georgia crackers

5. Employing nearly 4,000 workers at their United States headquarters in the Research Triangle Park, Glaxo is one of the world's largest producers of what type of product? (a) computer software (b) pharmaceuticals (c) pet products

6. The eighth-largest manufacturing employer in North Carolina for number of employees, Broyhill Furniture Industries Inc. has for decades made top-quality furniture. What town is the headquarters for Broyhill? (a) High Point (b) Lenoir (c) Winston-Salem

7. Second only to Oregon in production of Christmas trees, North Carolina ranks No. 1 nationally in sales with $90 million. Name the mountain community in Avery County on US Highway 221 that is one of our state's most productive Christmas tree-growing regions. (a) Boone (b) Ledger (c) Linville Falls

8. Manufacturing of automatic curb-making machines, Power Curbers Inc. brought North Carolina's heavy industry to international attention when its machinery was used in the construction of the English-French Chunnel project. What town, the seat of Rowan County, is home to Power Curbers? (a) Concord (b) Salisbury (c) China Grove

9. A top manufacturer of fabricated steel products for building and bridge construction, Carolina Steel is currently celebrating 75 years in business. Which city in the Triad region of our state is home to Carolina Steel? (a) Greensboro (b) Greenville (c) Fayetteville

10. With more than 6,000 workers, Greensboro-based Cone Mills is the 29th-largest employer in our state. Cone's other superlative is the fact that it is the world's largest producer of what type of cloth named for the city of Nimes, France? (a) khaki (b) seersucker (c) denim

11. Dating back to pre-Civil War days, Chatham Manufacturing is one of the largest blanket factories in the nation. What town in southwest Surry County near the Yadkin River and Interstate 77 is the home of Chatham Manufacturing? (a) Low Gap (b) Elkin (c) Bannertown

12. Chemical production, the third-largest segment of our state's manufacturing output, employs 40,000 Tar Heels. One of the top chemical firms in our state is Texasgulf Chemicals Co. What Beaufort County hamlet whose name literally glows is the site of Texasgulf? (a) Aurora (b) Shines Crossroads (c) Moon Creek

13. Chicago-based Sara Lee is the second-largest private employer in North Carolina with 22,000 workers. A diverse company, Sara Lee makes delicious frozen foods and which one of the following products as well? (a) farm tractors (b) microwave ovens (c) wearing apparel

Taste Of The State

Finally a quiz you can really sink your teeth into. Sample the answers to these homegrown North Carolina foods in this quiz.

1. The largest independent pickle manufacturer in the United States, Mount Olive Pickle Company in Mount Olive dates back to 1926. Producing more than 70 million jars of pickles annually, this company is located at the corner of what two whimsically named streets?
   (a) Cucumber and Vine   (b) Vinegar and Vine   (c) Pickle and Vine

2. T.W. Garner Food Co. in Winston-Salem is known for its delicious jellies, jams, and preserves made from a variety of fruits. Name the company's other famous product, which puts a punch in many dishes—drop by spicy drop?   (a) Boar and Castle Sauce   (b) Tabasco Sauce   (c) Texas Pete

3. Around the turn of the century, Caleb Bradham, a New Bern druggist, invented a refreshment known as "Brad's Drink," which eventually was patented as Pepsi-Cola. Although he would receive scant credit and little money for his mark on history, Bradham received his patent for Pepsi in what year?
   (a) 1895   (b) 1903   (c) 1910

4. The largest meat-snack maker in the nation, GoodMark Foods Inc. in Raleigh ships products around the world. It also has a front-row seat in NASCAR racing. What name of the GoodMark's spicy sausage snack is emblazoned on the nose of stock cars driven by the Labonte brothers?
   (a) Slim Jim   (b) Beef Jerky   (c) Ham I Am

5. With nearly 5,000 employees, Lance Inc. in Charlotte is the largest snack food manufacturing company in North Carolina. Started in 1913 when peanut salesman Philip Lance began grinding goobers to put between crackers, Lance's peanut butter sandwiches are often referred to by what colloquial name?
   (a) nabs   (b) toasts   (c) crisps

6. A North Carolina soft-drink legend, Cheerwine was invented in 1917 by L.D. Peeler in reaction to a sugar shortage caused by German submarines during World War I. Known as "the nectar of Tar Heels," Cheerwine's unique cherry taste is still manufactured in what historic Rowan County city?
   (a) High Point   (b) Salisbury   (c) Concord

7. Dating back to 1920, Dewey's Bakery in Winston-Salem was founded by Dewey Wilkerson Sr. A division of Dewey's, Salem Baking Company is famous for baking "the world's thinnest cookie," Made of imported spices, flour, and molasses, this type of cookie originated in what Eastern European nation?   (a) Transylvania   (b) Belgium   (c) Moravia

8. Country ham and biscuits have greeted many a Tar Heel morning. Several companies in North Carolina sell country ham, including Stadler's in Elon College, Hancock's in Franklinville, and Johnston County Hams, which is located in what town that hosts an annual Ham and Yam Festival?
   (a) Zebulon   (b) Smithfield   (c) Coats

9. Surely any idea of heaven must include Krispy Kreme doughnuts and a big pot of hot coffee. With a $25 investment, Vernon Rudolph and two friends began making these incredible edibles on July 13, 1937, in what Tar Heel town?   (a) Winston-Salem   (b) Lexington   (c) Asheville

10. In the 1920s barbecuer Adam Scott first blended up a sauce recipe that's still one of the state's most popular brands. Patented in 1946 by Adam's son Martel Scott, Scott's Barbecue Sauce ships more than 750,000 bottles of product annually from its facility in what city on the Neuse River in Wayne County?
    (a) Dobbersville   (b) Goldsboro   (c) Eureka

The Facts On Farming

Despite the fact that our state is becoming increasingly urbanized, farming still pays the bills in a great number of Tar Heel households. How much do you know about farming in North Carolina? Take the following quiz and find out.

1. With more than 70,000 farms on its land, North Carolina ranks as one of the nation's most important agricultural strongholds. According to the latest statistics, what is the average acreage of those farms? (a) 1,000 acres   (b) 150 acres   (c) 50 acres

2. As early as 1860, Governor John Ellis urged lawmakers to form an agency that would regulate and benefit agriculture in North Carolina. What year did the General Assembly finally form the North Carolina Department of Agriculture?   (a) 1877   (b) 1865   (c) 1885

3. Though many areas of our state are now urbanized, farms still provide a substantial number of North Carolinians with jobs. Of the 3.2 million total jobs in North Carolina, what percent are in agriculture? (a) 10 percent   (b) 60 percent   (c) 21 percent

4. Many North Carolina dairymen favor the Holstein cow for its high milk production and gentle nature. What color is a Holstein cow?   (a) reddish brown   (b) black and white   (c) gray

5. To further the development and marketability of all types of Tar Heel bovines, the North Carolina Cattlemans Association boasts 3,000 members in 75 of our 100 counties. What year did this influential group form?   (a) 1850   (b) 1975   (c) 1955

6. It tastes excellent baked or in pies. Far and away, North Carolina leads the nation in production of this particular tuber, with four million 100-pound bags produced annually. Name this popular vegetable. (a) rutabaga   (b) sweet potato   (c) parsnip

7. Whether raising crawdads or catfish, many North Carolina farmers are expanding their financial horizons by using their ponds for the production of tasty morsels for tables far and wide. What is this rapidly growing aspect of agriculture called?   (a) aquaculture   (b) aquatic ranching   (c) pond produce

8. Though NC ranks 12th nationally in production of this crop today, it has probably provided employment for more folks in its day than any other product in our state's history. Name this plant, which Eli Whitney's invention revolutionized in 1793. (a) soybeans (b) cotton (c) sorghum

9. Vital to the pollination of our state's crops, the 178,000 bee colonies that North Carolina's 15,000 beekeepers maintain help honey lovers and farmers alike. When traveling flower to flower, where do honeybees hold all that pollen they gather?
    (a) on their stinger   (b) on their hind legs   (c) on their antennae

10. Just about everyone knows that NC is the tobacco capital of the US, with more than 600 million pounds gown annually. Name the Wilson County town where more bright leaf tobacco is marketed than anywhere in America.   (a) Town Creek   (b) Wilson   (c) Elm City

11. Some North Carolina tobacco farmers, like Linwood Waters of Washington, are experimenting with raising seedlings in soilless beds that are constantly fed liquid nutrients. What is this growing technique called?   (a) hydroponics   (b) liquid smoke   (c) fluid dynamics

12. Since they raise more turkeys than any state (48 million in 1992), North Carolina "gobbler-growers" decided to name one month as "Turkey Month." What month has that honor?
    (a) November   (b) December   (c) June

13. Ranking fourth nationally in production of peanuts, North Carolina produces more than 450 million pounds of "goobers" annually. Contributing 88 million pounds to that total in 1992, what county, whose seat is Jackson, led the state in peanut production?
    (a) Northampton County   (b) Gates County   (c) Chowan County

North Carolina's Agricultural Excellence

Employing more than 20 percent of our state's work force, agriculture is big business in North Carolina. Hike up those bib overalls, crank up the tractor, and get ready to plant the correct answers to this quiz on Tar Heel farming.

1. The North Carolina Department of Agriculture was created by the General Assembly of 1876-77. Name the commissioner of this vital government agency who served from (1964-2000).
   (a) Calvin McGuirt   (b) James A. Graham   (c) Alex Frew McMillan

2. In 1993 North Carolina ranked third nationally in total net farm income and related industry sales. About how many dollars did this translate into for our Tar Heel economy?
   (a) $600 million   (b) $2 billion   (c) $42 billion

3. Each month the North Carolina Department of Agriculture prints 75,000 copies of a fine little newspaper that's loaded with farm news and classified advertising. Name this free publication, in which everything from an antique washpot to a 500-acre farm is listed for sale.
   (a) *Tar Heel Tattler*   (b) *Agricultural Review*   (c) *North Carolina Farmer*

4. With more than 60 million birds raised annually, North Carolina is the top turkey-producing state in the nation. Name the Hoke County town where residents and visitors gather each September for the annual North Carolina Turkey Festival.   (a) Raeford   (b) Quewhiffle   (c) Buckhorn

5. Ranked third nationally in production, North Carolina hog farmers are now shipping their product all over the world. Folks might start making barbecue in Vladivostok since 264,000 Tar Heel piggies recently went to market in what country?   (a) Germany   (b) Russia   (c) China

6. With more than $1 billion in total annual crop cash receipts, Johnston County is the champion farming county in our state. Name the town that is Johnston's seat and also claims to be the "Ham Capital of the World."   (a) Boon Hill   (b) Bentonville   (c) Smithfield

7. In recent years "king" cotton has made a comeback in North Carolina fields. In 1994 our state produced 600,000 bales of the fluffy stuff. How much does a standard bale of cotton weigh?
   (a) 480 pounds   (b) 700 pounds   (c) 800 pounds

8. Trailing only Oregon and Michigan in sales of Christmas trees, North Carolina raises some 30,000 acres of that product annually. Name the particular variety of Christmas tree that our state's farmers grow more of than any other state.   (a) white cedar   (b) Fraser fir   (c) yellow pine

9. Though most people associate the production of wheat with the country's midwestern states, North Carolina harvests about 20 million bushels of the amber waves each year. What county leads our state in wheat production and is also the site of Bath, our oldest town.
   (a) Beaufort County   (b) Craven County   (c) Dare County

10. Of course, tobacco is the crop that put North Carolina on the agricultural map. Our state accounts for two-thirds of the entire US production. Though it's labor-intensive, tobacco can bring Tar Heel farmers about how many gross dollars per acre?   (a) $500   (b) $1,000   (c) $4,000

11. Grown in China for 5,000 years, soybeans came to North Carolina in the 1870s. Used for everything from lipstick to food, soybeans are the last North Carolina crop to be harvested each year. In what month is our state's 1.5 million acres of soybeans scooped up? (a) August (b) September (c) December

12. In 1993 North Carolina retained its No. 4 national ranking in the production of broiler chickens. With 3.1 billion pounds of broilers going for about 32 cents a pound, how many dollars did that mean for Tar Heel chicken farmers?   (a) $74 million   (b) $1 billion   (c) $95 million

13. Fish farmers in our state raise more than 4 million pounds of trout annually. This works out to nearly $6 million in sales for a growing North Carolina agricultural industry that goes by what name?
    (a) aquaculture   (b) pond produce   (c) lake cropping

14. Vital to our state's agriculture, nearly 200,000 beehives kept by 15,000 North Carolina beekeepers see to it that farm crops and flowers are pollinated. What famous type of Tar Heel honey comes from a tree whose name belies its product?   (a) bitterwood   (b) wormwood   (c) sourwood

Tar Heel Harvest

North Carolina has been blessed with a cornucopia of agricultural and culinary abundance. Let's offer thanks as we guess the answers to this quiz on Tar Heel foods and feasts.

1. Given the fact that North Carolina leads the nation in turkey production, odds are good that the centerpiece of many Thanksgiving tables across the country will have come from our state. About how many Tar Heel gobblers go to market each year?   (a) 10 million   (b) 30 million   (c) 61 million

2. Baked in the jacket, poured into pies, or whipped up with a marshmallow topping, North Carolina sweet potatoes are not only a culinary treat but also the official Tar Heel state vegetable. What county, seated by Smithfield, leads North Carolina in sweet potato production?
(a) Duplin County   (b) Johnston County   (c) Wayne County

3. Made famous in the early 1970s by popular songwriter Tony Joe White, a North Carolina native plant whose scientific name is *Phytolacca americana* has provided many Tar Heel country homes with a green side dish since Colonial days. Name this leafy plant best sauteed with a chunk of fatback.
(a) Sorrel   (b) Poke sallet   (c) Squirrel corn

4. In 1995 North Carolina raised 347 million pounds of the versatile food that our South Carolina neighbors call "penders." Name this legume that's used to make everything from sandwiches to pies.
(a) soybean   (b) sorghum   (c) peanut

5. Gustatory times have not always been so plentiful in North Carolina. During the Civil War, Tar Heels who craved a good cup of coffee often had to resort to an ersatz brew made from parched corn or the stems of what blue, roadside flower?   (a) Chicory   (b) Salvia   (c) Indigo

6. Another Civil War taste sensation that many a Tar Heel rebel ate was made by swirling cornmeal in hot bacon grease, then cooked by wrapping the dough around a rifle ramrod held over the campfire. Name this dish that was a staple before cholesterol was even a word.
(a) Hoecake   (b) Swoosh   (c) Johnny cake

7. Steamed, or with their meat picked and fried into cakes, crabs are a Tar Heel coastal delicacy that most everyone loves. Name the species of crab that epicures prefer over all others and that North Carolina fishermen catch more than 20 million pounds of annually.
(a) Blue crab   (b) Fiddler crab   (c) She crab

8. More than 50 species of fin fish are caught commercially in North Carolina waters and make their way to tables across the country. One of the most popular types for eating is the whiting. What other name does this savory swimmer go by?   (a) Alewife   (b) Virginia mullet   (c) Puppy drum

9. Brunswick stew has long been a traditional North Carolina dish whether on its own or as a complement to barbecue. Besides corn, beans, chicken, and pork, what other ingredient was, in earlier times, an important addition to this hearty dish?   (a) raccoon   (b) squirrel   (c) deer

10. North Carolina pioneers who could not obtain raisins but wanted to add a bit of sweetness to puddings and pies often turned to a type of native berry that grew on trees. Name this tree, whose leaves also provide food for silkworms.   (a) Dewberry   (b) Gooseberry   (c) Mulberry

11. Founder of Old Salem, the Moravians brought to North Carolina their tradition of fine European cooking. Made with rich, black molasses and brown sugar, Moravian cakes are really crispy cookies that date back to the 1700s and help celebrate what holiday?   (a) Thanksgiving   (b) Easter   (c) Christmas

Down On The Farm

Test your knowledge of North Carolina agricultural history and statistics as you answer this quiz that takes you back down on the farm.

1. Although North Carolina's new 1868 state constitution provided for the establishment of a "Bureau of Statistics, Agriculture, and Immigration," it was not until 1877 that the General Assembly approved the measure. Name the former colonel from Anson County who became its first commissioner.
    (a) Leonidas Lafayette Polk   (b) Calvinius Calhoun McGuirt   (c) Jonathan Hall

2. In 1881 the NC Board of Agriculture purchased Raleigh's National Hotel for $13,000 as its headquarters. Although the hotel has long been gone, the NC Department of Agriculture still occupies offices on the original site. What busy Raleigh street named for our former colonial capital is our state's agricultural nerve center?   (a) Wilmington Street   (b) Wake Forest Road   (c) West Edenton Street

3. Agriculture is North Carolina's leading industry, with farm receipts approaching $7 billion annually. Our state has also been called the third most agriculturally diverse state in the nation. The number of working farms in North Carolina has remained fairly constant over the past several years at what figure?   (a) 40,000   (b) 45,000   (c) 58,000

4. In 1930, the Department of Agriculture took over control of the North Carolina State Fair. Held each October, the State Fair showcases our state's agricultural pride with livestock shows and other exhibitions of Tar Heel farm excellence. About how many folks visit the State Fair each year?
    (a) 200,000   (b) 700,000   (c) 400,000

5. Although a far cry from states like Texas where more than 14 million cattle cruise the range, North Carolina still has around 1.2 million head of beef and dairy cows. The leading Tar Heel county for cattle on farms is, curiously enough, on the border of our state's largest metropolis. Name North Carolina's number one cow county.   (a) Iredell County   (b) Orange County   (c) Guilford County

6. Ranking second in the nation, North Carolina raises more than 70,000 tons of cucumbers annually for pickles. A lot of those cukes go to a company in southern Wayne County where they're turned into pickles and relish of every description. Name the town that shares its name with the largest pickle factory in the country.   (a) Vlassicville   (b) Mount Olive   (c) Dillsboro

7. Bringing more than $1 billion in cash receipts to North Carolina farmers, tobacco is our state's most valuable crop. While flue-cured tobacco represents the largest portion of 1995's harvest at 253,000 acres, what other type of tobacco grown mainly in North Carolina's mountain region saw an 8,000-acre crop?   (a) Burley   (b) Cuban   (c) Turkish

8. Horses and ponies make up an important part of the Tar Heel farm scene with more than 130,000 head listed in 1996. Although some North Carolina counties have thousands of horses available for work or riding, Hyde County inventories only how many steeds?   (a) 220   (b) 95   (c) 30

9. Our official North Carolina state vegetable, sweet potatoes on Tar Heel farms top any state in the nation. The number one county in our state for sweet potato plantings also happens to top the list for statewide crop cash receipts. Name this county where more than 1,400 farms operate.
    (a) Mecklenburg County   (b) Johnston County   (c) Camden County

10. Thanks to the eradication of the boll weevil and the polyester leisure suit, cotton production in North Carolina is on the upswing. From an all-time high in 1926 of 2 million acres, to an all-time low in 1979 when just 49,000 acres of cotton were planted in our state, cotton was produced on 800,000 Tar Heel acres in 1995. How much does a bale of cotton weigh?
    (a) 700 pounds   (b) 480 pounds   (c) 300 pounds

Transportation

Spencer Shops

The Rudiments Of Railroading

North Carolina has a rich railroading history, and this quiz tests your knowledge of it. For those who aren't too sure of this subject, try reading some of the stories found in *The State* May 1991 issue.

1. Once running between Johnson City, Tennessee, and Boone, the narrow-gauge East Tennessee and Western North Carolina line acquired a nickname that lives on today at a mountain amusement park. What is that nickname? (a) Old Smoky   (b) Cannonball Express   (c) Tweetsie Railroad

2. Name the tycoon who founded not only American Tobacco Company, but also the Piedmont and Northern Railway. (a) James Buchanan Duke   (b) Phillip Morris   (c) Brown Williamson

3. As of 1990, about how many miles of track were owned and maintained by the railroad companies serving North Carolina? (a) about 4,000 miles   (b) about 3,000 miles   (c) about 2,000 miles

4. Alexander Railroad Company is headquartered in what Alexander County town?
(a) Love Valley   (b) Taylorsville   (c) Millersville

5. What state agency has jurisdiction over railroad operations in North Carolina?
(a) Department of Transportation   (b) Railway Commission of NC   (c) NC Utilities Commission

6. In what year did Piedmont and Northern Railway begin the switch from electric to diesel-powered engines? (a) 1950   (b) 1930   (c) 1920

7. During the Civil War, what railroad company took supplies from blockade-running ships to Confederate forces in Virginia and so became known as the "Lifeline of the South?"
(a) Wilmington and Weldon   (b) Wilmington and Richmond   (c) New Hanover and Petersburg

8. Known as the "Mullet Line," what railroad company served the burgeoning coastal fishing industry during the 1800s? (a) Coastal Plain Railroad   (b) Outer Banks Railroad   (c) Atlantic and NC Railroad

9. In what year did the North Carolina Railroad Company complete the full 223-mile route that ran between Raleigh, Goldsboro and Charlotte? (a) 1850   (b) 1856   (c) 1900

10. What railroad company, chartered in 1834, changed its name to the Wilmington and Weldon in 1854?
(a) Sandhills Railroad   (b) Wilmington and Raleigh Railroad   (c) Cape Fear Railroad

11. What Alamance County town began as a repair-shop site for the North Carolina Railroad?
(a) Burlington   (b) High Point   (c) Greensboro

12. Formed in 1894, this railroad company quickly obtained extensive track rights and soon dominated rail business in the Piedmont.
(a) Seaboard Coastline   (b) Southern Railway Company   (c) Piedmont and Northern Railroad

13. Following a 1986 name change, what is the former Seaboard System Railroad Inc. now known as?
(a) CSX Transportation   (b) SSR Railway   (c) Amtrak

14. What North Carolina city became the first in the state to operate an electric street railway?
(a) Charlotte   (b) Raleigh   (c) Asheville

15. Arriving from Columbia, the Charlotte and South Carolina Railroad was the first train to call on Charlotte. What was the year of that initial run? (a) 1852   (b) 1880   (c) 1890

Our Highways And Byways

North Carolina's extensive road network makes it a hub for the Eastern Seaboard and the South. To see how well you know our highways, try to answer as many of the following questions as you can—without looking at a map.

1. North Carolina has many nicknames. Which one is often used in reference to our highway system?
    (a) the Good Roads State   (b) the Pothole State   (c) the Interstate State

2. What national distinction does the North Carolina road system enjoy?
    (a) most bridges of any state   (b) more miles of guardrail than any state
    (c) nation's largest state-maintained road system

3. The state Division of Travel and Tourism offers free road maps for anyone who calls what "800" number listed below?   (a) 1-800-VISIT NC   (b) 1-800-MOVIN' ON   (c) 1-800-HIT ROAD

4. Which one of these interstates does *not* go through North Carolina?   (a) I-85   (b) I-77   (c) I-75

5. Which of the following highways passes Lake Hiwassee in the mountains and ends at Whalebone on the Outer Banks? It served the state long before the first mile of interstate was ever laid.
    (a) NC 27   (b) US 64   (c) NC 45

6. Ferries play an important role in North Carolina. Travelers who run out of road on Ocracoke Island can simply hop on a ferry, enjoy the ride and get off at what mainland dock?
    (a) Smith Island   (b) Knotts Island   (c) Cedar Island

7. Speaking of the Outer Banks, name the highway that not only travels their length, but also is sometimes buried under wind- and wave-driven sand.   (a) NC 12   (b) NC 55   (c) NC 301

8. For part of its length as it traverses our state, US 74 takes on the name of a former president. Name the president.   (a) Andrew Johnson   (b) Andrew Jackson   (c) James K. Polk

9. As part of a beautification program, the state Department of Transportation plants wildflowers along North Carolina's roads. Travelers can do *their* part in this effort by not littering our highways. Just in case you forgot...what is the fine for littering in North Carolina?   (a) $50   (b) $100   (c) $500

10. If you should be traveling US 52 in the Piedmont, and the irresistible aroma of barbecue strikes your nose, you know you're in what Barbecue Capital of the World?
    (a) Lexington   (b) Concord   (c) Wallburg

11. Shaking off the glitter of Myrtle Beach, South Carolina, US 17 eases into the Tar Heel State just north of Little River. Name the second town in North Carolina that this coast-skirting road passes through.
    (a) Supply   (b) Bolivia   (c) Shallotte

12. Clear across the state, US 321 wiggles through the foothills, then into the mountains. On its way it passes through the popular resort town of Boone. Name the college that helped put Boone on the map.
    (a) Mars Hill College   (b) Appalachian State University   (c) Western Carolina University

13. If it seems like there are a lot of roads and highways in North Carolina, well, that's a fact. Try to guess the approximate number of miles of road here.   (a) 76,500 miles   (b) 50,000 miles   (c) 100,000 miles

14. With so many excellent roads in our state, it's all too easy to go a bit faster than you should. Bearing this in mind, what is the maximum speed limit (unless otherwise posted) allowed in North Carolina?
    (a) 70 miles an hour   (b) 55 miles an hour   (c) 60 miles an hour

Take A Ride On The Waterway

The Intracoastal Waterway stretches from Gloucester, Massachusetts, to Key West, Florida. How well do you know its North Carolina segment?

1. Which one of these colorful nicknames is the Intracoastal Waterway sometimes referred to by sailors?
    (a) the Ditch   (b) the Inside Loop   (c) the Shortcut

2. What is the standard depth of the Waterway?   (a) 6 feet   (b) 12 feet   (c) 30 feet

3. How many miles of the Intracoastal Waterway are in North Carolina?
    (a) about 100 miles   (b) about 450 miles   (c) exactly 308 miles

4. Part of the Waterway follows a river in North Carolina named for a type of reptile. Name this river, between Tyrrell and Dare counties.   (a) Cooter River   (b) Alligator River   (c) Salamander River

5. If a boat were to take the starboard fork of the Waterway as it leaves Virginia and enters North Carolina, it would pass through a large swamp. What is that swamp's name?
    (a) Dreary Swamp   (b) Dismal Swamp   (c) Green Swamp

6. What huge US Marine Corps base does the Waterway skirt in Onslow County?
    (a) Camp Butner   (b) Fort Caswell   (c) Camp Lejeune

7. What government agency is responsible for the Waterway's upkeep?   (a) US Army Corps of Engineers
    (b) NC Department of Transportation   (c) NC Department of Commerce

8. Traveling along the Waterway, how many miles is it from New River Inlet to Topsail Island Inlet?
    (a) 5 miles   (b) 100 miles   (c) 20 miles

9. As the Waterway skirts Maw Point in Pamlico County, it enters a bay that shares its name with a type of furniture. What is that bay called?   (a) Rattan Bay   (b) Early American Bay   (c) Wicker Bay

10. Ships and boats of all sizes use the Waterway to gain access to the dock facilities at Morehead City. What county is this state port in?   (a) Pender County   (b) Carteret County   (c) Dare County

11. Beaufort is not only a busy port of call, but it also shares its name with a town in South Carolina. There's a difference of opinion on how the name should be pronounced, however. How do we North Carolinians pronounce it?   (a) Bo-fort   (b) Bew-fort

12. What highway crosses the Waterway near Fairfield in Hyde County?
    (a) Interstate 85   (b) US 74   (c) NC 94

13. The Albemarle Sound is named for George Monck, one of the Lords Proprietors of North Carolina. What title did George hold?   (a) Prince of Albemarle   (b) Duke of Albemarle   (c) Count Albemarle

14. What town, the last stop on the Waterway before South Carolina, is considered by many to be the fried-seafood capital of the world?   (a) Seaside   (b) Southport   (c) Calabash

The World Of Tar Heel Watercraft

With 3,375 miles of tidal coastline, and nearly 4,000 square miles of inland waters, North Carolina has more places to float a boat than you can shake an oar at. Set a course for correct answers, then launch into this quiz.

1. In 1820 the first United States Navy ship to be named the *USS North Carolina* was launched. Weighing 2,600 tons and sporting 102 guns, this mighty vessel was powered by what means?
   (a) coal   (b) sails   (c) diesel fuel

2. Rare is the person in our state who does not know that the World War II battleship also dubbed *USS North Carolina* rests at harbor in Wilmington. What is the nickname earned by this veteran dreadnought?
   (a) The Showboat   (b) Big Ben   (c) The Shangri-La

3. The first steamboat to be built in North Carolina slid down the waterways in 1818 Beaufort. What mythical Greek figure who brought fire to man was this craft named after?
   (a) Hercules   (b) Uranus   (c) Prometheus

4. Long before any white man plied the waters of our state, Native Americans paddled their way across North Carolina's waters. In our region, what material did the Indians prefer for the construction of their canoes?   (a) birch bark   (b) hollowed logs   (c) cork

5. Freshwater fishermen can often be seen these days on North Carolina lakes and rivers in boats decked out with depth finders, trolling motors and plenty of engine. What are these high-performance craft called?   (a) bass boats   (b) hydroplanes   (c) PT boats

6. The North Carolina state historic boat is a vessel made of native wood, 20 to 30 feet long and named after the quarry it was designed to catch. Developed on Roanoke Island more than 100 years ago, what is this workboat called?   (a) crab boat   (b) oyster boat   (c) shad boat

7. Because of our unique barrier island coastline, many Tar Heel travelers depend upon the ferry boats operated by the North Carolina Department of Transportation for time-saving rides. One of these boats heads northwest daily from Ocracoke to what Hyde County town?
   (a) Swan Quarter   (b) South Creek   (c) Stumpy Point

8. The same features which make necessary the ferries are the reasons why North Carolina has only two deep-water state ports for ships to dock. Wilmington is one port. What more northerly city on our coast boasts the other commercial wharf?
   (a) New Bern   (b) Washington   (c) Morehead City

9. Housed in an 18,000-square-foot facility, the North Carolina Maritime Museum displays both actual boats and artifacts relative to our state's long watercraft history. Name the Carteret County town where this popular attraction is located.   (a) Havelock   (b) Beaufort   (c) Kuhns

10. Speaking of maritime attractions in the Tar Heel State, few are more interesting or historically significant than the 70-foot-long replica of a 16th century sailing ship of the type used by early English explorers to our North Carolina coast. Moored at Manteo, what is this craft's name?
    (a) *Elizabeth II*   (b) *Queen Mary*   (c) *Golden Hind*

11. Civil War blockade-running etched many ships' names into Tar Heel history. One runner, the *Modern Greece,* struck a sandbar and went down in 1862. What fort near Wilmington displays some of this craft's Confederate cargo in a museum?   (a) Fort Macon   (b) Fort Wagner   (c) Fort Fisher

12. Another Rebel raider, the *CSS Raleigh,* also ran more afoul of the bottom than Federal guns. Launched in 1864, the *Raleigh* hit shoals near the mouth of the Cape Fear and was scuttled. What type of ship was the *Raleigh?*   (a) midget submarine   (b) ironclad   (c) mortar barge

13. Launched December 6, 1941, from the North Carolina Ship Corporation yards at Wilmington, the *Zebulon B. Vance* was the first of what type of fast-built cargo ships to see service in World War II?
    (a) Freedom ships   (b) Democracy ships   (c) Liberty ships

Fortresses By The Sea

With North Carolina's long seafaring tradition, it is fitting that ships have been named for people and places in our state. Try out your sea legs with this quiz on Tar Heel ship names.

1. The first *USS North Carolina* was a 2,633-ton, three-masted sailing ship called to action with the US Navy in the Atlantic and Mediterranean. This ship was launched in 1820 from the naval yard in what Pennsylvania city of brotherly love? (a) Harrisburg (b) Philadelphia (c) Pittsburgh

2. The present *USS North Carolina* is, of course, the highly acclaimed veteran of World War II anchored in the Cape Fear River at Wilmington. Known affectionately as The Showboat, the *USS North Carolina* wears what identifying numerals on her bow? (a) 33 (b) 22 (c) 55

3. The Civil War permitted many naval innovations to come of age including iron-plating of wooden ships. One of the most fearsome of these ironclads was the *CSS Albemarle*. For several months in 1864 the *Albemarle* threatened Union shipping around what river near Plymouth?
   (a) New River (b) Neuse River (c) Roanoke River

4. Another Confederate ironclad that saw action in the waning days of the Civil War was the *CSS Neuse*. Scuttled by her crew to avoid capture by Union forces, the *Neuse* ended her career near what town that serves as the seat of Lenoir County? (a) Kinston (b) Pink Hill (c) Falling Creek

5. Around the turn of the century, steam-powered packet ships were a popular means to transport goods and people along North Carolina's coastal waterways. One of these small ships was named for what New Hanover County city on the Cape Fear River it called home port?
   (a) Shallotte (b) Wilmington (c) Watha

6. During the World War I era and shortly thereafter, shipbuilding became a predominant activity in North Carolina ports. Commissioned in 1919 just after the Great War ended, one merchant ship produced by the Liberty Shipbuilding Company in Wilmington was christened after what state nickname?
   (a) Rip Van Winkle (b) Sooner (c) Old North State

7. World War II brought another frenzy of shipbuilding activity to North Carolina. Known as Liberty Ships, merchant vessels for wartime were produced in great numbers. The first Liberty Ship to be launched in 1941 was named for what former Tar Heel governor from Buncombe County?
   (a) Zebulon B. Vance (b) Luther Hodges (c) Josephus Daniels

8. Smaller than regular aircraft carriers, escort carriers performed many hazardous missions during World War II. Three US Navy escort carriers were named for North Carolina sounds: Bogue, Core, and what other sound near Roanoke Island? (a) Currituck Sound (b) Croatan Sound (c) Pamlico Sound

9. Modern-day US Navy aircraft carriers can weigh more than 80,000 tons and carry nearly 100 aircraft. One of the Navy's largest ships with more than 5,000 sailors and pilots on board, what carrier is named for a place made famous by the Wright brothers? (a) *USS Manteo* (b) *USS Dare* (c) *USS Kitty Hawk*

10. Launched in 1994, the *USS Charlotte* is a nuclear-powered US Navy warship based in Pearl Harbor. More than 350 feet long, and displacing 7,100 tons, the *Charlotte*'s number SSN 766 designates this vessel as what kind of craft? (a) sonar ship (b) submarine (c) supply ship

11. Built in Newport News, Virginia, the *USS Asheville* is a US Navy submarine manned by a crew of 116 enlisted personnel and 30 officers. Armed with torpedoes, as well as Harpoon and Tomahawk missiles, the *Asheville* is capable of what speed? (a) 10 knots (b) 15 knots (c) 20-plus knots

North Carolina Ferries

Coastal ferries are a vital link to our state's transportation network. They also float images of romance, fun, and adventure. Hop a ride on this quiz to test your nautical knowledge.

1. Ferry service on the North Carolina coast traverses five separate bodies of water. Besides Currituck and Pamlico sounds, the Department of Transportation Ferry Division serves citizens on the Cape Fear River, Pamlico River, and what other waterway that flows from Durham County past New Bern?
    (a) Tar River   (b) Powhatan River   (c) Neuse River

2. Current Tar Heel coastal ferry service has its roots in a line that was briefly operated during the spring of 1924 by a chap named Jack Nelson. Carrying passengers across Oregon Inlet, Nelson called what fishing village near Kill Devil Hills home base?   (a) Corolla   (b) Colington   (c) Frisco

3. In the early 1940s, Kitty Hawk native T.A. Baum operated a ferry business that took folks across Croatan Sound on two wooden boats that could carry 10 cars each. With the help of James and McDonald Clark, Baum ran his business from Manteo to what town in Dare County?
    (a) Manns Harbor   (b) Buxton   (c) Duck

4. Following World War II, The State Highway Commission purchased two surplus ships from the US Navy and began operating them as ferries on Croatan Sound. Named *Governor Cherry* and *Sandy Graham,* these vessels were LCTs, a military acronym for what?
    (a) Landing Craft Transport   (b) Landing Craft Tank   (c) Large Cargo Transport

5. Around 1950, ferryboat pioneer and Outer Banker Toby Tillett sold his Oregon Inlet operation to the State of North Carolina. Keeping Tillett's crews, the state ran his two 11-car capacity ferries, which were called *New Inlet* and what other name reminiscent of a large seaport in Spain?
    (a) *Jaurez*   (b) *Lisbon*   (c) *Barcelona*

6. The year 1961 saw North Carolina's first toll ferry begin operation on Pamlico Sound between Ocracoke Island and the Atlantic Ocean. The ferry that provided this service was a 128-foot craft constructed by the West India Fruit and Steamship Co. based in what Carteret County town that is the boat's namesake?
    (a) Sea Level   (b) Sneads Ferry   (c) Gull Rock

7. During 1965, two new ferries began operating from Ocracoke Island to Cedar Island. Still in operation, one of these crafts is named *Pamlico* for the body it plies, and the other ferry takes its name from what scenic body of water on Ocracoke Island?   (a) Lake Mattamuskeet   (b) Silver Lake   (c) Lake Waccamaw

8. The Hatteras Inlet ferry operation currently handles nearly 40 percent of all vehicle traffic in the North Carolina coastal ferry system. Between 1988 and 1991, five new ferries were added to the Hatteras route, including one named for what town on NC Highway 12 halfway between Buxton and Hatteras?
    (a) Waves   (b) Salvo   (c) Frisco

9. In 1977, the seventh North Carolina coastal ferry operation began service with the 30-car capacity ship *Governor Edward Hyde.* Traversing Pamlico Sound in a two-and-a-half-hour trip, this jaunt goes from Ocracoke Island to what Hyde County town whose name has an avian ring to it?
    (a) Duck   (b) Sanderling   (c) Swan Quarter

10. The 23rd vessel to enter service with the NC Department of Transportation's Ferry Division was completed and began operations in early 1995. Measuring 220 feet in length, this craft is named for what Carteret County island on which there's a town called Lola?
    (a) Durant Island   (b) Cedar Island   (c) Knotts Island

11. Operating about two dozen ferries with more than 200 daily departures in summer and 150 departures in winter makes North Carolina the nation's second-largest coastal ferry system. What state has a larger fleet?   (a) Oregon   (b) California   (c) Washington

Port Authorities

Our state's deep-water seaports in Morehead City and Wilmington are immersed in a history of commercial activity. Ship a load of correct answers with this quiz on state ports.

1. An important part of the Tar Heel transportation scene for over two centuries, Wilmington's position on the Cape Fear River made it an ideal location for a seaport. Part of a trade zone originally called the Port of Brunswick, Wilmington was incorporated in what year? (a) 1710 (b) 1739 (c) 1779

2. Port development in Morehead City began in the 1850s. Originally called Shepherd's Point, Morehead City, named for North Carolina governor John Motley Morehead (1796-1866), is located along what river? (a) Tar River (b) Neuse River (c) Newport River

3. Both Morehead City and Wilmington have their own small railways, operated by the NC State Ports Railroad Commission, that shuttle goods between the docks and main rail lines. With seven miles of track, what is the name of the little railroad at Wilmington?
   (a) Cape Fear Railroad (b) Wilmington Terminal Railroad (c) New Hanover Railroad

4. World War II saw the ports of Wilmington and Morehead City provide valuable service to the Allied cause. On May 15, 1999, a celebration took place in Wilmington honoring the 25,000 North Carolina Shipbuilding Co. workers who built what type of cargo ships at yards currently occupied by the state port? (a) Victory ships (b) Amphibious ships (c) Liberty ships

5. In 1949, the General Assembly approved the issue of $7.5 million in bonds for construction and improvement of North Carolina ports. What year during the Korean War era were terminals equipped to handle ocean-going ships completed at Wilmington and Morehead City?
   (a) 1952 (b) 1956 (c) 1957

6. In 1945, the state legislature created the NC State Ports Authority. In addition to the ports of Wilmington and Morehead City, the Ports Authority operates a small boat harbor near the entrance to the Cape Fear River down stream from Wilmington at what town? (a) Town Creek (b) Winnabow (c) Southport

7. Excellent highway access to the ports at Wilmington and Morehead City has done much to expedite the exchange of both imports and exports from those facilities. In Wilmington, the State Port is just off Highway 421. What major road leads to the docks at Morehead City?
   (a) US Highway 17 (b) US Highway 70 (c) NC Highway 49

8. With cargoes arriving daily from around the world, the ports of Wilmington and Morehead City see a variety of goods and commodities enter the country through their docks. What branch of the federal government has offices at both North Carolina State Ports?
   (a) US Customs (b) US Border Patrol (c) FBI

9. With more than 6,700 feet of wharf frontage on the Cape Fear River, the Port of Wilmington uses a variety of equipment, including four gantry cranes, a mobile crane, 59 life trucks, and nine top-lift container handlers to unload ships. How many ships are unloaded at Wilmington each year?
   (a) 150 (b) 250 (c) 500

10. The Port of Morehead City recently saw completion of a new $8 million railroad trestle to a nearby island where the port plans expansion. The new trestle replaces a wooden structure originally built in 1907. To what island, the site of a large aviation fuel depot, does the trestle go?
    (a) Radio Island (b) Roanoke Island (c) Bald Head Island

11. During 1999, the Port of Wilmington saw more than 1 million tons of exports and 1.2 million tons of imports pass over its wharves. With 456,000 tons exported, what renewable resource commodity leads all others leaving Wilmington? (a) Iron ore (b) Sulfur (c) Wood pulp

First In Flight

Since the time the Wright Brothers lifted their biplane over the sands of Kitty Hawk on December 17, 1903, North Carolina has had a proud history in the field of aviation.

See how much you know about North Carolina aviation by testing yourself with these questions.

1. Brothers Paul and Kiffin Rockwell of Asheville flew with what famous World War I group?
    (a) Red Barons   (b) Black Sheep Squadron   (c) Lafayette Escadrille

2. This small Cape Hatteras airport is named for what controversial Air Corps leader of the 1920s?
    (a) Billy Mitchell   (b) Jimmy Doolittle   (c) Curtis LeMay

3. What year did Charlotte/Douglas Municipal Airport begin operations?   (a) 1917   (b) 1945   (c) 1936

4. Charles Lindbergh once paid Greensboro a visit in the *Spirit of St. Louis*. On what date did he land there?   (a) December 7, 1941   (b) October 14, 1930   (c) October 14, 1927

5. What government agency recommended Kitty Hawk to the Wright brothers?
    (a) US Weather Bureau   (b) NASA   (c) FAA

6. Morris Field was named after World War I aviator William C. Morris of Cabarrus County. Where was this World War II training base located?
    (a) Concord   (b) Kannapolis   (c) Charlotte/Douglas Municipal Airport

7. Robert Morgan of Asheville flew a famous B-17 bomber for 25 missions over Europe in WWII. What was that plane's name?   (a) *Memphis Belle*   (b) *Bad Penny*   (c) *Diamond Lil*

8. What public airports have the highest and lowest elevations in North Carolina?
    (a) highest: Ashe County Airport, 3,173 feet above sea level—lowest: Ocracoke Island Airport, 5 feet above sea level   (b) highest: Mt. Mitchell Airpark, 5,000 feet above sea level—lowest: Craven County Airport, 190 feet above sea level   (c) highest: Cherokee Regional Airport, 3,000 feet above sea level—lowest: Hyde County, 80 feet above sea level

9. On what date did Wilbur Wright first arrive at Kitty Hawk?
    (a) September 3, 1903   (b) September 13, 1900   (c) December 17, 1900

10. What was the wingspan of the Wrights' 1903 flyer?
    (a) 30 feet, 6 inches   (b) 40 feet, 4 inches   (c) 45 feet, 2 inches

11. What three civilian airports in North Carolina have runways 10,000 feet long?
    (a) New Hanover International, Kinston Regional, Seymour Johnson
    (b) Charlotte/Douglas International, Raleigh Durham International, Piedmont Triad International (Greensboro)   (c) Fayetteville Regional, Morganton/Lenoir, Concord Regional

12. In what year was Seymour Johnson Air Force Base established?   (a) 1917   (b) 1941   (c) 1952

13. When and where did Piedmont Airlines' first flight take place?   (a) January 1, 1947 in Winston-Salem   (b) February 20, 1948 in Wilmington   (c) October 1, 1950 in Charlotte

14. Frank Lawlor was a member of the legendary Flying Tigers during the early days of World War II. What North Carolina city was he from?   (a) Winston-Salem   (b) Fayetteville   (c) Durham

15. In 1927, the Air Corps repeatedly bombed a large concrete highway bridge near Albemarle. What river did that bridge span?   (a) Uwharrie River   (b) Tar River   (c) Pee Dee River

North Carolina Potpourri

Biltmore Estate, Asheville, NC

Books About The Tar Heel State

No matter the year, authors who have chosen North Carolina as the subject matter of their literary efforts always seem to have a wealth of colorful material to draw upon. Read on, then see if you can reach the right answers to this quiz on Tar Heel books.

1. A member of Sir Walter Raleigh's 1585 colony at our shores, Thomas Hariot wrote a book about that adventure that took the misleading title *A briefe and true report of the new found land of Virginia*. What settlement in North Carolina was Hariot's work really written about?
   (a) Sullivan's Island   (b) Roanoke Island   (c) Isle of Palms

2. William S. Powell wrote a book first published in 1968 that gives a brief description of every city, town, mountain and body of water in our state. Name the text that chronicles our Tar Heel geography from the 19th century Avery County community of Aaron to Zoar near Lanes Creek in Union County.
   (a) *The North Carolina Gazetteer*   (b) *Tar Heel Towns*   (c) *Our Carolina Landscape*

3. In 1986 popular Tar Heel author Jerry Bledsoe came out with a book that related his 600-mile, five-month trek down NC's longest highway. Bledsoe's title named two towns at the ends of US 64?
   (a) *From Whalebone to Hothouse*   (b) *From Columbia To Cashiers*   (c) *From Bethel To Brevard*

4. Listing information and opinions on everything from red wolves to ramps, Robert Beverley did an incredible amount of research on our state's mountain region and turned it into a book published in 1993. Taking a note from Poor Richard, what is Beverley's title?
   (a) *Poor Robert's Almanac*   (b) *The Mountain Almanac*   (c) *The Western North Carolina Almanac*

5. Tar Heel historians LeGette Blythe and Charles Brockman collaborated in 1960 to write a book tracing the history of Charlotte and Mecklenburg County. Borrowing from that area's nickname, what title did their work take?   (a) *Panther's Den*   (b) *Hornet's Nest*   (c) *State of Mecklenburg*

6. In addition to founding *The State* in 1933, Carl Goerch also hosted a 1930s radio show on Raleigh's WPTF and authored several books. One of Goerch's most popular works took its title from what Outer Banks island?   (a) Ocracoke Island   (b) Cedar Island   (c) Bald Head Island

7. Born in 1913 in Dare County, Nell Wechter began writing at an early age. In 1957 she published a novel for young people based on World War II Outer Banks experiences with German U-Boats. What was this award-winning and still popular book called?
   (a) *Depth Charges Off Dare*   (b) *Taffy of Torpedo Junction*   (c) *Pursuit Off Pamlico*

8. Yet another classic book about our state's Outer Banks region was authored by Ben Dixon McNeill in 1958. Profiling Bankers and their relationship to that unique area in both a historical and sociological sense, McNeill's title echoed what type of resident there?
   (a) *Hattersman*   (b) *Core Sound Folk*   (c) *Citizens of Corolla*

9. Said to have written more about the history of our state than any other person, Hugh Talmadge Lefler had a long and distinguished career as an author and educator. Name the North Carolina history book that Lefler and Albert R. Newsome published way back in 1954 that is still highly regarded.
   (a) *Tar Heel History*   (b) *North Carolina's Past*   (c) *North Carolina: The History of a Southern State*

10. In addition to publishing this magazine from 1951 to 1970, Bill Sharpe also wrote a four-volume set of books about all 100 North Carolina counties. Originally appearing as articles in *The State,* what title did Sharpe give his completed project?
    (a) *Carolina 100*   (b) *A New Geography of North Carolina*   (c) *Tar Heel Counties and Towns*

11. Since 1941 the North Carolina secretary of state has regularly issued a comprehensive compilation of information about our state. Containing everything from the name of our state dog to brief biographies on legislators, this book goes by what title?
    (a) *North Carolina Manual*   (b) *Carolina Factbook*   (c) *Tar Heel Tally*

The Power Of The Press

Since colonial times Tar Heels have held dear their freedom of the press. Put your knowledge of names, locations, and dates to the test as you try this quiz on North Carolina newspapers.

1. The Haywood County town of Canton's newspaper dates back to 1903. Hitting the newsstands each Wednesday, this local paper has a name similar to a famous World War II US Navy aircraft carrier. With a circulation of 2,000, what is the name of Canton's paper?
    (a) *The Blue Ridge*   (b) *The Enterprise*   (c) *The Nimitz*

2. Burlington's newspaper, the *Times-News,* has a circulation of 30,000 readers. Published by Freedom Communications, the *Times-News* has a weekday evening edition and morning editions on Saturday and Sunday. When this newspaper was first published in 1887, who was our state's governor?
    (a) Alfred M. Scales   (b) Jonathan Hall   (c) J.W. Goins

3. Although its journalistic life lasted barely two months, the Raleigh *Register* was the first newspaper in our state to offer daily distribution. The year this event took place was one year after the North Carolina Railroad was chartered. In what year was the *Register* published daily?   (a) 1862   (b) 1850   (c) 1812

4. On November 1, 1985, what had been the Carolinas' largest afternoon daily ceased publication after 97 years. Name this newspaper that had been founded by Wade Hampton Harris in December 1888.
    (a) *Charlotte Times*   (b) *Charlotte Tattler*   (c) *Charlotte News*

5. Owner of the first printing press in North Carolina, James Davis published the first newspaper in our state, the *North Carolina Gazette,* in 1749. Name the coastal Carolina town that was Davis' home and still is the seat of Craven County.   (a) New Bern   (b) Avon   (c) Oriental

6. Boasting 3,000 paid subscribers today, Bryson City's weekly newspaper dates back to 1884. Widely read in Swain County, the paper takes what name after the hills that surround the town?
    (a) *Blue Ridge Banner*   (b) *Brush Mountain Chronicle*   (c) *Smoky Mountain Times*

7. Published weekly, *The Chatham News* was founded in 1923. The newspaper of choice for nearly 5,000 subscribers, this little giant of Tar Heel journalism is headquartered in what Chatham County town that was first known as Matthews Cross Roads?   (a) Siler City   (b) Pittsboro   (c) Silk Hope

8. Dispensing stories and opinion since 1893, the *News of Orange County* fills its 4,500 readers with information each Wednesday. The *News of Orange County* is based in what county seat town located about 12 miles northwest of Durham?   (a) Carr   (b) Hillsborough   (c) Bahama

9. At the extreme western end of the Tar Heel state, the town of Murphy and its neighbors enjoy a semiweekly newspaper that was founded in 1889. What is the name of this journal, which reflects both the county of its publication and American Indian tribe?
    (a) *Cherokee Scout*   (b) *Catawba Carrier*   (c) *Lumbee Leaflet*

10. Winner of the 1971 Pulitzer Prize for public service, the *Winston-Salem Journal* daily enlightens its 100,000 or so subscribers. What year, sandwiched between the election of Gov. D.L. Russell and the Spanish-American War, did this paper first hit the streets?   (a) 1882   (b) 1890   (c) 1897

11. The largest newspaper in the Carolinas has had a long history of journalistic excellence, including a Pulitzer Prize for exposing corruption at Jim and Tammy Bakker's PTL Club. Name this newspaper whose Sunday circulation alone exceeds 300,000.
    (a) *The Asheville Orator*   (b) *The Charlotte Observer*   (c) *The Raleigh Herald*

12. Raleigh's newspaper has had some fine editors, including Josephus Daniels who also served as secretary of the US Navy and ambassador to Mexico. *The News and Observer* traces its roots to what year near the end of the Civil War?   (a) 1865   (b) 1867   (c) 1868

13. The state's first weekly newspaper to ever win a Pulitzer Prize, the *Tabor City Tribune,* took this honor in 1952 for editorials against the Ku Klux Klan. With a current circulation approaching 4,000, the *Tribune* comes from what county?   (a) Robeson County   (b) Bladen County   (c) Columbus County

*Circulation figures and founding dates for most questions came from the reference source *Gale Directory of Publications* and *Broadcast Media 1996.*

Tar Heel Spooks And Specters

North Carolinas has more than its share of haunts, haints, and hobgoblins. Don't get the willies as you guess the answers to this quiz on grisly goings-on in our state.

1. Just south of Siler City is a 40-foot circle of bare earth that has scared folks silly for decades. Although scientists have tried to explain the phenomenon, most people blame another being and offer a different name for this site. (a) Satan's Shuffle (b) Devil's Tramping Ground (c) Mephisto's Meander

2. Made famous in song by country music star Tommy Faile, mysterious lights have been spotted on a mountain top along the Burke-Caldwell county line since the late 1700s. Name these eerie illuminations that have even drawn the attention of the Smithsonian Institution.
    (a) Linville Lights (b) St. Elmo's Fire (c) Brown Mountain Lights

3. Tales of human-like creatures abound in North Carolina lore. During the 1870s, rail workers in Northampton County came across a mound filled with humanoid skeletons nine feet tall. What Northampton County town on Highway 301 had those bones?
    (a) Garysburg (b) Rich Square (c) Galatia

4. At the opposite end of the yardstick are Tar Heel stories about mysterious "little people." One of the best tales revolves around a Cherokee legend of elves who live near what prominent landmark overlooking Lake Lure? (a) Table Rock (b) Chimney Rock (c) Devil's Garden

5. Witnesses from local farmers to President Grover Cleveland have claimed they saw a mysterious light along railroad tracks near Maco. Said to be the ghost of a trainman killed in an 1867 crash, the Maco light is located in what county? (a) Brunswick County (b) Beaufort County (c) Hertford County

6. Besides spooks, spaceships have been known to throw a scare into Tar Heels. In the mid-1970s more than 50 UFO sightings took place in a single week near the seat of Robeson County. Name this community that was under an alien air raid. (a) Whiteville (b) Pembroke (c) Lumberton

7. Taking the form of a young woman, a ghostly hitchhiker has been seen by motorists near Jamestown in Guilford County since the 1920s. Name the highway where this lithesome specter floats for a tote.
    (a) US 70 (b) NC 29 (c) US 421

8. Built for the Western North Carolina Railroad, Cowee Tunnel near Bryson City was constructed by prison labor. The ghosts of 20 convicts who drowned crossing what river near the worksite are said to haunt this dank passage? (a) Catawba River (b) South Fork River (c) Tuckasegee River

9. Said to be ghosts of Tory riders taking an urgent dispatch to Lord Cornwallis from Kings Mountain battlefield, the "King's Riders" date back to just after the American Revolution. Name the British commander who sent this futile plea for help to his superior in Salisbury.
    (a) Colonel Patrick Ferguson (b) Colonel Harlan Sanders (c) Colonel Alexander McLeod

10. "Ephraim's Light" is a spooky glow in Northampton County said to have its origins when a plantation slave there was burned for killing his master. Name the town a few miles northwest of Gumberry on NC 186 where this flickering fantasy appears. (a) Lasker (b) Seaboard (c) Potecasi

11. Back in 1956, watermelons were on the mind of a mysterious Tar Heel monster that left its foot-long footprints in an Anson County garden. What town was the site of this strange creature's quest for melons? (a) Polkton (b) Hydro (c) Wadesboro

12. Hertford County residents tell a weird tale about a woman who cursed so much that a huge spotted creature flew out of the sky and stabbed her with a pitchfork. Como in Hertford, where this incident allegedly took place, is named for a lake in what European nation?
    (a) Italy (b) Spain (c) The Netherlands

13. Since the 1700s, residents of a North Carolina county, seated by Winton, have told tales about a giant bird called the Shike Poke that carries away naughty children to its nest in the swamps. Name the county where pocosin and forest are said to harbor this avian apparition.
    (a) Martin County (b) Dare County (c) Hertford County

Tar Heel Haunts And Hobgoblins

Hobgoblins of every type have fueled the fears and fancies of North Carolinians since our state's earliest days. Don't get spooked in your quest for the answers to this quiz.

1. Killed in an 1867 train wreck, Joe Baldwin is said to still walk the tracks just west of Wilmington swinging a lantern. What town on US 74 between Leland and Delco is the site of Joe's famous light?
    (a) Maco (b) Maxton (c) Whiteville

2. Possum hunters Jim Weaver and Joe Lewis never forgot the night in 1905 when they claimed to have witnessed a Civil War battle near Goldsboro fought by ghosts. What battlefield were they near when the action started? (a) Cold Harbor (b) Fort Fisher (c) Bentonville

3. Located near Bryson City, Cowee Tunnel was built by convict labor for the Western North Carolina Railroad. The ghosts of 20 cons who drowned crossing the river by boat to get to work are said to still haunt the shaft. What river at Cowee claimed the men?
    (a) Broad River (b) Tuckasegee River (c) Pigeon River

4. In Northampton County an eerie story still circulates about ghostly flames on a plantation where a slave was burned for killing his master. What town on NC 186 four miles northeast of Gumberry is the scene of "Ephraim's Light?" (a) Oxford (b) Soul City (c) Seaboard

5. In a swamp near Smithfield the ghosts of Yankee renegades hung for murdering a local plantation owner and his wife are said to haunt the island where they were executed. What county is home to Smithfield and the spooks? (a) Johnston County (b) Carteret County (c) Dare County

6. As far back as 1923, motorists passing through the Guilford County hamlet of Jamestown have reported a ghostly figure asking for a ride to High Point. What form does this haunting hitchhiker take?
    (a) a teenager (b) a little boy (c) a young woman

7. Many eerie tales have been told about the ghost of Charlotte Cabarrus at Somerset Place plantation in Washington County. The former estate of Josiah Collins, Somerset Place and Charlotte's ghost are located near what large natural lake? (a) Jordan Lake (b) Lake Phelps (c) Lake Lure

8. Just off NC 171 not far from Jamesville is Diamond City, a North Carolina ghost town that had its heyday more than 100 years ago. Stories about Diamond City include strange fireballs and ghostly railroad workers. What coastal county is Diamond City located in?
    (a) Martin County (b) New Hanover County (c) Onslow County

9. To this day, near the former Cherokee Indian capital of Echota, a ghostly brave's spirit is said to walk the mountain ridges. Who is this Cherokee leader who gave up his own life in 1838 so that his people could be free? (a) Tsali (b) Tecumseh (c) Red Cloud

10. Located 10 miles west of Siler City is one of North Carolina's most famous "supernatural" sites. What is the name of this 40-foot diameter circle of bare earth where not plant or tree will grow?
    (a) Boogerman's Walk (b) Witch's Walk (c) Devil's Tramping Ground

11. Between Hot Springs and Marshall once stood a haunted inn named Chunn's Tavern. The ghost of the murderous innkeeper Alfred Chunn, who was himself killed in self-defense by a young Civil War veteran, is said to haunt the banks of what nearby river?
    (a) Neuse River (b) French Broad River (c) Tar River

12. Two ghostly riders sometimes seen on October evenings between Kings Mountain and Salisbury, "The King's Messengers" are said to be the spirits of Tory militiamen from the American Revolution. What ill-fated British Major dispatched these men to Cornwallis from Kings Mountain seeking reinforcements.
    (a) Patrick Ferguson (b) Geoffrey Page (c) Thomas Tallis

13. Another phantom rider, the heartbroken lover of a slain Civil War soldier, is said to guide her eerie steed past Old Calvary Church at Fletcher. Many who have seen this sight compare it to the headless horseman in what famous story by Washington Irving?
    (a) *Legend of Sleepy Hollow* (b) *Ichabod Crane* (c) *Last of the Mohicans*

North Carolina's State Symbols

North Carolina's state symbols reflect the abundance of good things in our state as well as the excellence of its people. Test your knowledge of Tar Heel nature and natives with the correct answers to this quiz.

1. The official song of North Carolina was chosen by the General Assembly of 1927. Written by Judge William Gaston of New Bern way back in 1840, this lyric tune goes by what title?
   (a) "Carolina On My Mind"   (b) "Tar Heel Heaven"   (c) "The Old North State"

2. Appearing on our state flag and seal, North Carolina's official motto is Esse Quam Videri. Found in Cicero's classic essay on friendship, this Latin phrase has what meaning:
   (a) "To be rather than to seem"   (b) "To act rather than to seem"   (c) "To sew rather than to seam"

3. Even though our state flag had shown these shades since its earliest days, it was not until 1945 that the General Assembly adopted what tones as the official colors of North Carolina?
   (a) gold and blue   (b) red and blue   (c) white and red

4. The only type of canine to have originated in our state, North Carolina's official state dog was chosen in 1989. Name this breed, whose magnificent call and noble face are the source of hunting reverence and awe.   (a) Soonerhund   (b) Plott hound   (c) Tar Heel terrier

5. Named for the type of fish it was especially adept at pursuing, North Carolina's official state boat is a traditional sailing ship once handcrafted on Roanoke Island. What craft is this, built of native cypress and juniper?   (a) Shad boat   (b) Bass boat   (c) Crappie boat

6. Although some might say moonshine, North Carolina's state drink is actually a much more nourishing product of our state's many farms. In 1987 the General Assembly voted what drink our official state beverage?   (a) Apple cider   (b) Pinto bean wine   (c) Milk

7. North Carolina's state rock was chosen for its strength and character—qualities our citizens possess in great abundance. A quarry near Mount Airy is the world's largest mine of what stone, which has been our mineral symbol since 1979?   (a) Granite   (b) Marble   (c) Feldspar

8. A denizen of our state's gardens and forests, the type of turtle that the General Assembly chose in 1979 to be North Carolina's official reptile can live to be 100 years old. Slow but steady, what species of turtle is this that portrays the patience of the Tar Heel people?
   (a) Eastern Snapping Turtle   (b) Eastern Box Turtle   (c) Terrapin

9. In 1971 the General Assembly voted the Channel Bass our official state saltwater fish. Weighing up to 75 pounds, this fighting quarry of surfcasters all along our coast also goes by what name?
   (a) Red Drum   (b) Virginia Mullet   (c) Croaker

10. In 1965 North Carolina became first in the nation to designate an official state seashell. Generally found in deep waters off our coast, what type of 4-inch-long, plaid-colored shell holds this honor?
    (a) Whelk   (b) Coquina   (c) Scotch Bonnet

11. A symbol of cooperation and industry, our state's official insect produces a valuable commodity in addition to helping farmers pollinate their crops. What busy creature has been North Carolina's insect symbol since 1973?   (a) honey bee   (b) yellow jacket   (c) hornet

12. A familiar sight in parks, forests, and at birdfeeders, our official North Carolina mammal is loved by some and considered a pest by others. What furry scamp has since 1969 been so honored by the General Assembly?   (a) Red squirrel   (b) Gray squirrel   (c) Raccoon

13. In 1963 the General Assembly voted for an official North Carolina state tree. Name this species that since colonial days has been a vital part of our economy, and even helped give us the nickname "Tar Heels."   (a) Oak   (b) Poplar   (c) Pine

14. A year-round resident in North Carolina, our official state bird was chosen in March 1943. Always lending a brilliant splash of color during drab winter days, what species of feathered friend did the General Assembly pick during World War II to represent our state?
    (a) Scarlet Tanager   (b) Goldfinch   (c) Cardinal

Space Invaders

One of the nation's Unidentified Flying Object hot spots, North Carolina receives reports of all kinds of spaceship sightings. Explore our alien connection in this quiz on Tar Heel UFOs.

1. One of America's top UFO investigators, George D. Fawcett of Lincolnton, has donated his research of more than 1,200 sightings to the Center for UFO Studies in Roswell, New Mexico. The center has given North Carolina what rank among the 50 states in UFO sightings? (a) first (b) second (c) fourth

2. The highway that runs between Lincolnton and Cherryville has seen many alleged alien craft encounters, including one in 1978 in which a motorcycle chased a UFO. Name this road, which also had reported alien encounters in 1973, 1992, and 1993.
(a) NC Highway 49 (b) NC Highway 150 (c) US Highway 28

3. In 1979 a reported chase between a helicopter and UFO occurred in Charlotte. Radar at Charlotte-Douglas Airport reportedly detected unexplained objects traveling east as the chopper and UFO began their flight from what cultural center next door to the old Charlotte Coliseum?
(a) Ovens Auditorium (b) Park Center (c) Memorial Stadium

4. Some folks argue that one of North Carolina's most famous curiosities is a landing site for UFOs. What 40-foot circle near Siler City, where vegetation refuses to grow, could be a place where space ships alighted? (a) Widow's Walk (b) Devil's Tramping Ground (c) Satan's Crop Circle

5. Several UFO sightings have occurred near Lake Norman and the upper end of Mecklenburg County. What major electricity-producing facility on Lake Norman seems to draw these alleged visitors from outer space? (a) Allen Steam Plant (b) Oconee Nuclear Station (c) McGuire Nuclear Station

6. On March 16, 1998, witnesses reportedly saw a glowing silver disc flying toward Lenoir. Folks said the disc was larger than the three military jets escorting it from what resort town northwest of Lenoir on US Highway 321? (a) Vale (b) Blowing Rock (c) Granite Falls

7. North Carolina's first reported visit from a manned UFO came in April 1952, when a 10-foot-wide saucer-shaped disc struck businessman Jim Allen's house in Robeson County. The "spaceman" pilot, said to be three feet tall, climbed back into his ship and left Allen speechless in what town?
(a) Lumberton (b) Hope Mills (c) Peachland

8. Another North Carolina UFO lakeside sighting occurred on April 8, 1998, when triangular-shaped UFOs were filmed with a camcorder. As reported by CBS News, the ships were flying near what lake on the Yadkin River near Salisbury? (a) High Rock Lake (b) Lake Adger (c) Lake Tillery

9. At least nine cases of electromagnetic effects, such as car engines cutting off and radio malfunctions, have been attributed to UFOs in North Carolina. A few of the places where these effects have been noted are Greensboro, Mount Airy, Lincolnton, and what Hoke County town known as the turkey capital of our state? (a) Marshville (b) Arabia (c) Raeford

10. In 1994, at least a half dozen people in Shelby reported seeing a strange object in the western sky that was red and green on top with glowing lights like a chandelier. Heading west from Shelby would have put the UFO on a course to what town on US Highway 74?
(a) Mooresboro (b) Patterson Springs (c) Kings Mountain

11. On October 23, 1950, ex-United States Air Force pilot Frank Risher spotted a large dirigible-shaped UFO with three portholes in Chatham County. The craft hovered for several seconds, then sped southeast away from what Chatham County town on the Norfolk Southern Railway line?
(a) Silk Hope (b) Bonlee (c) Bynum

Turn Of The Centuries

Pop the cork on this quiz—the answers just might help North Carolinians ring in the new millennium.

1. Located in Hertford County, the Tar Heel community of Millennium is possibly the only spot in the nation so named. Situated northeast of Aulander and southwest of Ahoskie, Millennium can be reached by what highway? (a) NC 11   (b) US 74   (c) NC 77

2. The year 1700 saw English explorer John Lawson take a trip up the Santee-Wateree-Catawba River into the Piedmont of North Carolina. One thing Lawson discovered during his expedition was a dish prepared by Native Americans that many today consider the "state food" of North Carolina.
    (a) fried chicken   (b) fried catfish   (c) barbecue

3. In 1800, one of the most significant documents in North Carolina history was reportedly destroyed in a fire that leveled the home of prominent Mecklenburg County citizen John McKnitt Alexander. Name this paper that has been called the first official act of independence from the British in the American colonies.
    (a) Mecklenburg Bill of Rights   (b) Charlotte Resolves   (c) Mecklenburg Declaration of Independence

4. The turn of the 20th century saw the first load of automobiles shipped to the South arrive in Charlotte by railroad. From this lot, Queen City resident Osmond Barringer purchased a steam-powered car of what brand name? (a) BMW   (b) Locomobile   (c) Triumph

5. North Carolina's population is undoubtedly growing. The 1990 US Census reported our state's population to be 6,632,000. As of January 1, 2000, how many folks does the US Bureau of the Census predict will reside in the Old North State? (a) 7,777,000   (b) 8,100,000   (c) 8,550,000

6. For decades, roving groups of gentlemen have made New Year's Eve unique in the Gaston County town of Cherryville by recreating an ancient tradition designed to scare off witches and evil spirits. January 1, 2000, arrived with a roar in Cherryville as what raucous activity took place?
    (a) drag racing   (b) musket shooting   (c) hollering contest

7. As revelers ushered in the new millennium on December 31, 1999, there were plenty of fireworks to light up the evening sky. Shining down on the festivities was a Carolina moon in what phase?
    (a) last quarter   (b) first quarter   (c) full moon

8. A fun-filled New Year's Eve party, complete with dancing, fireworks, and a falling beach ball at the stroke of midnight, hit the board walk at a New Hanover County beach known for its good times atmosphere. The "Shag," is a dance that can trace much of its history to that boardwalk at what beach below Wilmington? (a) Carolina Beach   (b) Topsail Beach   (c) Atlantic Beach

9. Chetola Resort in the North Carolina mountains is planning a Millennium Masquerade for New Year's Eve that will feature 250 famous folks from the past 100 years—actually the party goers dressed as those celebrities. The resort is located near what Watauga County village incorporated in 1889 near the head of the Yadkin River? (a) Zionville   (b) Deep Gap   (c) Blowing Rock

10. Charlotte plans a big New Year's Eve celebration that will include everything from a countdown for kids to a "Midnight in Western Europe" observance. What uptown Charlotte street named for North Carolina's royal governor from 1765-1771 will be the spot where the Queen City rings in the new millennium? (a) Brevard Street   (b) Tryon Street   (c) Davidson Street

Plenty To Brag About In The Tar Heel State

Proud, productive and progressive, North Carolina is a state that thrives on excellence. This quiz focusing on some of our state superlatives will provide any Tar Heel with plenty of braggin' rights.

1. The world's largest natural habitat zoo is our very own North Carolina Zoological Park. More than 1,400 acres of open countryside provide habitats for a variety of animals. Situated in a rural area just outside of Asheboro, the North Carolina Zoo can be reached by what highway?
   (a) US 74   (b) NC 159   (c) NC 47

2. Bargain hunters from all over "shop until they drop" at North Carolina's many factory outlet stores. Name the Alamance County city with so many outlets that its nickname is "Outlet Center of the South."
   (a) Burlington   (b) High Point   (c) Statesville

3. Its 255 rooms filled with priceless art treasures and furnishings, Asheville's famous Biltmore House is not only the largest private home in North Carolina, it's also the largest private residence in the world. George Vanderbilt's edifice to opulence is constructed in what architectural style?
   (a) Greco-Roman   (b) English Tudor   (c) French Renaissance

4. North Carolina's status as a golfer's paradise can best be understood by considering the fact that the Southern Pines-Pinehurst area is known as the "Golf Capital of the World." About how many golf courses are available for play in our state?   (a) 200   (b) 300   (c) 400

5. Always at the forefront in the performing arts, North Carolina is home to the world's first outdoor drama, *The Lost Colony*. Presented each summer since its debut in 1937, the play was cancelled for a spell by what occurrence?   (a) World War II   (b) Hurricane Hazel   (c) Cuban Missile Crisis

6. North Carolina turkey farmers have led the nation in production of turkeys moving ahead of Minnesota in 1982. The combination of hard work and high-tech allows Tar Heel turkey growers to raise how many gobblers annually?   (a) 20 million   (b) 60 million   (c) 80 million

7. Known for many years as the "Good Roads State," North Carolina provides more miles of paved highway for its visitors and residents than any other state in America. About how many miles of paved roads do we boast?   (a) 50,000 miles   (b) 60,000 miles   (c) 76,000 miles

8. To keep all those miles of roadside beautiful, more than 7,000 North Carolina groups have joined the "Adopt a Highway" program. About how much litter do these groups annually clean from our Tar Heel roads?   (a) 5 million pounds   (b) 1 million pounds   (c) 3 million pounds

9. Recreational opportunities abound in North Carolina. One of the most popular places in the state for boating, fishing and water skiing is 32,000-acre Lake Norman. The largest lake in North Carolina, this 34-mile-long body of water goes by what nickname?
   (a) Mecklenburg Mediterranean   (b) Inland Sea   (c) Catawba Gold Coast

10. Snow skiing is another outdoor activity that North Carolina excels in. The Tar Heel State has nine resorts and 80 slopes available for use. A 1,200-foot vertical drop, the slope at Sugar Mountain in Avery County is the steepest in the South. What skiing boomtown is nearest Sugar Mountain?
    (a) Highlands   (b) Etowah   (c) Banner Elk

11. Literally going from rags to riches, the multimillion dollar sport of stock car racing got much of its start in North Carolina. Each May the Charlotte Motor Speedway stages the Coca-Cola 600, the second-largest spectator event in the United States. What is the event that just tops the 600?
    (a) Indy 500   (b) Kentucky Derby   (c) Super Bowl

12. The most visited national park in the United States, the Great Smoky Mountains National Park, has over half of its 514,000 acres located in North Carolina. The highest peak in the park is located in Swain County. What is the name of this 6,642-foot mountain?
    (a) Mount Mitchell   (b) Clingmans Dome   (c) Mount Pisgah

13. Another North Carolina mountain superlative is the Joyce Kilmer Memorial Forest. One of the finest areas of virgin forest in the United States, its 3,840 acres are located within Nantahala National Forest in Graham County. What was the occupation of Joyce Kilmer?   (a) bear hunter   (b) botanist   (c) poet

The Year In Review

The end of the year is always a time for reflection. This quiz should help spark some memories.

1. June 1991 saw the crowning of a new Miss North Carolina. Who won that honor?
    (a) Mitta Isley (b) Jennifer Smith (c) Joy Rankin

2. What North Carolina university won the NCAA basketball championship April 1991?
    (a) Duke University (b) University of NC at Chapel Hill (c) Western Carolina University

3. When the US Census released its 1990 population figures, which number below is closest to North Carolina's population? (a) 10,000,000 (b) 3,000,000 (c) 6,000,000

4. History was made this legislative session when the first black man to serve as Speaker of the North Carolina House of Representatives took office. What is his name?
    (a) Dan Blue (b) Everett Blackmon (c) William Baxter

5. In October 1991, the *USS North Carolina* marked 30 years of mooring on the Cape Fear at Wilmington. What type of World War II ship is it? (a) aircraft carrier (b) battleship (c) cruiser

6. The North Carolina School of the Arts also celebrated an anniversary this year—its 25th. What North Carolina city is home to this fine institution? (a) Hickory (b) Monroe (c) Winston-Salem

7. Thankfully not another Hugo, a hurricane did take a good swipe at our coast August 1991. What was its name? (a) Bob (b) Wally (c) Marcus

8. In July 1991, the Charlotte Hornets basketball team announced it was once again changing head coaches. Who became the team's new leader? (a) Ryan Hunter (b) Allan Bristow (c) Robert Fulghum

9. Many NASCAR fans no doubt shed a tear when this stock car racing legend from Level Cross announced in October 1991 that he would drive just one more season. Name the driver known as "The King."
    (a) Ken Butler (b) Calvin McGuirt (c) Richard Petty

10. Operation Desert Storm veterans paraded to a hero's welcome in Fayetteville on July 4. What base, near Fayetteville, is home to one of that group's proudest contingents, the 82nd Airborne?
    (a) Fort Bragg (b) Fort Knox (c) Fort Caswell

11. June 1991 witnessed the maiden flight of the world's largest blimp from an aerodrome in Weeksville. In what North Carolina county is Weeksville located?
    (a) Rowan County (b) Pasquotank County (c) Avery County

12. Name the lucky fellow who pocketed $225,000 in prize money April 1991 after winning the Greater Greensboro Open golf tournament. (a) Mark Barringer (b) Mark Brooks (c) Mark Clark

13. North Carolina's growing movie industry got a boost last summer when a $40 million production of the classic *The Last of the Mohicans* was filmed near Lake James. Who wrote *The Last of the Mohicans?*
    (a) James Fenimore Cooper (b) Samuel Shapiro (c) Ernest Hemingway

14. The new World League of American Football began playing in 1991, with a team in Raleigh-Durham. What was its name? (a) Raleigh-Durham Raiders (b) Triangle Terrors (c) Raleigh-Durham Skyhawks

Looking Back On 1992

1992 was an eventful year in North Carolina, with politics and sports taking center stage much of the time. To see if you've kept up to date, take the following quiz on the year in review.

1. During 1992, Raleigh marked the bicentennial of its role as our state capital. It was not, however, the first city in North Carolina to have that honor. What town preceded Raleigh as capital?
    (a) Washington   (b) New Bern   (c) Goldsboro

2. With a possible $12 billion impact on North Carolina's economy, plans to construct a huge air freight terminal in our state surged ahead in 1992. What town was selected to be the home for the Global Air Cargo Complex?   (a) Albemarle   (b) Cary   (c) Kinston

3. North Carolina scored a major business coup in 1992 when Metroline Studios announced plans to build a sprawling studio facility that would employ hundreds in Cabarrus County. What type of studio does Metroline plan to build?   (a) film studio   (b) pottery studio   (c) family portrait studio

4. North Carolina poultry farmers retained their national championship this year by raising more of what type of fowl than any other state in the Union?   (a) pea fowl   (b) turkeys   (c) Bantam roosters

5. Billed as North Carolina's largest celebration of the musical blues, the Fifth Annual Bull Durham Blues Festival was held in Durham during 1992. What month did this musical milestone take place?
    (a) September   (b) October   (c) November

6. At the 1992 Summer Olympic Games in Barcelona, Spain, Charlotte's Melvin Stewart did our state proud by capturing a gold medal in what type of sport?   (a) pole vault   (b) discus   (c) swimming

7. Winning its second consecutive NCAA national basketball title in April of 1992, Duke University romped over the Michigan Wolverines. What was the final score of that game?
    (a) 85-63   (b) 71-51   (c) 79-60

8. Making golfing history in 1992, Fayetteville native Raymond Floyd became the first golfer ever to win a Senior PGA Tour and regular PGA Tour tournament in one season. Belying his competitive nature, what is Raymond's nickname?   (a) Sleepy   (b) Drowzy   (c) Droopy

9. The CIAA, a conference which organizes the nation's oldest and most famous black college basketball tournament, decided in 1992 to move their event from Richmond, Virginia to Winston-Salem in 1994. What does the acronym CIAA stand for?   (a) College Intramural Athletic Association   (b) Carolina Invitational Athletic Association   (c) Central Intercollegiate Athletic Association

10. Many were the long faces in Chapel Hill shortly after the 1992 college football season began. Defeated for the fifth time in a row by the North Carolina State University Wolfpack, the University of North Carolina Tar Heels will have to wait yet another year for revenge. Who was the quarterback who led NC State to its 27-20 win?   (a) Terry Jordan   (b) Bernie Henderson   (c) David McNeill

11. Politics was big news in 1992. In North Carolina, we elected a new "gubernator." Gubernator is Latin for what post?   (a) Peanut Inspector   (b) Governor   (c) Chief Judge

12. In the May 1992 Republican primary for the United States Senate, Lauch Faircloth defeated former Charlotte mayor Sue Myrick. Somewhat ironically, given his party affiliation, what town in our state is Lauch from?   (a) Democrat   (b) Carter   (c) Clinton

13. Democrat Melvin Watt won the North Carolina congressional primary race in May 1992 as well. In what newly formed North Carolina US House district did Watt achieve his win?
    (a) 14th Congressional District (b) 13th Congressional District (c) 12th Congressional District

The Tar Heel Year In Review

The year 1995 witnessed news milestones in sports, politics and a variety of other subjects in our state. Hit the headlines and call out the news hounds as you search for answers to this quiz on Tar Heel happenings of 1995.

1. Many Tar Heel farmers started out 1995 with good news concerning one of their most profitable crops. With an estimated value of $273 million, the commodity once called "King" posted its highest harvest since 1937. Ranking 11th nationally in production, North Carolina is seeing a resurgence of what crop?
    (a) cotton   (b) peanuts   (c) soybeans

2. Breaking a record that dated back 56 years, Cal Ripken Jr. of the Baltimore Orioles baseball team surpassed Lou Gehrig's streak of 2,130 consecutive games in September. Baseball fans in North Carolina were especially proud of Ripken's feat since he spent some of his early pro baseball career with what Tar Heel minor league team?   (a) Hickory Crawdads   (b) Gastonia Rangers   (c) Charlotte O's

3. After much political wrangling, the 1995 General Assembly voted on a state vegetable for North Carolina. Urged on by students at Wilson's Elvie Street Elementary School, lawmakers finally gave the nod to what vegetable our state leads the nation in production of?
    (a) tomato   (b) turnip greens   (c) sweet potato

4. Proving that politics and religion can make for some unique relationships, 1995 saw United States Senator Jesse Helms and the Dalai Lama of Tibet pay a cordial and informative visit to a Union County college. What school, which shares its name with the local community, did they stop by?
    (a) Indian Trail University   (b) Wingate University   (c) Monroe Technical Institute

5. The University of North Carolina at Chapel Hill basketball team went to the NCAA Final Four in 1995 seeking yet another national championship, but it was not to be. Playing in Seattle's Kingdome, the Tar Heels came up short in the shooting department, sinking just 37.5 percent of their shots from the field in the national semifinals. When the final buzzer sounded, what team had defeated the Tar Heels 75-68?   (a) Arkansas Razorbacks   (b) Florida Gators   (c) Michigan Wolverines

6. Shooting a 14-under-par 274 in blustery April weather, Mississippi native Jim Gallagher Jr. went on to victory in one of North Carolina's most prestigious golf tournaments. Pulling off the biggest final round comeback on the PGA Tour in years, Gallagher took home $274,000 for his win in the GGO. What does the acronym GGO stand for?
    (a) Greater Gastonia Open   (b) Greater Greensboro Open   (c) Greater Guilford Open

7. April saw sportscar fans from all over the Southeast gather near Lake Lure for the 50th and final running of one of their favorite events. When the final flag fell and the engines were silent, what racing event faded into Tar Heel history?
    (a) Chimney Rock Hillclimb   (b) Lake Lure Rally   (c) Hickory Nut Gorge Gymkhana

8. June 13 witnessed a crowd of nearly 14,000 faithful gather at the Charlotte Coliseum for services and prayer led by one of the world's most influential religious figures. Name this lady who, though small in size, had a heart as big as the world.
    (a) Sister Mary Edwards   (b) Sister Ernestina Evangelista   (c) Mother Teresa

9. Beating out nearly 150 applicants, Lumberton was one of just 10 communities nationwide to be named an "All-American City" in 1995. Factors that helped sway the judges included the town's decreasing crime rate and a beautification program which saw the planting of 15,000 flowers. What North Carolina county is Lumberton the seat of?   (a) Robeson County   (b) Pender County   (c) New Hanover County

10. Meredith College senior Lisa Bamford was crowned Miss North Carolina in 1995. A talented pianist, Bamford's rendition of a piece by Hungarian composer Franz Listz swept the talent portion of the pageant. What Wake County town on Interstate 40 southeast of Raleigh does she call home?
    (a) Rolesville   (b) Lizard Lick   (c) Garner

Sixty Years Of 'Down-Home' Trivia

Many milestones, firsts and features have occurred at *The State* during the six decades it has tried to inform and entertain its readers. Check those back issues and your own memory for the answers to this 60th anniversary quiz.

1. On June 3, 1933, the very first issue of *The State* hit the newsstands. What North Carolina governor had the supreme honor of gracing the cover of that inaugural copy of *The State?*
   (a) Clyde Hoey   (b) J.C.B. Ehringhaus   (c) Robert Cherry

2. The founder of *The State,* Carl Goerch, worked as a newspaperman before he went into the magazine business. Which one of the following newspapers did he write for prior to launching *The State?*
   (a) *The Wilson Mirror*   (b) *The Charlotte Post*   (c) *The Winston-Salem Journal*

3. Still a bargain today, the early issues of *The State* offered much good reading for the money. How much did those first issues cost?   (a) 25 cents   (b) 40 cents   (c) 10 cents

4. Though currently produced in Charlotte, *The State* was founded, and for many years published, in Raleigh. What building in our capital city held the offices of *The State?*
   (a) Lawyers Building   (b) Dobbs Building   (c) Cotton Buildling

5. In late December 1952, *The State* acquired its present motto, "Down Home In North Carolina." In all the years prior to that date, what had the magazine used as its slogan?
   (a) "Roving Around Carolina"   (b) "News and Views of North Carolina"
   (c) "A Weekly Survey of North Carolina"

6. With his relationship with *The State* dating all the way back to 1935, former University of North Carolina cheerleader, radio personality and writer Billy Arthur has contributed an inestimable amount of knowledge and entertainment to *State* subscribers. As noble as his heart, what is Billy's full name?
   (a) William Jennings Bryan Arthur   (b) William Tecumseh Sherman Arthur
   (c) William Joseph Eudy Arthur

7. Always eager to inform its readers, *The State* has featured an informational quiz on a wide range of topics since its earliest issues. What was the precursor to the current "State's Quiz" called?   (a) "Guess What"   (b) "How Many Can You Answer"   (c) "Truth Or Consequences"

8. Furthering literary enlightment for decades, *The State* has long featured a page or two of book reviews between its covers. Currently called "The Book Corner," what was the original *State* book review column named?   (a) "Book Larnin"   (b) "Tar Heel Texts"   (c) "Carolina Copies"

9. With a regular column in *The State* that ran from 1936 until recently, Carol Dare's "Merely A Woman's Opinion" was a wealth of recipes, womanly musings and wise opinions. Just who was Carol Dare?
   (a) Carol Goerch's daughter   (b) Virginia Dare's great-granddaughter   (c) a fictional character

10. A column of news media bits and pieces, "Turpentine: Drippings From the Tar Heel Press," was a *State* feature that ran for many years. Name the WRAL radio personality who was not only a frequent "Turpentine" contributor, but went on to become a US senator.
    (a) Luther Hodges   (b) Doug Mayes   (c) Jesse Helms

11. Author, sportsman and publicist Bill Sharpe helmed *The State* from 1951 to 1970. In addition to his duties at the front office, Mr. Sharpe also wrote a page about goings on across North Carolina. What was this column called?
    (a) "Hatteras To Highlands"   (b) "Murphy To Manteo"   (c) "Southport To Spruce Pine"

12. The late Bill Wright took over *The State* in 1970 when Bill Sharpe passed away. What issue of the magazine saw Mr. Wright not only assume the leadership role but also write an eloquent tribute to his friend and partner Bill Sharpe?   (a) January 15, 1970   (b) February 21, 1970   (c) March 1, 1970

Sixty-five And Still Growing

June 3, 1998, marked the 65th anniversary of *Our State* magazine. Take a tour down memory lane as you answer the questions in this quiz on the history of one of North Carolina's oldest and most loved publications.

1. June 3, 1933, saw the first issue of *The State* go on sale. The depression-era brainchild of publisher Carl Georch, this first issue consisted of how many copies?   (a) 500   (b) 1,000   (c) 2,500

2. A man of many talents, Goerch held jobs as a newsman, radio host, and television personality before and during his stint as publisher of *The State*. In addition to his love of the news media, Goerch had another passion that, at one time, made him the oldest person in North Carolina to hold what type of license?   (a) commercial fisherman   (b) airplane pilot   (c) hunting guide

3. Priced so anyone with a love of North Carolina can afford reading about the wonderful Tar Heel land in which we live, copies of *Our State* are just $2.95. When Carl Goerch first put out the magazine, a copy of *The State* sold for what price?   (a) 5 cents   (b) 10 cents   (c) 25 cents

4. Since 1935 Billy Arthur has contributed his own unique blend of North Carolina knowledge and wit to *Our State* magazine. Besides his talents as a journalist and radio broadcaster, Billy was once upon a time adept at cartwheels in his role as cheerleader for what school?
   (a) East Carolina University   (b) North Carolina State University   (c) University of North Carolina

5. In December 1952, *The State* began using the motto it carries to this day, "Down Home in North Carolina." Before this, the magazine had used what nickname that also reflected its frequency of publication?   (a) "A Weekly Survey of North Carolina"   (b) "This Month in North Carolina"
   (c) "Tar Heel Weekly News"

6. From its earliest years *Our State* has featured a page with reviews of books by Tar Heel authors or about our region and its lore. Currently called "Tar Heel Literature," these pages were originally known by what title?   (a) "Book Smart"   (b) "Readin' Review"   (c) "Book Larning"

7. Teasing the minds of *State* readers for decades, an informative and entertaining quiz on some aspect of North Carolina history or culture has always been a part of the magazine. Before its present name of *"Our State* Quiz," this department was called what?
   (a) "Tar Heel Teasers"   (b) "How Many Can You Answer"   (c) "Carolina Clues"

8. In 1951, sportsman and author Bill Sharpe took over *The State* helm as publisher—a position he held until 1970. Prior to joining *The State* team, Sharpe had served under three governors in what division of the North Carolina state government?
   (a) advertising and promotion   (b) travel and tourism   (c) parks and recreation

9. During its long history *Our State* has had several well-known North Carolinians as editorial contributors. Just as outspoken now as he was years ago, Senator Jesse Helms once added his thoughts to the magazine in a segment that featured news items and was named after what pungent pine product?
   (a) "North Carolina Naval Stores News"   (b) "Turpentine: Drippings From the Tar Heel Press"
   (c) "Pinenuts: Just Say No"

10. In early 1996 *The State* underwent another change in ownership when entrepreneur Bernard Mann became owner and publisher. Bringing the magazine full circle in a geographical sort of way, both *State* founder Carl Goerch and Bernie Mann originally hailed from what state?
    (a) Ohio   (b) Massachusetts   (c) New York

11. Setting *The State* firmly on a course of bigger and better doings, Mann Media made a slight adjustment to the magazine's title. With a cover photograph featuring horses cavorting in a lush Carolina field, what month saw *The State* assume its present name of *Our State* magazine?
    (a) June 1996   (b) July 1996   (c) August 1996

Answers

Page 2 ~ Our Four Fine National Forests
1. (b) US Forest Service
2. (a) approximately 3,000,000 acres
3. (b) Cherokee Indians
4. (c) Moses
5. (b) 1933
6. (a) Badin Lake
7. (a) NC 24/27
8. (c) France
9. (c) Rhododendron
10. (b) Waterwheel plant
11. (a) Pocosins
12. (c) Cherokee County

Page 3 ~ A Cascade Of Waterfall Trivia
1. (b) Transylvania County
2. (a) Blue Ridge Escarpment
3. (c) 411 feet
4. (b) Cullasaja River
5. (a) Pisgah National Forest
6. (b) Little Switzerland
7. (c) New Year's Creek
8. (b) Georgia
9. (a) Hernando de Soto
10. (a) South Mountains
11. (c) Wilkes County
12. (a) Hanging Rock State Park
13. (c) Qualla Reservation

Page 4 ~ Follow A North Carolina River
1. (b) Interstate 26
2. (c) Nile River
3. (c) Belgrade
4. (c) New Bern
5. (a) High Shoals Falls
6. (c) Bryson City
7. (c) Broad River
8. (b) Transylvania County
9. (c) England
10. (b) Nixonton

Page 5 ~ Creeks And Streams
1. (c) Swain County
2. (a) Cypress
3. (c) Sacramento Creek
4. (a) Andrew Jackson
5. (b) Bridle Creek
6. (b) Carteret County
7. (c) Lilliput
8. (b) Compass Creek
9. (c) Colt Creek
10. (a) Chinquapin
11. (b) Cape Fear River

Page 6 ~ Playing The Name Game With Tar Heel Towns
1. (a) Archdale County
2. (c) Fishtown
3. (b) Kullaughee
4. (a) Pershing
5. (c) Martinsborough
6. (b) Black River
7. (a) Hickory Tavern
8. (c) Scuppernong Lake
9. (a) Shepherd's Point
10. (b) Huntersville
11. (c) Mt. Ararat
12. (a) Wake Court House
13. (c) Sahara of North Carolina

Page 7 ~ How They Were Named
1. (c) Ivanhoe
2. (b) Japan
3. (a) Hillsborough
4. (c) Hiddenite
5. (a) Canton
6. (a) Dallas
7. (b) High Point
8. (a) Genlee
9. (c) Seven Springs
10. (a) Spencer Mountain
11. (c) Valle Crucis
12. (b) Wanchese
13. (c) Zirconia
14. (c) Louisburg
15. (a) Eden
16. (c) Conover
17. (b) LaGrange
18. (c) Fremont
19. (b) Naples
20. (a) Pembroke

Page 8 ~ Tar Heel Crossroads
1. (b) Cat Square
2. (a) Noah's Ark
3. (c) longitude and latitude
4. (c) I-40
5. (b) Mulberry
6. (a) Alamance County
7. (c) chiggers
8. (b) Tar Heel
9. (b) Chatham County
10. (a) NC 43 and 102
11. (c) foxes
12. (c) Clinton
13. (a) Mitchell River

Page 9 ~ Name That Town
1. (b) Brevard
2. (a) Andrew Jackson
3. (c) Albemarle Sound
4. (a) steel
5. (b) Avery
6. (c) I-85
7. (b) Troy
8. (a) Taylorsville
9. (c) Grover Cleveland
10. (c) Carteret
11. (a) Lord Proprietor of Carolina

Page 10 ~ Street Wise
1. (b) Dale Earnhardt
2. (a) Catawba County
3. (c) Girl Scout Road
4. (a) Bubba Boulevard
5. (b) Gangplank Road
6. (a) Tobacco Road
7. (c) The Road to Nowhere
8. (a) Easy Street
9. (c) Poverty Lane
10. (a) Jesse Helms
11. (b) Rabbit Skin Road

Page 11 ~ County Courthouses Past And Present
1. (c) marble
2. (a) Pittsboro
3. (b) Edenton Bay
4. (a) 107
5. (b) 2076
6. (c) Wilkesboro
7. (a) Bolivia
8. (b) first woman hanged in North Carolina
9. (c) William Percival

10. (a) Bryson City
11. (b) Civil War
12. (a) New Bern
13. (c) Richmond

Page 12 ~ North Carolina Military Camps
1. (c) Camp Polk
2. (a) first Confederate killed in Civil War
3. (b) Camp Lejeune
4. (a) Revolutionary War
5. (b) Marston
6. (c) Colonel Zebulon B. Vance
7. (a) Onslow County
8. (c) Crowders Mountain
9. (b) Burlington
10. (a) Clingmans Dome
11. (b) Battle of Kings Mountain
12. (c) Durham/Granville/Person

Page 13 ~ All You Wanted To Know About Tar Heel
    Mansions
1. (a) 1895
2. (c) Davie County
3. (b) Mecklenburg County
4. (a) James B. Duke
5. (c) Orton Plantation
6. (a) State Prison
7. (c) Scotts Hill
8. (b) Edenton
9. (a) William Tryon
10. (b) Reidsville
11. (c) Salisbury
12. (b) Bertie
13. (a) Pungo River

Page 14 ~ Historic North Carolina Churches
1. (b) Bath
2. (c) Edenton
3. (a) cruciform
4. (b) Mary Anna Morrison Jackson
5. (c) Ashe Co.
6. (a) Cornelius Harnett
7. (b) Hurricane Hazel
8. (c) East Flat Rock
9. (a) New Bern
10. (c) Biltmore House
11. (b) Moravians
12. (a) Catholic
13. (b) Jefferson Davis

Page 15 ~ Graves And Graveyards...

1. (b) East Street
2. (a) Napoleon Bonaparte
3. (c) 1942
4. (b) Wake Co.
5. (a) Harnett
6. (b) "Fort Fisher Hermit"
7. (c) Old Burying Ground
8. (a) his arm
9. (c) Randolph Scott
10. (b) *Look Homeward, Angel*
11. (c) Catawba River
12. (a) Carbine
13. (a) rum

Page 16 ~ Much Ado About Museums

1. (b) Bailey
2. (a) Laurinburg
3. (c) Spruce Pine
4. (b) Dallas
5. (c) Beaufort
6. (a) Fort Bragg
7. (c) Kenly
8. (a) Winston-Salem
9. (b) Sanford
10. (c) Cherokee
11. (a) Lake Junaluska
12. (a) Wilmington
13. (a) Durham
14. (c) Charlotte
15. (b) Valdese

Page 17 ~ Public Gardens In North Carolina

1. (c) Wilmington
2. (b) Fort Raleigh
3. (b) Cape Fear River
4. (a) Pinehurst
5. (b) Raleigh Little Theatre
6. (a) Winston-Salem
7. (c) Eno
8. (b) West Campus
9. (c) Robeson County
10. (a) NC 115
11. (c) UNC at Asheville
12. (b) Horn in the West Theater
13. (b) Wrightsville Sound
14. (c) Oconaluftee Village

Page 18 ~ Inlets And Islands

1. (a) Ocracoke Island
2. (c) Camp Lejeune Marine Base
3. (b) Smith Island
4. (b) Cedar Island
5. (a) fish
6. (b) Currituck Sound
7. (c) NC 12
8. (a) Bogue Sound
9. (b) "The Lost Colony"
10. (c) Brunswick County
11. (a) Sunset Beach
12. (b) Herbert C. Bonner Bridge
13. (a) Intracoastal Waterway
14. (c) Native Americans
15. (b) White Oak River

Page 19 ~ Curiosities Of Our Colonial Capital

1. (c) Switzerland
2. (a) 1746-1792
3. (c) Tuscaroras
4. (b) The Athens of NC
5. (a) Trent and Neuse Rivers
6. (b) US 70
7. (c) 1770
8. (a) Terry Sanford
9. (b) George Washington
10. (a) Ambrose Burnside
11. (c) 1989
12. (b) hospital
13. (a) King George II
14. (c) crape myrtle
15. (c) 1,000 years old

Page 20 ~ Wandering Through Wilmington

1. (c) New Liverpool
2. (a) Pender County
3. (b) Bellamy Mansion
4. (a) The Cotton Exchange
5. (b) 1960
6. (c) US 421
7. (b) 1875
8. (a) Thalian Hall
9. (c) *Wilmington Morning Star*
10. (b) George Washington
11. (a) Woodrow Wilson
12. (b) Laney High School
13. (c) Lumina

Page 21 ~ Go East, Young Man
1. (b) Seymour-Johnson Air Force Base
2. (c) Mickey Rooney
3. (a) Richard Caswell
4. (b) Imagination Station
5. (b) US Highway 64
6. (a) National Hollerin' Contest
7. (b) 1776
8. (c) Bay Tree Lake
9. (b) Duplin Winery
10. (c) North Carolina Wesleyan College
11. (b) France

Page 22 ~ A Capital Quiz
1. (c) 1771
2. (b) Margaret
3. (b) Wake Forest
4. (a) Greek Revival
5. (a) Neuse River
6. (b) William Tecumseh Sherman
7. (c) Andrew Johnson
8. (b) 1956
9. (b) mules
10. (a) Masonic Temple Building
11. (b) 1932
12. (c) NC College of Agriculture and Mechanic Arts
13. (a) a former North Carolina governor
14. (c) Daniel Fowle
15. (a) 1865

Page 23 ~ Mountain Trivia
1. (c) goats
2. (b) Tennessee Valley Authority
3. (a) Old Woman
4. (c) Maggie Valley
5. (a) Chimney Rock Hillclimb
6. (b) Cherokee
7. (c) Daniel Boone
8. (b) Lake Lure
9. (a) Black Dome
10. (c) William Sydney Porter
11. (b) Brevard Music Center
12. (a) Sugar Water
13. (c) Little Switzerland
14. (b) 6,643 feet

Page 24 ~ Highland Heritage
1. (c) Morristown
2. (b) 250
3. (b) Western North Carolina Railroad
4. (a) US 25

5. (c) Thomas Edison
6. (a) attorney
7. (c) Mary Pickford
8. (a) Dixieland
9. (c) National Climatic Center
10. (c) Basilica of St. Lawrence
11. (a) *Thunder Road*

Page 25 ~ High And Mighty
1. (b) Black Dome
2. (a) Governor of North Carolina
3. (b) Jackson County
4. (c) Novel
5. (a) Cherokee Tribe
6. (c) Moses
7. (a) Grandfather Mountain
8. (c) Clay County
9. (b) Alphabet
10. (a) Plott hound
11. (c) Minister

Page 26~Tar Heel Mountain Names And Places
1. (a) Kings Mountain
2. (c) Moses
3. (b) *Our Southern Highlanders*
4. (a) Polk County
5. (a) alphabet
6. (c) 1765-1771
7. (a) Rutherford County
8. (b) Hernando de Soto
9. (b) Swiss
10. (c) Cherokees
11. (a) Mount Mitchell State Park
12. (c) Utah Mountain
13. (b) Andrew Jackson

Page 27 ~ North Carolina Inns Abound From Mountains To Sea
1. (a) US 64
2. (c) Lake Toxaway
3. (b) 1913
4. (c) Gaelic
5. (a) Mary Pickford
6. (b) Burnsville
7. (a) Naval officers' quarters
8. (c) James Tufts
9. (b) Pamlico Sound
10. (a) Southern Railroad
11. (c) Great Trading Path
12. (c) Carl Sandburg
13. (b) Cotton mill

Page 28 ~ Tar Heel Eats And Eateries
1. (b) milk
2. (a) tomato base
3. (c) Cheddar
4. (a) Moravians
5. (c) Wayne County
6. (b) strawberries
7. (a) onion
8. (c) bugs
9. (c) cornmeal
10. (b) Continental Divide
11. (b) Tuckasegee River
12. (a) NC 16
13. (b) Trent River
14. (a) Masonic flag

Page 29 ~ The Inn Crowd
1. (c) 1913
2. (a) Sunset Mountain
3. (c) Biltmore Dairy
4. (c) F. Scott Fitzgerald
5. (a) Franklin D. Roosevelt
6. (b) Dwight Eisenhower
7. (b) National Register of Historic Places
8. (c) William Shakespeare
9. (a) Arts and Crafts
10. (c) George Vanderbilt

Page 30 ~ Historic Restaurants
1. (a) Dillsboro
2. (c) Ashe County
3. (a) National Register of Historic Places
4. (b) Blowing Rock
5. (a) Sears
6. (c) Trent River
7. (b) Carl Sandburg
8. (c) Valle Crucis
9. (a) Four Diamond Award
10. (b) Grocery
11. (c) Bryson City

Page 32 ~ The Lowdown On NC College Regalia
1. (c) catamount
2. (b) seahawk
3. (a) *Chanticleer*
4. (c) black and gold
5. (b) bulldog
6. (b) blue and gold
7. (a) *Buccaneer*
8. (c) burgundy and gray
9. (b) ram
10. (a) Crusaders
11. (c) *Agromeck*
12. (a) camel

Page 33 ~ Making The Grade
1. (c) Cougar
2. (a) Carteret County
3. (b) Wilmington
4. (c) Eastover
5. (c) 77 years
6. (b) Fletcher
7. (a) Cherokee County
8. (c) Taylorsville
9. (b) Duke University
10. (a) Pitt County

Page 34 ~ Tar Heel Patriots To Remember
1. (a) Bertie County
2. (c) governor
3. (b) Cherokee Indians
4. (a) pistol duel
5. (c) UNC at Chapel Hill
6. (b) State of Franklin
7. (a) Joseph Hewes
8. (c) Scotland
9. (b) 1784-1787
10. (a) French
11. (a) Abner
12. (c) Stovall

Page 35 ~ Revolutionary Places
1. (b) Hezekiah Alexander
2. (c) House in the Horseshoe
3. (a) Belmont Abbey College
4. (c) Patrick Ferguson
5. (c) Mount Vernon Springs
6. (a) Hillsborough
7. (b) Barbecue Church
8. (a) Currie
9. (b) Revolutionary War cannon
10. (c) Salisbury

Page 36 ~ A Nation Divided
1. (c) July 3, 1863
2. (a) Southport
3. (b) May 20, 1861
4. (c) John W. Ellis
5. (a) *USS Monitor*
6. (b) Salisbury
7. (a) Charlotte
8. (b) Wilmington
9. (a) Fort Fisher
10. (b) Colonel
11. (b) Raleigh
12. (c) Battle of Bentonville
13. (a) Thomas' Highland Legion

Page 37 ~ History Marks The Spot
1. (a) Stonewall Jackson
2. (c) William T. Sherman
3. (b) Jefferson Davis
4. (c) Asheville
5. (b) General Burnside
6. (a) Joseph E. Johnston
7. (c) ironclad
8. (a) Jewish
9. (b) Plymouth
10. (c) *USS Monitor*
11. (b) bricks
12. (a) James Martin

Page 38 ~ Put On Those Tar Heel Civil War
   Thinking Caps
1. (a) Burlington
2. (c) Stanley
3. (b) Thomas Wolfe
4. (a) Robert E. Lee
5. (b) Virginia
6. (a) Stonewall Jackson
7. (c) Fort Fisher
8. (b) Joseph E. Johnston
9. (a) Battle of Sharpsburg
10. (a) Same was a woman, Malinda Blalock
11. (a) George Meade

Page 39 ~ Regimental Nicknames From A Tar Heel
   Perspective
1. (b) Trojan Regulators
2. (a) Pee Dee Wildcats
3. (c) Waxhaw Jackson Guards
4. (a) Haywood Fire Shooters
5. (c) Burke and Catawba Sampsons
6. (a) Tuckahoe Braves
7. (c) Duplin Turpentine Boys

8. (b) Nantahala Rangers
9. (b) Lone Star Boys
10. (a) Scuppernong Grays
11. (c) Sandy Run Yellow Jackets
12. (a) Haw River Boys
13. (b) Caldwell Rough and Ready Boys

Page 40 ~ Sherman's March
1. (a) Pee Dee River
2. (c) Wilmington
3. (b) Laurel Hill
4. (b) Egypt
5. (a) Joseph Johnston
6. (b) Johnston County
7. (a) Kilpatrick's Pants
8. (b) April 12, 1865
9. (a) 26th North Carolina
10. (b) Morrisville

Page 41 ~ Tar Heel Officers Offered Inspiration In
   Civil War
1. (c) "Stand ye fast, and prepare"
2. (a) Hickory
3. (b) Newton
4. (b) Mecklenburg Declaration of Independence
5. (a) Ireland
6. (c) Cumberland County
7. (a) Wadesboro
8. (c) Yadkin County
9. (c) 1929-1933
10. (c) Broad River

Page 42 ~ Reconstruction In North Carolina
1. (b) 1867-1877
2. (c) Andrew Johnson
3. (a) Gettysburg
4. (b) Freedmen's Bureau
5. (b) Pitt County
6. (c) carpetbaggers
7. (b) Grand Dragon
8. (a) 14th
9. (b) Republicans
10. (a) impeachment
11. (c) Ohio
12. (b) 1868
13. (a) Warren County

Page 43 ~ The Corps Of Civilians
1. (b) 1933
2. (a) $30
3. (c) 60,000
4. (a) more than 60
5. (c) kudzu
6. (b) Mount Mitchell
7. (b) Blue Ridge Parkway
8. (a) Graham County
9. (c) Cherokee
10. (a) Appalachian Trail
11. (c) Frying Pan Gap
12. (b) Bryson City
13. (a) Marion

Page 44 ~ NC's Role In World War II
1. (b) 362,000
2. (a) Showboat
3. (c) P51 Mustang
4. (a) Johnston County
5. (b) cargo shipping
6. (c) Victory Gardens
7. (b) "Torpedo Junction"
8. (a) Fort Bragg
9. (c) *Memphis Belle*
10. (a) Andrew Jackson
11. (c) "Devil Dogs"
12. (c) United Service Organizations

Page 45 ~ Preserving Our History
1. (a) Department of Cultural Resources
2. (c) Catawba River
3. (c) Blackbeard
4. (c) Carl Sandburg
5. (a) US 441
6. (b) George Washington Vanderbilt
7. (c) Forsyth County
8. (a) Wilmington
9. (b) Albemarle Sound
10. (c) Seaboard Air Line
11. (a) Tryon Palace
12. (b) North Blount Street

Page 46 ~ Tar Heel State Historic Sites
1. (a) Morrow Mountain State Park
2. (c) Statesville
3. (b) Cape Fear River
4. (b) sand
5. (a) railroading
6. (c) Log cabin
7. (b) James K. Polk
8. (a) Cabarrus County

9. (b) *The Hills Beyond*
10. (a) Johnston and Sherman
11. (c) George Washington
12. (a) a river

Page 48 ~ Tar Heel Greats
1. (b) Brad's Drink
2. (a) Lillian Exum Clement
3. (c) NC Supreme Court Associate Justice
4. (a) Washington Duke
5. (c) Faison
6. (a) Laney High School
7. (b) Market Street
8. (c) 26th Regiment NC Troops
9. (c) Smithfield
10. (c) *Memphis Belle*

Page 49 ~ North Carolina's Early Explorers
1. (c) Pacific Ocean
2. (a) Cape Fear River
3. (b) Hernando de Soto
4. (b) Pamlico River
5. (c) Chesapeake Bay
6. (a) Cape Hatteras
7. (a) Sir Walter Raleigh
8. (b) Pamlico Sound
9. (c) Sir Francis Drake
10. (a) Croatoan
11. (b) Chowan River
12. (a) Durants Neck

Page 50 ~ North Carolina's Wonderful Women
1. (c) James Madison
2. (b) Cornelius
3. (a) secretary of labor
4. (b) chief justice of the NC Supreme Court
5. (c) Loray Mill
6. (a) Guilford County
7. (b) Sedalia
8. (c) painting
9. (b) Mary Anna Morrison
10. (a) Louisburg
11. (c) Edenton
12. (b) Lillian Exum Clement

Page 51 ~ North Carolina's African-Americans
1. (b) Salisbury
2. (a) Jefferson Davis
3. (c) Concord
4. (b) William McKinley
5. (a) Hertford
6. (c) Tar River
7. (a) Liberia
8. (b) Spanish-American War
9. (c) 1868
10. (b) Methodist
11. (a) yellow
12. (c) Livingstone College
13. (a) US 401

Page 52 ~ A Potpourri Of Political Trivia
1. (a) Ralph Lane
2. (b) Thomas Miller
3. (a) William Tryon
4. (a) Richard Caswell
5. (b) Richard Dobbs Spaight Jr.
6. (c) William Richardson Davie
7. (a) James Iredell Jr.
8. (c) John Willis Ellis
9. (a) Zebulon B. Vance
10. (b) Charles B. Aycock
11. (c) Joseph M. Broughton
12. (a) William Kerr Scott
13. (b) Terry Sanford

Page 53 ~ Tar Heel Politicos Past And Present
1. (c) Monroe
2. (b) Lincolnton
3. (c) Morganton
4. (a) Research Triangle Park
5. (a) mayor of Charlotte
6. (b) Democrat
7. (a) Rockingham
8. (c) Polkton
9. (b) *The Clansman*
10. (c) Greensboro
11. (a) secretary of the Navy
12. (b) Rural Free Delivery

Page 54 ~ Tar Heel Mountains Rich With Writers
1. (b) Asheville
2. (a) Zebulon Vance
3. (c) Weaverville
4. (a) *The Winter People*
5. (a) The French Broad
6. (b) Sylva
7. (c) 1st North Carolina Sate Poet Laureate

8. (b) Moravian Falls
9. (a) Canton
10. (c) *A Mother and Two Daughters*
11. (b) Western Carolina University
12. (a) The Land of the Sky

Page 55 ~ Show Business Tar Heel Style
1. (a) Hot Nuts
2. (c) Beaufort
3. (c) "NYPD Blue"
4. (a) Henderson
5. (c) *Deliverance*
6. (b) "Moms" Mabley
7. (a) *The Color Purple*
8. (b) Grabtown
9. (c) saxophone
10 (b) William Samuel
11. (a) Robbinsville
12 (c) Lisa

Page 56 ~ Tuneful Tar Heels
1. (a) Fred Kirby
2. (c) Earl Scruggs
3. (b) Arthur Smith
4. (c) Arthel Watson
5. (a) Stonewall Jackson
6. (a) The Moody Brothers
7. (b) Ronnie Milsap
8. (c) John D. Loudermilk
9. (a) Clyde Moody
10. (b) The Radio Building
11. (c) Charlie Poole
12. (a) Donna Fargo

Page 57 ~ North Carolina Indian Tribes
1. (c) 30
2. (b) Roanoke Island
3. (c) Montgomery County
4. (b) Tuscarora Indians
5. (a) Eastern Band of the Cherokee Indians
6. (c) Bryson City
7. (c) William Thomas
8. (a) Joyce Dugan
9. (b) Katapa
10. (a) Yaupon

Page 58 ~ Tales From Tar Heel Tribes
1. (a) Seven
2. (c) Gatesville
3. (b) Chief Junaluska
4. (a) Lake Mattamuskeet
5. (a) Blowing Rock
6. (b) corn, beans, squash
7. (c) Bertie County
8. (a) Caffena-tree
9. (c) Raven Rock State Park
10. (b) Lake Waccamaw
11. (b) hemlock

Page 60 ~ Flower Power
1. (b) Solomon's seal
2. (c) Yucca
3. (a) Soapwort
4. (c) Bull bay
5. (b) Thunderwood
6. (a) Maypops
7. (c) Wild carrot
8. (a) Apple of Peru
9. (a) Chicory
10. (c) Black-eyed Susan
11. (b) Cow lily

Page 61 ~ Native Plants Plentiful In NC
1. (b) yaupon tea
2. (a) Catawba rhododendron
3. (c) NC 107
4. (a) Wilmington
5. (b) sourwood
6. (a) goat's rue
7. (a) ginseng
8. (c) epiphyte
9. (b) toothache tree
10. (a) poke sallet
11. (c) tobacco
12. (a) Catawba County
13. (c) swamp cabbage

Page 62 ~ Coastal Carolina Flora And Fauna
1. (b) puppy drum
2. (a) pineapple
3. (c) up to 500 pounds
4. (b) menhaden
5. (a) Carolina anole
6. (c) osprey
7. (a) sea oats
8. (c) bluefish
9. (a) yaupon
10. (c) live oak

11. (b) croaker
12. (c) Scotch Bonnet
13. (a) ghost crab
14. (c) quahog

Page 63 ~ A Bird Baffler
1. (a) Cardinal
2. (b) National Audubon Society
3. (b) Anson County
4. (c) Osprey
5. (c) Lake Mattamuskeet
6. (a) Wild Turkey
7. (a) American Robin
8. (b) Wood Duck
9. (a) Great Horned Owl
10. (c) Mockingbird
11. (a) Crow
12. (c) Chickadee
13. (a) Goldfinch
14. (b) Starling

Page 64 ~ A Tar Heel Quiz For The Birds
1. (c) Lake James
2. (c) peregrine falcon
3. (a) Moore County
4. (c) NC 12
5. (a) Oteen
6. (c) wild turkey
7. (b) ferry boat
8. (c) Gaston County
9. (a) New River
10. (b) 16,600
11. (a) Hyde County
12. (c) raven
13. (b) Haywood County

Page 65 ~ NC's Mineral Magnificence
1. (c) 300
2. (a) Museum of NC Minerals
3. (b) Egypt Mine
4. (c) 1st in the world
5. (a) Mount Airy
6. (c) Iron Station
7. (b) no other state
8. (a) Granville County
9. (b) January
10. (b) Reed Gold Mine
11. (a) California
12. (b) Hiddenite

Page 66 ~ Tar Heel Gold
1. (a) Reed Gold Mine
2. (c) US 52
3. (b) agriculture
4. (a) Philadelphia
5. (c) art museum
6. (a) West Morehead Street
7. (b) Rutherford County
8. (c) Thomas Edison
9. (c) Belmont
10. (a) Stanly County
11. (b) City of Gold
12. (a) Person County
13. (c) Franklin County

Page 67 ~ The Answers Are Blowin' In The Wind
1. (b) 1954
2. (a) eye
3. (c) $7 billion
4. (b) 1775
5. (a) Pamlico Sound
6. (c) black square in center of red background
7. (b) counterclockwise
8. (a) New Hanover County
9. (c) Division of Emergency Management
10. (b) 1979
11. (a) August and September
12. (c) 74 mph or more

Page 70 ~ Try To Tackle This
1. (b) Chicago Bears
2. (a) Walter "Bill" Anderson
3. (c) Lenoir-Rhyne College and ECU
4. (a) Al Groh
5. (c) The first forward pass
6. (b) Gater Bowl
7. (a) Roman "Gabe" Gabriel
8. (b) Charlie "Choo-Choo" Justice, Cotton Sutherland, Art Weiner, Andy Bershak, George Barclay
9. (c) Fred E. "Freddie" Crawford
10. (a) Richard Christy
11. (b) "The Battering Ram"
12. (b) Pat Dye
13. (a) Charlie Woollen
14. (b) Art Weiner
15. (c) Florida State

Page 71 ~ Gridiron Greatness In The Tar Heel State
1. (a) University of North Carolina
2. (c) Salisbury
3. (a) Durham
4. (c) 22
5. (b) New York Giants
6. (a) "Ace"
7. (c) Washington Redskins
8. (c) NC State University
9. (a) Atlantic Coast Conference
10. (a) Ficklen Stadium
11. (c) Jethro Pubh
12. (c) purple and gold

Page 72 ~ "What It Was Was Football"
1. (c) University of North Carolina
2. (a) Livingstone College
3. (b) Wake Forest College
4. (c) Rose Bowl
5. (a) Georgia
6. (b) Heisman Trophy
7. (c) Wilmington
8. (b) Los Angeles Rams, Philadelphia Eagles
9. (c) WBTV
10. (a) New York Giants
11. (b) 1960, 1961, 1962
12. (c) Tangerine Bowl
13. (a) San Francisco 49ers

Page 73 ~ North Carolina Roundball Roundup
1. (a) Greensboro
2. (c) 1966
3. (b) Flaming Five
4. (a) Bones
5. (c) Dixie Classic
6. (b) "Pistol" Pete
7. (b) Cornbread
8. (a) Raleigh
9. (b) New York
10. (c) Wildcat
11. (a) 5 foot 3
12. (b) 4
13. (c) Charlie Scott

1. (c) Fayetteville
2. (b) Black Mountain Golf Club
3. (a) 1895
4. (c) No. 2
5. (b) Donald Ross
6. (b) Arnold Palmer
7. (a) Linville Ridge
8. (b) Gerald Ford
9. (a) Bald Head Island
10. (a) 1909
11. (a) Lee Trevino
12. (c) 1977
13. (a) Sam Snead
14. (b) Wake Forest University
15. (b) 1961

Page 75 ~ Golf Is More Than Just A Game In NC
1. (b) 400
2. (a) $20 billion
3. (c) Puerto Rico
4. (c) High Point
5. (b) He was a Confederate general.
6. (a) Roxboro
7. (a) Military school office
8. (b) 1903
9. (c) Pisgah National Forest
10. (a) Paine Webber Invitational
11. (c) Jesse Haddock
12. (b) Jack Nicklaus
13. (a) 1980

Page 76 ~ Par For The Course
1. (b) Waterfowl hunting
2. (c) US 158
3. (c) Washington Duke Golf and Country Club
4. (a) Michael Jordan
5. (b) Campbell University
6. (c) US Women's Open
7. (a) dairy farm
8. (b) Scotland
9. (b) Tanglewood
10. (b) Pinehurst No. 2

Page 77 ~ Batter Up!
1. (a) South Atlantic League
2. (c) Kevin Costner
3. (b) Minnesota Twins
4. (b) Fort Mill
5. (a) Piedmont League
6. (c) Clark Griffith Park
7. (b) Winston-Salem

8. (a) Mudcats
9. (c) National Association of Professional Baseball Leagues
10. (b) Alexander Julian
11. (a) 1928
12. (b) Birmingham
13. (a) McCormick Field
14. (b) Chicago Cubs
15. (c) Raleigh

Page 78 ~ Who's On First?
1. (c) Alamance County
2. (b) Jim Thorpe
3. (a) George Herman Ruth
4. (c) Lou Gehrig
5. (a) Dan Boone
6. (c) Cal Ripken, Jr.
7. (b) Pitcher
8. (c) "Country"
9. (a) Knuckleball
10. (a) Williamston
11. (b) "Catfish"

Page 79 ~ Fishing For Answers
1. (b) Cape Point at Cape Hatteras
2. (c) Top-water, floating fishing lures
3. (a) Power-pendulum or English casting
4. (c) 94 lbs. 2. oz.
5. (b) a strong, 10-foot-long saltwater casting rod
6. (a) large bluefish
7. (c) puppy drum, redfish, spottail
8. (a) Virginia mullet
9. (c) Mummichog, Chog, Gudgeon
10. (b) International Game Fishing Association
11. (a) Grifton
12. (c) Fort Fisher
13. (a) little tunny
14. (c) 13 inches
15. (a) *Fanny and Jenny*

Page 80 ~ Coastal Piers And Fishing
1. (c) 24 piers
2. (b) steel
3. (a) Red Drum
4. (b) Spot
5. (c) Yellowfin tuna
6. (a) Bogue Inlet
7. (c) Lemonfish
8. (b) Red
9. (c) Pivoting drawbridge
10. (a) 20 feet
11. (a) Theodore Roosevelt

1. (a) first ski resort to open in NC
2. (b) Tom Alexander
3. (c) Norway and Spain
4. (c) 1977
5. (c) 1964
6. (a) 1966-67
7. (a) Skier Safety Act
8. (b) French-Swiss Ski College
9. (b) Jean Claude Killy
10. (c) Southeastern Winter Special Olympics
11. (a) Nordic skiing
12. (c) Larchmont Engineering
13. (a) Beech Mountain
14. (b) Hound Ears
15. (b) Banner Elk
16. (a) Black Mountain Crest Trail
17. (b) Sugar Mountain, 1,200 foot drop

Page 82 ~ Hitting The Slopes
1. (b) 1962
2. (a) Maggie Valley
3. (b) April
4. (c) 8,000
5. (b) 5,506 feet
6. (a) Mars Hill
7. (b) Top Gun
8. (c) 641,000
9. (a) Jackson County
10. (b) Nordic skiing
11. (c) Asheville

Page 83 ~ Hunting Down Some Answers
1. (b) $15
2. (a) 10 gauge
3. (c) 30 pounds
4. (b) pistol
5. (a) crossbow
6. (b) October 5-10
7. (a) November 21-February 27
8. (b) blaze orange
9. (c) 10 daily
10. (a) red
11. (b) Dare County
12. (c) 50 pounds in weight
13. (a) NC state regulations
14. (b) they are in the nest

Page 84 ~ Tar Heel Hiking Trails
1. (a) Uwharrie Trail
2. (c) Durham
3. (b) Pea Island National Wildlife Refuge

4. (c) Little Santeetlah Creek
5. (a) Carolina Bay
6. (b) Sandhills
7. (c) 200
8. (a) Linn Cove Viaduct
9. (b) Fontana Lake
10. (a) Bryson City
11. (c) Mount LeConte
12. (b) Catawba rhododendron

Page 85 ~ The Appalachian Trail
1. (b) 305.1 miles
2. (a) Pittsboro
3. (c) Clay County
4. (a) Burlington
5. (a) highest dam
6. (a) Cherokee
7. (c) Arnold
8. (a) US 19 W
9. (c) Roan Mountain
10. (b) Kings Mountain
11. (a) Avery County

Page 86 ~ Stock-Car Stars
1. (a) Lee Petty
2. (c) Ronda
3. (b) 1960
4. (b) Elvis
5. (a) Dale Jarrett
6. (b) North Carolina Motor Speedway
7. (a) Monroe
8. (c) 1970
9. (b) Hudson
10. (c) High Point

Page 87 ~ Start Your Engines For Tar Heel Racing
   Quiz
1. (c) wooden planks
2. (a) Charlotte
3. (b) corn squeezins
4. (c) 1937
5. (a) Plymouth
6. (b) Raleigh
7. (c) Buck Baker
8. (a) Ironhead
9. (b) Scotland
10. (a) Joe Lee Johnson
11. (c) Elvis Presley
12. (b) .625 miles long
13. (a) US 64/70 W
14. (a) "The Gentleman"

Page 88 ~ Stating The Facts About Our Parks
1. (a) New Hanover County
2. (c) river
3. (b) Bear Island
4. (c) Civil War
5. (a) Governor
6. (c) Gastonia
7. (b) Nags Head
8. (a) Carteret County
9. (c) oldest river in North America
10. (b) B. Everett Jordan
11. (a) Daniel Boone
12. (c) Linville and Catawba rivers

Page 89 ~ Roughing It—Tar Heel Style
1. (b) Blowing Rock
2. (c) Chimney Rock
3. (b) Roanoke Sound
4. (a) Pungo River
5. (c) Denver
6. (b) Dobson
7. (b) Boonville
8. (a) Lake Toxaway
9. (b) Cherokee
10. (c) Columbus
11. (a) Franklin
12. (b) The Last Supper

Page 90 ~ Taking An Artsy Look At The Tar Heel
   State
1. (a) Lost Colony
2. (c) North Carolina Arts Council
3. (b) Federal Art Project
4. (a) 1971
5. (b) 1949
6. (a) Mitchell County
7. (c) North Carolina Zoological Park
8. (b) Rural Realism
9. (a) Gnomes
10. (c) Black Mountain College
11. (b) dime
12. (a) Southern Highland Handicraft Guild

Page 91 ~ The Undisputed King Of Outdoor Drama
1. (b) 11
2. (a) *The Lost Colony*
3. (c) $80 million
4. (c) Chapel Hill
5. (a) Tsali
6. (c) more than 100,000
7. (b) Daniel Boone
8. (c) White Oak

9. (a) Kenansville
10. (b) Lumbee Indians
11. (a) Quakers
12. (c) Andrew Jackson
13. (b) the Alamo
14. (a) Halifax Resolves
15. (c) Italy

Page 92 ~ Mayberry, U.S.A.
1. (b) 1960
2. (c) *The Lost Colony*
3. (b) Mount Airy
4. (a) 1989
5. (c) Greensboro and Raleigh
6. (a) Helen Crump
7. (c) WASG
8. (b) September
9. (a) 1963 Ford Galaxie
10. (b) Mount Pilot
11. (c) "A Girl for Goober"

Page 93 ~ Music Makers
1. (a) Madison County
2. (c) "On Top of Old Smoky"
3. (b) Bascom Lamar Lunsford
4. (a) "The Hoke County Special"
5. (b) Knoxville
6. (a) Dulcimer
7. (a) WWNC
8. (b) Asheville
9. (c) Randolph County
10. (a) Watauga County
11. (a) Durham

Page 94 ~ The Beat Goes On
1. (a) 3,000,000
2. (b) Duke Chapel
3. (a) North Carolina School of the Arts
4. (b) Winston-Salem
5. (b) Transylvania County
6. (c) *Die Fledermaus*
7. (b) Catawba College
8. (a) Hickory
9. (c) Spoleto Festival USA
10. (c) Pulitzer Prize
11. (c) East Carolina University

Page 95 ~ A 'Fair' Test Of Knowledge
1. (b) 1853
2. (a) North Carolina State Agricultural Society
3. (b) October
4. (c) North Carolina State University
5. (a) J. Melville Broughton
6. (c) Theodore Roosevelt
7. (a) William Jennings Bryan
8. (b) Charles Aycock
9. (c) aeroplane
10. (c) Head, Heart, Hands, Health
11. (b) influenza
12. (a) Siamese
13. (b) Department of Agriculture

Page 96 ~ Tar Heel Celebrations
1. (b) Asheville
2. (a) Davidson
3. (c) Fish Camp Jam
4. (b) Lake Junaluska
5. (b) Carteret County
6. (a) Harkers Island
7. (c) Coon Dog Days
8. (b) Scuppernong River Festival
9. (a) Gaston County
10. (c) Wrightsville Beach

Page 97 ~ Christmas In The Old North State
1. (a) Flat Rock
2. (c) Wake County
3. (b) NC 200
4. (a) Revolutionary War
5. (c) Intracoastal Waterway
6. (b) James B. Duke
7. (a) William T. Sherman
8. (c) Aberdeen
9. (c) F. Scott Fitzgerald
10. (b) Christmastown USA
11. (a) Kenansville
12. (c) Zebulon Vance
13. (b) High Point

Page 100 ~ The Business Of Banking
1. (c) William T. Graham
2. (b) Mechanics and Farmers Bank
3. (b) 60 stories
4. (c) 1927
5. (b) Wachovia
6. (a) 1810
7. (b) Bank of New Bern, Bank of Cape Fear
8. (b) Edenton
9. (c) 1899 in Rocky Mount

10. (a) Union National Bank
11. (b) NCNB
12. (b) West Trade Street
13. (c) Jefferson Davis
14. (a) Central Bank and Trust Co. of Asheville
15. (b) Bank of Belmont

Page 101 ~ North Carolina Means Business
1. (c) red and black
2. (a) textile mills
3. (b) John Belk
4. (a) The Chunnel
5. (b) 22,000
6. (c) Gunk
7. (b) Salisbury
8. (c) NC 8
9. (a) Little Miss Sunbeam
10. (b) Guilford County
11. (c) poultry products
12. (a) Research Triangle Park
13. (c) Cajun

Page 102 ~ Manufacturing In The Tar Heel State
1. (a) East Spencer
2. (c) Pisgah Forest
3. (b) High Point
4. (a) nabs
5. (b) pharmaceuticals
6. (b) Lenoir
7. (c) Linville Falls
8. (b) Salisbury
9. (a) Greensboro
10. (c) denim
11. (b) Elkin
12. (a) Aurora
13. (c) wearing apparel

Page 103 ~ Taste Of The State
1. (a) Cucumber and Vine
2. (c) Texas Pete
3. (b) 1903
4. (a) Slim Jim
5. (a) nabs
6. (b) Salisbury
7. (c) Moravia
8. (b) Smithfield
9. (a) Winston-Salem
10. (b) Goldsboro

Page 104 ~ The Facts On Farming
1. (b) 150 acres
2. (a) 1877
3. (c) 21 percent
4. (b) black and white
5. (c) 1955
6. (b) sweet potato
7. (a) aquaculture
8. (b) cotton
9. (b) on their hind legs
10. (b) Wilson
11. (a) hydroponics
12. (c) June
13. (a) Northampton County

Page 105 ~ North Carolina's Agricultural Excellence
1. (b) James A. Graham
2. (c) $42 billion
3. (b) *Agricultural Review*
4. (a) Raeford
5. (b) Russia
6. (c) Smithfield
7. (a) 480 pounds
8. (b) Fraser fir
9. (a) Beaufort County
10. (c) $4,000
11. (c) December
12. (b) $1 billion
13. (a) aquaculture
14. (c) sourwood

Page 106 ~ Tar Heel Harvest
1. (c) 61 million
2. (b) Johnston County
3. (b) Poke sallet
4. (c) peanut
5. (a) Chicory
6. (b) Swoosh
7. (a) Blue crab
8. (b) Virginia mullet
9. (b) squirrel
10. (c) Mulberry
11. (c) Christmas

Page 107 ~ Down On The Farm
1. (a) Leonidas Lafayette Polk
2. (c) West Edenton Street
3. (c) 58,000
4. (b) 700,000
5. (a) Iredell County
6. (b) Mount Olive

7. (a) Burley
8. (c) 30
9. (b) Johnston County
10. (b) 480 pounds

Page 110 ~ The Rudiments Of Railroading
1. (c) Tweetsie Railroad
2. (a) James Buchanan Duke
3. (a) about 4,000 miles
4. (b) Taylorsville
5. (c) NC Utilities Commission
6. (a) 1950
7. (a) Wilmington and Weldon
8. (c) Atlantic and NC Railroad
9. (b) 1856
10. (b) Wilmington and Raleigh Railroad
11. (a) Burlington
12. (b) Southern Railway Company
13. (a) CSX Transportation
14. (c) Asheville
15. (a) 1852

Page 111 ~ Our Highways And Byways
1. (a) the Good Roads State
2. (c) nation's largest state-maintained road system
3. (a) 1-800-VISIT NC
4. (c) I-75
5. (b) US 64
6. (c) Cedar Island
7. (a) NC 12
8. (b) Andrew Jackson
9. (c) $500
10. (a) Lexington
11. (c) Shallotte
12. (b) Appalachian State University
13. (a) 76,500 miles
14. (b) 55 miles an hour

Page 112 ~ Take A Ride On The Waterway
1. (a) the Ditch
2. (b) 12 feet
3. (c) exactly 308 miles
4. (b) Alligator River
5. (b) Dismal Swamp
6. (c) Camp Lejeune
7. (a) US Army Corps of Engineers
8. (c) 20 miles
9. (a) Rattan Bay
10. (b) Carteret County
11. (a) Bo-fort
12. (c) NC 94
13. (b) Duke of Albemarle
14. (c) Calabash

Page 113 ~ The World Of Tar Hee Watercraft

1. (b) sails
2. (a) The Showboat
3. (c) Prometheus
4. (b) hollowed logs
5. (a) bass boats
6. (c) shad boat
7. (a) Swan Quarter
8. (c) Morehead City
9. (b) Beaufort
10. (a) *Elizabeth II*
11. (c) Fort Fisher
12. (b) ironclad
13. (c) Liberty ships

Page 114 ~ Fortresses By The Sea

1. (b) Philadelphia
2. (c) 55
3. (c) Roanoke River
4. (a) Kinston
5. (b) Wilmington
6. (c) Old North State
7. (a) Zebulon B. Vance
8. (b) Croatan Sound
9. (c) *USS Kitty Hawk*
10. (b) submarine
11. (c) 20-plus knots

Page 115 ~ North Carolina Ferries

1. (c) Neuse River
2. (b) Colington
3. (a) Manns Harbor
4. (b) Landing Craft Tank
5. (c) *Barcelona*
6. (a) Sea Level
7. (b) Silver Lake
8. (c) Frisco
9. (c) Swan Quarter
10. (b) Cedar Island
11. (c) Washington

Page 116 ~ Port Authorities

1. (b) 1739
2. (c) Newport River
3. (b) Wilmington Terminal Railroad
4. (c) Liberty ships
5. (a) 1952
6. (c) Southport
7. (b) US Highway 70
8. (a) US Customs
9. (c) 500
10. (a) Radio Island
11. (c) Wood pulp

Page 117 ~ First In Flight

1. (c) Lafayette Escadrille
2. (a) Billy Mitchell
3. (c) 1936
4. (c) October 14, 1927
5. (a) US Weather Bureau
6. (c) Charlotte/Douglas Municipal Airport
7. (a) *Memphis Belle*
8. (a) highest: Ashe County Airport, 3,173 feet above sea level—lowest: Ocracoke Island Airport, 5 feet above sea level
9. (b) September 13, 1900
10. (b) 40 feet, 4 inches
11. (b) Charlotte/Douglas International, Raleigh Durham, Piedmont Triad International (Greensboro)
12. (b) 1941
13. (b) February 20, 1948 in Wilmington
14. (a) Winston-Salem
15. (c) Pee Dee River

Page 120 ~ Books About The Tar Heel State

1. (b) Roanoke Island
2. (a) *The North Carolina Gazetteer*
3. (a) *From Whalebone to Hothouse*
4. (c) *The Western North Carolina Almanac*
5. (b) *Hornet's Nest*
6. (a) Ocracoke
7. (b) *Taffy of Torpedo Junction*
8. (a) *Hattersman*
9. (c) *North Carolina: The History of a Southern State*
10. (b) *A New Geography of North Carolina*
11. (a) *North Carolina Manual*

Page 121 ~ The Power Of The Press

1. (b) *The Enterprise*
2. (a) Alfred M. Scales
3. (b) 1850
4. (c) *Charlotte News*
5. (a) New Bern
6. (c) *Smoky Mountain Times*
7. (a) Siler City
8. (b) Hillsborough
9. (a) *Cherokee Scout*
10. (c) 1897
11. (b) *The Charlotte Observer*
12. (a) 1865
13. (c) Columbus County

1. (b) Devil's Tramping Ground
2. (c) Brown Mountain Lights
3. (a) Garysburg
4. (b) Chimney Rock
5. (a) Brunswick County
6. (c) Lumberton
7. (a) US 70
8. (c) Tuckasegee River
9. (a) Colonel Patrick Ferguson
10. (b) Seaboard
11. (c) Wadesboro
12. (a) Italy
13. (c) Hertford County

Page 123 ~ Tar Heel Haunts And Hobgoblins
1. (a) Maco
2. (c) Bentonville
3. (b) Tuckasegee River
4. (c) Seaboard
5. (a) Johnston County
6. (c) a young woman
7. (b) Lake Phelps
8. (a) Martin County
9. (a) Tsali
10. (c) Devil's Tramping Ground
11. (b) French Broad River
12. (a) Patrick Ferguson
13. (a) *Legend of Sleepy Hollow*

Page 124 ~ North Carolina's State Symbols
1. (c) "The Old North State"
2. (a) "To be rather than to seem"
3. (b) red and blue
4. (b) Plott hound
5. (a) Shad boat
6. (c) Milk
7. (a) Granite
8. (b) Eastern Box Turtle
9. (a) Red Drum
10. (c) Scotch Bonnet
11. (a) honey bee
12. (b) Gray squirrel
13. (c) Pine
14. (c) Cardinal

Page 125 ~ Space Invaders
1. (c) fourth
2. (b) NC Highway 150
3. (a) Ovens Auditorium
4. (b) Devil's Tramping Ground
5. (c) McGuire Nuclear Station

6. (b) Blowing Rock
7. (a) Lumberton
8. (a) High Rock Lake
9. (c) Raeford
10. (a) Mooresboro
11. (b) Bonlee

Page 126 ~ Turn Of The Centuries
1. (a) NC 11
2. (c) barbecue
3. (c) Mecklenburg Declaration of Independence
4. (b) Locomobile
5. (a) 7,777,000
6. (b) musket shooting
7. (a) last quarter
8. (a) Carolina Beach
9. (c) Blowing Rock
10. (b) Tryon Street

Page 127 ~ Plenty To Brag About In The Tar Heel State
1. (b) NC 159
2. (a) Burlington
3. (c) French Renaissance
4. (c) 400
5. (a) World War II
6. (c) 80 million
7. (c) 76,000 miles
8. (a) 5 million pounds
9. (b) Inland Sea
10. (c) Banner Elk
11. (a) Indy 500
12. (b) Clingmans Dome
13. (c) poet

Page 128 ~ The Year In Review
1. (b) Jennifer Smith
2. (a) Duke University
3. (c) 6,000,000
4. (a) Dan Blue
5. (b) battleship
6. (c) Winston-Salem
7. (a) Bob
8. (b) Allan Bristow
9. (c) Richard Petty
10. (a) Fort Bragg
11. (b) Pasquotank County
12. (b) Mark Brooks
13. (a) James Fenimore Cooper
14. (c) Raleigh-Durham Skyhawks

Page 129 ~ Looking Back On 1992
1. (b) New Bern
2. (c) Kinston
3. (a) film studio
4. (b) turkeys
5. (a) September
6. (c) swimming
7. (b) 71-51
8. (a) Sleepy
9. (c) Central Intercollegiate Athletic Association
10. (a) Terry Jordan
11. (b) Governor
12. (c) Clinton
13. (c) 12th Congressional District

Page 130 ~ The Tar Heel Year In Review
1. (a) cotton
2. (c) Charlotte O's
3. (c) sweet potato
4. (b) Wingate University
5. (a) Arkansas Razorbacks
6. (b) Greater Greensboro Open
7. (a) Chimney Rock Hillclimb
8. (c) Mother Teresa
9. (a) Robeson County
10. (c) Garner

Page 131 ~ Sixty Years Of 'Down-Home' Trivia
1. (b) J.C.B. Ehringhaus
2. (a) *The Wilson Mirror*
3. (c) 10 cents
4. (a) Lawyers Building
5. (c) "A Weekly Survey of North Carolina"
6. (c) William Joseph Eudy Arthur
7. (b) "How Many Can You Answer"
8. (a) "Book Larnin"
9. (a) Carol Goerch's daughter
10. (c) Jesse Helms
11. (b) "Murphy To Manteo"
12. (a) January 15, 1970

Page 132 ~ Sixty-five And Still Growing
1. (c) 2,500
2. (b) airplane pilot
3. (b) 10 cents
4. (c) University of North Carolina
5. (a) "A Weekly Survey of North Carolina"
6. (c) "Book Larning"
7. (b) "How Many Can You Answer"
8. (a) advertising and promotion
9. (b) "Turpentine: Drippings From the Tar Heel Press"
10. (c) New York
11. (c) August 1996

Bibliography

A History of Sports in North Carolina by Jim Sumner

Birds of the Carolinas by Eloise Potter, James Parnell, Robert Teulings

The Civil War in North Carolina by John Barrett

First in Flight: The Wright Brothers in North Carolina by Stephen Kirk

First on the Land: The North Carolina Indians by Ruth Whetmore

Guide to North Carolina Highway Historical Markers NC Department of Archives and History

Hornet's Nest: The Story of Charlotte and Mecklenburg County by LeGette Blythe and Charles Raven Brockman

Mayberry, My Hometown: The Ultimate Guide to America's Favorite TV Small Town by Stephen Spignesi

North Carolina County Fact Book, Volumes I and II by Beverly and Glenn Tetterton

The North Carolina Gazetteer by William Powell

North Carolina Illustrated by H.G. Jones

North Carolina: Reflections of 400 Years by JCP Corporation and Branch Banking and Trust Company

N.C. Roadmap NC Department of Transportation

North Carolina: The History of a Southern State by Hugh Lefler and Albert Newsome

North Carolina Through Four Centuries by William Powell

North Carolina Troops: A Roster by Weymouth Jordan

On This Day in North Carolina by Lew Powell

Touring the Carolinas' Civil War Sites by Clint Johnson

Western North Carolina Almanac by Robert Beverley

Wild Flowers of North Carolina by William S. Justice and C. Ritchie Bell

various websites

Index

Who is Alan Hodge?
(a) a newspaper reporter
(b) a Civil War reenactor
(c) a surf fisherman
All of the above.

MY BIO...BY ALAN LEE HODGE

My family on my mom's side has lived in the Belmont, North Carolina area since around 1768...I'm old time and hard core North Carolina. I first started with *The State* magazine in 1990 when the editor Angela Terez gave me a chance at creating the "State's Quiz". I worked in libraries for 13 years. Now besides my job as reporter for the *Kings Mountain Herald* newspaper I also free-lance for *Business North Carolina* magazine. I'm an avid surf fisherman, but my passion is Civil War reenacting which I have been doing for about five years. My wife Sharon, also a reenactor, portrays a 19th century Southern lady of refined demeanor yet modest means. In real life she is a banker with Wachovia in Belmont, and we have been married 13 years.

The thing that has amazed me most about doing the quizzes is how much there is to know about North Carolina. When I first started doing them, I was afraid I would quickly run out of subjects...now, 10 years later, I am still awed by the depth of our state's lore. I hope this book helps young and old alike come to a greater understanding of where we have been as Tar Heels and where we are going in the future. I am greatly indebted to Bernie Mann, the present publisher of *Our State*. Without his permission this publication could never have happened.

ML